THE INVISIBLE ART

TO HIS BOOKE.

Goe little Booke: thy ſelfe preſent,
As child whoſe parent is vnkent,
To him that is the preſident
Of nobleneſſe and chiualrie:
And if that Enuie barke at thee,
As ſure it will, for ſuccour flee
Vnder the ſhadow of his wing.
And, asked who thee forth did bring,
A Shepheards ſwaine ſay did thee ſing,
All as his ſtraying flocke hee fed:
And when his Honour hath thee read,
Craue pardon for thy hardy head.
But if that any aske thy name,
Say, thou wert baſe begot with blame:
For why thereof thou takeſt ſhame.
And when thou art paſt ieopardie,
Come tell me what was ſayde of mee,
And I will ſend more after thee.

Immerito.

A page of Edmund Spenser's *Shepheard's Calender*, as published by John Harrison in London in 1617, re-set by H.W. Caslon & Co. Ltd, 82-83 Chiswell Street, London E.C.1, and published in that firm's typebook entitled *Caslon Old Face*, early 1920s. (78% of original size) The 'president of noblenesse and chiualrie' was presumably Spenser's dedicatee, Philip Sidney, but for the present purpose the phrase signifies the gentle reader.

CHRISTOPHER HURST

THE INVISIBLE ART

THE PURSUIT OF BOOK MAKING

HURST / LONDON

First published by C. Hurst & Co. (Publishers) Ltd,
38 King Street, London WC2E 8JZ

A Cataloguing-in-Publication data record for this book is available from the British Library.

Printed in Malaysia

ISBN 1-85065-587-1

'The typographical art should be invisible, the hand which seeks perfection, but which is never actually seen.' (John Ryder [1917–2001], quoted in the *Guardian* obituary, 26 January 2001)

'One of the weaknesses of our country is that we're satisfied with the second or third best in everything. The basic attitude of us Indians is *chalega, ayega, dekhega* [it'll work, it'll do, let's make do]. You can only achieve a standard by aiming at something more: so if you want excellence, you must aim at perfection. I know that aiming at perfection has its drawbacks—it makes you go into detail that you could avoid, it takes a lot of energy out of you, but that's the only way you finally actually achieve excellence. So in that sense being finicky is essential.' (J.R.D. Tata [1903–93], Indian industrialist*)

'Costly thy habit as thy purse can buy,
But not express'd in fancy; rich, not gaudy:
For the apparel oft proclaims the man.' (*Hamlet*, Act I, sc. iii)

'What can go wrong will go wrong.' ('Sod's Law')

'The difficult can be done at once; the impossible takes a little longer.' (Saying attributed to the Royal Navy)

*When J.R.D. Tata made these comments it might have been difficult for a British publisher to see them as applying to his own industry. Today it is not so difficult.

CONTENTS

Part 2. THE SCHOLARLY PUBLISHER

A PERSONAL NOTE

This opus is concerned with running a small scholarly publishing house. That may seem a rather specialised occupation, but its performance requires a full complement of publishing skills. To do it successfully, especially starting from scratch, one has to be a Jack or Jill of all trades connected to the book business, and perhaps a master or mistress of one or two of them.* For the person running a large modern publishing house it is in theory unnecessary to have any of these skills at all; I sometimes wonder if it may not actually be a hindrance. At least in the old family-owned and -managed firms, cadets from the proprietorial dynasty, before graduating to an executive position, had to pack parcels in the warehouse under a strict foreman, go out on the road as a 'rep' (sales representative) under a demanding sales manager, and work on manuscripts or proofs under the beady eye of the chief editor or production manager. Further experience might be garnered in an overseas branch of the parent company, or in a friendly family-run publishing or bookselling firm on the continent.

One cannot but respect the classic publishers' reference works, Judith Butcher's *Copy-editing*† and *Hart's Rules*,‡ and no editorial

*I am already exhausted by the effort to be inclusive, and from here on will generally use the male pronoun when either sex is referred to.

†*Copy-editing: The Cambridge Handbook for Editors, Authors and Publishers*, CUP, 1st publ. 1975, 3rd edn 1992.

‡*Hart's Rules for Compositors and Readers at the University Press, Oxford*, OUP, 1st publ. 1893, 15th edn (1st for general sale) 1904, 39th edn 1983 (re-issued with corrections 1989).

or production department should be without them. So why should I venture to propose what may seem to be rules of my own? One powerful reason is that Butcher assumes her readers to be working in sizeable presses with functions neatly compartmentalised. For example, there is frequent reference to 'the commissioning editor', 'the line editor' and so on. I know of no such distinctions. Having at times in the past done everything, I recognise only one main rule: that the 'Publisher', the head of the house, can and should depend ultimately on no one but himself. He can delegate work, but the buck stops with him. Another work of great importance, which also happens to be an inexhaustible source of stimulation and entertainment, is *The New Fowler's Modern English Usage* (revised 3rd edn by R.W. Burchfield, Oxford, 1998).

Not only have I written this book with almost no reference to existing published works, other than dictionaries; but I only cover areas of publishing activity where I can pretend to authority based on experience, and I will here say finally what could be added in many places: that my own personal taste is conservative, and what I see as objective may strike others as subjective. As C. Hurst & Co. (founded in 1967) has grown, although its personnel remain few, I have come to concentrate on certain areas more than others: the editorial and production processes in relation to individual books, and the drafting of agreements of different kinds, or their interpretation when they are offered to us by trading partners; for the tasks relating to contracts, editorial skills conveniently complement business acumen (see final chapter). Of course I am also involved in editorial policy—the development of the list—but this is an area full of subjective feelings, not to mention trade secrets, about which a publisher is best advised to remain guarded.

A special caveat for the reader is need here. I make no pretense to being informed about the technology of book production that involves transferring the corrected pages, cover artwork etc. directly from the publisher to the printer via a compact disk (CD). It is wondrously time- and effort-saving, and can thereby enable the publisher to boost his rate of production and thus the volume and value of his business. (Whether this gets him into the vortex of expansion leading to loss of control and independence is another question.) I could have informed myself about the point which the cutting edge has currently reached in order to represent the matter with tolerable accuracy, or have asked an expert to write a chapter for me, but how soon would all this be out of date? The book may be vulnerable to the accusation that not many publishers now operate in the way I describe as normal—I even recommend in some eventualities the use of paste and scissors—but instant redundancy in the area of technology would be worse. And here I come to the justification of my 'method': hands-on human involvement at all the vital interfaces in the production process—call it fine-tuning or quality control—is for me the very essence of the publisher's vocation, and some of this must be lost when the CD is the sole vehicle of the images which get into print.

Publishers of my type run a moral risk if they make claims for themselves beyond trying to do their job competently and, above all, staying solvent. So what aim can we reasonably profess? Conscientious publishers have to be content with knowing that readers of their books without a professional interest in book making will merely not suffer the annoyance of encountering sloppy editing, inadequate proof-reading, ham-fisted design and bad printing. In other words, the aim of high standards of book production in all its ramifications can be seen as a negative one—the avoidance of disagreeable sensations. I call it the invisible art* because, while its absence is extremely noticeable, its successful application will pass unnoticed—which is its object. (It may impart a warm glow, the source of which is hard to identify.) Practising the invisible art is expensive, whether you do it yourself or farm it out to others. Some may consider the result not worth the expense: they have their reward.

Publishers of printed books are inheritors of a mighty tradition that goes back more than half a millennium. It goes without saying that in the West the concept of lettering as an art goes back far beyond the invention of moveable type, to Greek and Roman

*I had written this before becoming aware that John Ryder had crystallised the concept in the words which form the first epigraph to this book. While he does not extend it beyond typography, I see it as applying equally to the work of the editor.

inscriptions. One should not confuse it with calligraphy, although the two almost converged in the Renaissance, and have certainly influenced each other since then. Some of the earliest books ever printed and bound in the modern way are also among the most beautiful. There was much beautiful book making in the 20th century—mostly perhaps in the 1920s and '30s—across Europe including Britain. But what we have seen since the demise of letterpress printing from metal type in classic fonts re-created by the Monotype Corporation is a bifurcation: typography practised as an art has largely deserted mainstream commercial publishing and flowed into backwaters such as book clubs—like the Folio Society in England, which prints standard works of literature in fancy editions for the 'connoisseur' (what can be more artificial or alien to the idea of a scholar's library?)—and tiny private presses, which do indeed labour to uphold true typography.

We should honour our ancestors and keep their spirit alive.

I acknowledge gratefully the help of the following friends who read the MS. at successive stages of its evolution and made valuable criticisms and suggestions: Michael Dwyer, Anthony Rota, Iain Stevenson, Diana Davies, Rukun Advani, Robert Gomme, and Bela Malik whose comments on the text were invaluable.

London, January 2002 C. H.

Part I. THE PHYSICAL BOOK

We will start immediately on a journey through the book from beginning to end. First things first: the next 24 pages are devoted to the Preliminary Pages (hereafter 'Prelims' with the accent on the first syllable), a far from excessive allowance considering their importance. Some of the prescriptions for type size and layout of individual pages cannot be claimed to do more than reflect my personal taste, which—as already stated—is conservative, but I will defend stoutly my attention to details large and small, to order and balance, and to traditional taboos such as starting certain items on rectos. Every detail is important, and it does no harm to remind oneself that 'a chain is strongest at its weakest link'.

The main text requires plentiful attention to detail too; if it is not girded round with a solid, unshakeable (but 'invisible') framework of orderliness combined with elegance, it will languish, and risks failing, partly at least, to achieve its object. With that provided, it is—to change the metaphor—a broader territory in which, for the publisher, broader considerations come into play. Hence the concentration on linguistic integrity. My insistence on retaining time-honoured distinctions of meaning does not imply a hankering for an arid academicism which would hallow classical usage and prohibit all further development; I am all for flexibility and easy language where its use is appropriate. As in poetry, so in prose, and so in scholarly writing.

A leitmotiv of this book is the sovereign value of distinctions—typographical and linguistic.

THE PRELIMS, I

The half-title

The presence of this virtually blank opening page immediately preceding the title-page is desirable for reasons well spelt out by Oliver Simon in his *Introduction to Typography*.* It seems rough-and-ready if the all-important title-page faces the front endpaper: even if the two appear identical in colour, they are not so in weight and quality. As Simon says, a spot of binder's glue could show in the 'gutter' (where the pages join), which would be regrettable; it is still worse when excessive glueing causes the endpaper to cover part of the left side of the all-important title-page, thus upsetting its design. These dangers apart, a half-title affords a momentary breathing-space before you get to the title-page, like an ante-room before a banqueting hall.

Half-titles can occur at intervals throughout a book which is divided into 'Parts'. If the book has a somewhat magisterial character, I would support this being done. The author may want to attach an epigraph to a Part title. But if it is not one that seems to demand such spacious treatment, then the Part number and Part title can be set above the number and title of the first chapter in that Part, with no loss of elegance, provided they are properly differentiated from each other typographically by weight.

*First published by Faber and Faber, 1945; new edition 1963.

The issue of possibly omitting such an intangibly important part of a book as the half-title only arises seriously when the overall page extent of the book, including Prelims, slightly exceeds an 'even working' (i.e. a multiple of 32 or 16, the length of a standard printed section), say by one or two pages, and to omit the half-title would save printing an extra section. The consequence of printing an extra section for a page or two of type is to be left with a bunch of blank pages at the end or be obliged to cut away a lot of paper to waste—an extravagant procedure in either case and one best avoided. But before deciding to omit the half-title, one should explore all other possible ways of saving a page. But such ways are limited, and none may prove to be available—except to print a mini-section consisting of the half-title only. It should never be forgotten that in book making the seemingly impossible can often be made possible.

What should appear on the half-title? First and foremost the title of the book. The subtitle should only be added if, without it, the title would appear too short and inexplicit, indeed when the subtitle is integral to the title (so much so that a qualifying subtitle of the normal type could be added to it). An example might be 'ALBANIA: A SHORT HISTORY'.

The publisher could follow the example of certain paperback publishers and place a short biography of the author under the half-title if this is a paperback, and if the back cover, for whatever reasons, is fully occupied by the blurb of the book with the possible addition of advance reviews by well-known authorities, or indeed if the cover designer has extended his artistic conception over the whole of the back as well as the front. It is also expedient, with jacketless hardcover editions (see pp. 142–3), to place the whole blurb, including a few lines about the author, on the half-title page slightly reduced in size to fit.

Simple though it may be, the half-title legend (assuming that no additional matter is to appear below it) has to be treated with due care. Just as the 'spine brass'* used to be designed independently from the setting on the jacket spine (it is now often shot from that setting), so the half-title legend has an existence independent

*The block used for imprinting the legend on the spine of the binding case.

from the setting on the title-page, and should not be made uniform with it. A median rendering would be in 11 point* roman capitals or a slightly larger size in upper-and-lower-case (u.l.c.). The 'golden' placing of the line is between one-sixth and one-fifth of the way down the page from the top trim.

In the unlikely event that you decide to make the frontispiece consist of a picture which bleeds† off top, bottom and fore-edge‡, a good place to caption it is the bottom right corner of the half-title page.

The dedication

(This refers in particular to one displayed solus on a page, not merely included as a final sentence or two in the Acknowledgements.) To many authors the dedication is of the utmost importance, and the publisher should never so much as demur over a request to include one. However, he should reserve the right to edit it, decide on the punctuation if any, and position it. One that is too long, too effusive or in the publisher's opinion irrelevant, provocative to the author's enemies or in doubtful taste obviously needs further thought by all concerned. The present writer was asked by one author to include a dedication '*To my beloved son* —', the son in question being a middle-aged lawyer. Because I knew the father well and thought that a straight '*To* —' would meet the case better, I suggested it and he agreed.

It should be set (depending on its length) an average of two point-sizes larger than the main text. A very short one of two or three words looks fine in roman type; a longer one might

*One of the many meanings of 'point' is a unit of measurement for type (hereafter rendered as 'pt'). According to the duodecimal system, there are 72 points to 1 inch, and 12 in one pica 'm' or, more conveniently, 'em'—hence 6 pica ems are equal to 1 inch. For practical (i.e. our) purposes, it is used horizontally to designate column width, and vertically to designate the size of the 'body' of metal type. The amount of 'leading', i.e. space between lines, is measured in points: e.g. 10 pt type with 2 pt leading is expressed as '10/12 pt'.

†Pictures are said to 'bleed' when their edges over-run one or more of the trimmed edges of a page (historically by one-eighth of an inch). They are said (rather unpleasantly) to 'bleed into the gutter' when one side disappears into the cleft between two facing pages. The word is also used as a noun.

‡The edge of the book opposite the binding; rhymes with 'porridge'.

look more striking in italic. Nouns (other than proper names) and verbs should be set entirely in lower-case.

The classic position for it is on (unnumbered) page v, facing the title verso, with page vi blank, but if shortage of space rules this out, it can go on the verso of the half-title, facing the title-page (see next section). If this is occupied by other essential matter, an alternative position of last resort is on the title-verso (i.e. the page backing the title-page), well displayed above or below the bibliographic data, but this position cannot avoid looking somewhat cramped and should never be chosen if there is room for it to go solus elsewhere.

The frontispiece

The word is used to designate page ii, the verso of the half-title, whatever the use to which it is put. For us its main alternative uses number five:

1. *Pictorial.* If the book is a biography or an autobiography, here is a good place for a picture of the subject. This is undoubtedly the best place for it if there is no illustration section inside the book, but it can be a good idea to put a particularly striking picture here even if there are illustrations further on. In the latter case the decision must be a subjective one on the part of the publisher, and he must then get the author to agree.

The publisher can unashamedly go for dramatic effect, if the subject calls for it, by 'bleeding' or by, say, blowing up the subject's face or, if the subject is not a person, a significant detail. Or one can equally well go for a conventional treatment, with the picture placed centrally with due balance of margins, and a caption under.

The effect of show-through on the half-title page—the rectangle of the picture forming an intrusive shadow—can be avoided if space permits by having both the half-title and the frontispiece unbacked, the latter being treated as if it were an old-fashioned tipped-in art-paper plate, and left out of the page numbering.

2. *Extension of the title.* By this I do not mean extending the typography of the elements that usually go on the title-page across

a double-page spread—this is sometimes done and, unless the artistry is superb, it seems self-indulgent and affected. Rather, I am referring, in my firm's case, to books about China, Japan and the Arab world, where we have evolved the custom of placing on the frontispiece an equivalent of the title and phonetic rendering of the author's name in Chinese, Japanese or Arabic as the case may be. We will always opt for calligraphy if the author is sufficiently skilled at it or has access to someone who is; we have occasionally paid for it. The size-enlargement or reduction—and positioning—are matters for careful aesthetic judgement. This device must surely enhance the pleasure felt by users on opening the book.

3. *List of the author's previous works.* This is self-explanatory, and although it offers little latitude for self-expression, there is ample opportunity to use the elements either with elegance or cack-handedly. The type-size and style used for the titles and the weight and style of the heading and the spacing have to be carefully designed.

4. *The rubric.* Although we have only once originated a (small) *series* of our own that was recognisable as such, it is quite possible that what for us is a free-standing publication our American co-publisher will want to include in a series of his own. We have also sometimes (though not often) published works sponsored by institutes. In cases such as these the editor of the American series or the director of the institute may want a blurb included about the said series or institute, and the obvious place for it is the frontispiece, set a size or even two sizes smaller and in a slightly narrower measure than the main text.

5. *The dedication.* See above.

The title-page

'The title-page ... gives to the book the general tone of its typographical treatment. When a lover of books handles a new volume he instinctively opens it at the title-page, ready to receive a sensation of delight or a sense of disappointment.' (Oliver Simon, 'The Title-page', *The Fleuron*, I [1923], pp. 93–7)

One should not totally forget that some of the title-pages of the Renaissance and later were substantial works of decorative art in their own right. (There is always the risk of the quality of such a title-page outweighing that of the book's content [see p. 146, footnote], which would defeat its intention.) In the Augustan and even the Victorian eras they went to another extreme: simplicity, compounded of a classical sense of balance. To achieve our wider aims we should tend towards the latter, but bear in mind the importance the early fathers of printing, and such as Oliver Simon, accorded to this page.

It is impossible to prescribe absolute standards, and it would be hubristic to do so since the title-page is a justifiable arena for the publisher's self-expression. Even so, a sense of balance (not the same as symmetry), lightness and elegance—the qualities that please the eye—is the aim. Anything lumpish should be avoided, and this includes all 'bold' faces*: contrast can be obtained by much subtler means.

Lumpishness can come from anything being too large for comfort, and a related but opposite sensation—starvation?—from anything being disproportionately small. In the days of Monotype metal faces, large sizes were individually designed and made, not magnified from small sizes as they inevitably are today—to ill effect—by use of the computer. It may not be self-evident why the former should have been aesthetically more satisfying, but perhaps Nicholas Hilliard and Hans Holbein the Younger would have agreed that the art of portrait-painting in miniature does not obey identical rules of balance to those that operate in full-size portraiture.

The elements will now be dealt with individually.

Author's name. In earlier times it was usual to place it below the title and to precede it with the word 'by'. Our style is to place it above the title, usually in 18 pt capitals. Where the volume is an 'edited' or collective one with a number of contributors, one could follow the above pattern and place '*editor*' in 12 pt lower-

*By these I mean the heavy faces of standard typefaces, but exclude interesting 'designer' faces used for the title itself.

case (l.c.) italic, or do what we would never do with a single-author volume, namely place

edited by
JOHN BROWNE

below the title. This doesn't have the naive ring of 'by' on its own. Where there are two editors, the neatest formula would be to have, first on the page,

JOHN BROWNE
JASON STEPTOE
editors

Also in earlier times, authors used often to blazon below their names decorations, honorary degrees (Sir Stanley Unwin proudly advertised his 'Hon. LL.D.'), current and past academic or public service affiliations and so on. But modern packaging has made this unnecessary: the jacket of a hardcover book or the back cover of a paperback enable as many of the author's strong points as there is space for to be spelt out.

Certain edited volumes have a quite small number of co-equal authors: then surely it is appropriate to set out all their names in a column, with the editor's name distinguished by having 'editor' following it on the same line, with or without parentheses. For names displayed in this way 12 pt* capitals work well (see illustration).

The title and subtitle. This is an enormous subject. If you want adventure within safe limits, consult a book on traditional typography such as Oliver Simon's classic *Introduction to Typography* (Faber, 1945, and reprints) and any volume of *The Fleuron* (1923–30). Our preference is for a large size of the text face in upper-and-lower-case (u.l.c.) roman. The shorter the title, the larger it can be set; the longer it is, the smaller it must be set. An overloaded title-page (overloaded by the type-sizes chosen rather than by the quantity of necessary information) is an eyesore.

*Naturally, what is suited for demy or royal 8vo may be too big for 12mo, and too small for folio. But we are concerned here with the 'human sciences' (to use the French term), where demy and royal are the standard sizes.

Roosevelt to Reagan

The Development of the Modern Presidency

JOHN HART
RICHARD HODDER-WILLIAMS
JOHN D. LEES
DAVID MERVIN
MALCOLM SHAW (*editor*)
PHIL WILLIAMS
ROBERT WILLIAMS

Handset in Caslon Old Face (Monotype series 128) by Mould Type, Preston. (Actual size)

Some combinations of a small number of words fall naturally into a harmonious composition, whereas others, even after much juggling, refuse to do so; in the latter case 'ranging' (i.e. vertically aligning) the lines and, necessarily, all the other matter on the title page on the left may produce a more harmonious result than centring them.

Subtitles are very common in scholarly books, and cannot be considered apart from titles, with which they are symbiotic. Provided the subtitle is not integral to the title (as it is in 'ALBANIA: A SHORT HISTORY', already cited), its subordination should be made clear but not to excess (there are of course *degrees* of subordination, involving a subjective element in the choice of type-size). It can be set in either roman (assuming the title to be set in roman) or italic u.l.c. (A roman subtitle to an italic title would look strange unless expertly handled.)

Times italic, a rather bulky face with a large x-height, was never particularly graceful even during the reign of Monotype, and is today even less so and should therefore be avoided; roman will have to do instead. Although the italics of Bembo, Baskerville and Garamond are still attractive, a roman subtitle in those faces can also look good.

Italic implies a degree of contrast to the roman item with which it is juxtaposed. Thus the choice of which to opt for—roman or italic—is dictated by the subjectmatter and is subjective, but it can be influenced by the physical shape of the title. If the title contains, say, two long words and two short ones like 'the', 'a', 'of' or 'and', and it seems necessary to set the words in big sizes because of their nature, e.g.

The
Phenomenology
of
Fundamentalism

it will have a vertical rather than a horizontal accent and therefore it would improve the balance to lessen the weight of the subtitle; the most obvious way of doing this is to italicise it. In some cases setting the two short words smaller than the big ones works well; in others, particularly when there is only one short word, it may look uncomfortable, and a uniform large size will therefore be preferable.

In other instances the nature of the title, especially if it contains more words than the above example, may require it to be set in a smaller size than if there were only few words, and this could enable the accent to be more horizontal.

Ancillary information. This is likely to take a form such as

WITH AN INTRODUCTION BY

HAROLD J. BLOGGS

or

TRANSLATED FROM THE GERMAN BY

JOHN AND HILDEGARDE SMITH

or even

TRANSLATED, EDITED AND WITH AN INTRODUCTION BY

HAROLD. J. BLOGGS

To have this in capitals nicely echoes the author's name, also in capitals, and differentiation can be introduced by having the upper, subordinate line in small capitals and the lower line in fullsize capitals of the same font. A good size would be 11 pt—or 12 pt if the individual's name is deemed to be a selling point.

The imprint. 'HURST & COMPANY, LONDON', in 12 pt roman capitals, has become our standard, the initial 'C.' having been dropped over time. In the rare instances where the publication has benefited, editorially and/or financially, from association with some institution, we will insert its name conjoined to ours in the following form—

HURST & COMPANY, LONDON

in association with the

Bundesinstitut für Ostwissenschaft, Munich

—the ancillary lines in 11/12 pt italic u.l.c.

The word 'Limited' or 'Ltd' following the publisher's name should surely never appear on a title-page.

Colophons. We used one in our early days, based on the time-ball on the top of the old Greenwich Observatory (we started life in Greenwich), but have dropped it. Colophons, logos, trade-marks—call them what one will—can be memorable (consider only the windmill of Heinemann, the flower-bowl of Jonathan Cape, the sailing ship of Longman and the eponymous Penguin), and our (commission) reps have said we should have one. However, it has to be superbly designed in order to be both appropriate* and memorable, as well as small and compact, and rather than have one that in any way misses the target, it is better to have none.

The title-verso or 'copyright page'

The title-verso is a most important page, and from this three desiderata follow:

1. the information presented therein should be correct and it should be unambiguous;
2. it should be confined to the minimum necessary;
3. its presentation should be elegant, which is impossible unless desideratum no. 2 is met.

The essential elements are the following:

—A statement that the book was first published in [country] by [publisher's name and address]. It is now usual to add the publisher's website.

—A statement that the work is copyrighted in the name of the author, the publisher or a sponsoring body, whichever the case may be. Who holds the copyright is of course a legal and not a typographical question, and becomes important when the sale of certain subsidiary rights is in question, and in legal cases where the ownership of copyright has to be proved: this is easier when the owner is the pubisher, and some authors, who naturally wish to see themselves named as copyright owner, may need some gentle persuading of this. This problem is lucidly explained in Lynette Owen's *Selling Rights* (4th edn, Routledge, 2001).

There are variations in the way copyright ownership is stated. As simple a formula as any is '© Harold J. Bloggs, 1979'. An American publisher might well say 'Copyright ©1979 by Harold J. Bloggs'. Which way you say it makes no difference, provided the date is not omitted.

*The 'ff' adopted by Faber and Faber, a firm whose name alone always used to be its best advertisement, is a case in point. The obvious pun on '*fortissimo*', the very antithesis of the traditional Faber style, seems misconceived.

We include the year of publication only in the copyright line, and advance it to the following year if finished copies are not due to be delivered in bulk before the beginning of November.

—A line stating the country in which the book has been printed. It is not uncommon for the name of the typesetter (and even the typeface and software used) and of the printer to be stated, but normally we prefer not to do this. Where a book of ours has been printed in our own country, we put 'England' or 'Scotland' rather than 'the United Kingdom', a political and not a geographical term.

—The International Standard Book Number (ISBN) or Numbers. If both hardcover and paperback are being issued, we would put

ISBNs
0-00000-000-1 *casebound*
0-00000-005-1 *paperback*

with a half-line space above. One should routinely check that the barcode on the jacket or cover corresponds with the ISBN inside the book.

—Cataloguing-in-Publication. The Library of Congress (the American spelling of the first word is 'Cataloging', which suggests a soft 'g') uses an extensive formulation, which is brutally unaesthetic in both form and content; the string of words and cryptograms has no rhyme or reason for anyone reading a book for pleasure or instruction. The formulations used by other national libraries tend to be simpler. For a long time the panel of CIP Data has been printed below the principal information on the copyright page as a matter of course, but it is now no longer required. All that needs to be said is 'A Cataloguing-in-Publication Data record for this book is available from the [name of library].' Librarians and library suppliers will have no difficulty in finding out how to access the CIP Data.

Two common legal formulae occupying several lines are often included, asserting (1) the author's 'moral' rights and (2) the publisher's control over all subsidiary rights. Since the first of these needs to be asserted in this way to have legal validity, it must clearly be included. The second is hardly a defence against infringement, any more than the all-embracing formula 'All rights reserved', which we invariably include. Such an ensemble at least need not be displeasing to the eye.

Additions are necessary in the following instances:

New editions or impressions of a published book. A line for each such reissue must appear under the original copyright line, e.g.

© Harold J. Bloggs, 1979
2nd impression, corrected 1981
3rd impression 1983
4th impression, with new Introduction by the author, 1987
2nd edition, revised and updated, 1993

In any subsequent impressions of the 2nd edition, the lines concerning the 2nd, 3rd and 4th impressions of the *first* edition can reasonably be omitted.

The distinction between a re-impression and a new edition cannot be too strongly stressed. A new impression contains no change to the original text except corrections of typographical or, at a stretch, minor factual errors. To qualify as a new edition, a book must contain substantial changes, possibly including a new concluding chapter or more than one, and to call a new impression a new edition will raise expectations and possibly result in a purchase, the consequence of which would be a sense in the purchaser of having been cheated. It is possible to incorporate, say, a new chapter and other alterations, if sufficiently localised, without re-setting the whole book (provided the typefaces can be exactly matched), and to this end I would consider that to index an additional chapter separately is a legitimate expedient. Such acrobatics require the kind of skill this book has set out to encourage. Deciding when the point has been reached when re-setting is preferable is a matter of fine editorial and financial judgement.

Books originated in another English-speaking country. Add after the address line 'under license from' followed by the publisher, city and state.

Books translated from another language. Begin the entry with 'Originally published as [foreign title in full] by [name of publisher and date of publication]'. The copyright line should then read: 'English translation © C. Hurst & Co. (Publishers) Ltd, [date]'.

Books re-published by a publisher other than the original one, but in the original form, with a new introduction by someone other than the author. Add after the copyright line 'New Introduction ©[name and date]'. If the author is deceased, precede the name with 'Estate of' or 'Exors of', or insert the name of the present copyright owner if the latter so prefers.

The epigraph(s)

Two books we published by the historian Stevan Pavlowitch contained copious epigraphs to the book as a whole. In *The Improbable Survivor* (1988) a single extended one filled a side and a quarter; in *Tito* (1992; see illustration on p. 16) there were six, completely filling one side. They immediately preceded the opening of the main text, but we made one error in my retrospective judgement: instead of occupying the last page(s) of the Prelims, they should have been the first (unnumbered) pages of the main text, with Chapter 1 opening on page 3.

Some authors, with the same instinct as Pavlowitch but not necessarily with the same discrimination, are obviously fond of epigraphs and use them as a flourish to introduce every chapter, or nearly every one (this Pavlowitch did not do). The publisher should look them over to make sure they truly seem appropriate; and if troubled on this score can tactfully mention the matter along with other points to the author, who may be slightly vain about it and wish to show off.

The epigraph to a chapter or sub-chapter should be set a size smaller than the main text, *with quote marks*, and followed by the source in proper bibliographical style, either in parentheses or following an em-dash. Whether to set it to the full text measure or indented on the left (and possibly on the right too) must be a matter of taste, but I do believe it should be set in roman type and not in italic, even when it is entirely in a foreign language—its position and smaller size distinguish it sufficiently from the main text.

'I believe that not only the Yugoslavs but all the Balkan peoples will one day revere Tito as the great man in whose achievements their aspirations also had a stake [. . .] The new Yugoslavia brings freedom, democracy and social justice not only to Yugoslavs. The turning point in the history of the Balkans has been reached. Just as the new Yugoslavia can only be Tito's Yugoslavia, so the new Balkans can only be Tito's Balkans.' (Michael Padev, *Marshal Tito*, London, 1944)

'De tous les roitelets rouges des Balkans, Tito était le plus glorieux.' (Raymond Aron, 10 July 1948, in *Les Articles du Figaro*, I, ed. by Georges-Marie Soutou, Paris, 1990)

'When the Century of the Common Man approaches its last quarter, one cannot help feeling grateful for a few uncommon men who are still left to us. Tito, whatever view you take of him, is certainly one of these.' (Fitzroy Maclean, in *The Sunday Times*, 3 May 1970)

'The great leader and world statesman who has led the Yugoslav peoples out of the ruins of the war, to stability at home, to respect and prestige in the world.' (Alexander Haig, US Secretary of State, in the visitors' book at Tito's tomb, as quoted in *Politika*, Belgrade, 4 May 1982)

'Tito? Who's he?' (second-year history student at Southampton University, starting a Balkan History course, 5 October 1989)

'Tito is ours! Tito is yours! Tito was ours, and you were Tito's, but that's not my fault. . . .' (parody of the old propaganda song 'Tito is ours, we are Tito's', popularised by the Belgrade rock-singer Bora Djordjević, known as Bora Čorba)

1

THE EARLY YEARS, 1892–1920: GASTARBEITER AND N.C.O.

Childhood

Marshal Tito, ruler of Communist Yugoslavia from the end of the Second World War to his death in 1980, as secretary-general of the Party, head of government, commander-in-chief and then life president, was born Josip Broz on 7 May 1892,[1] in the village of Kumrovec, in the region of Croatia known as Zagorje, some 50 kilometres north-west of Zagreb, in what was then Austria-Hungary.

The crown of Croatia had been united with that of Hungary since 1102 — a date that marks the beginning of Croatia's eight-centuries-long association with, and domination by, Hungary. In 1526–7, when a large part of its territory had been conquered by the Ottoman Turks, the Habsburgs were elected to what remained of the Hungaro-Croatian realm before proceeding to reconquer in their entirety the 'dominions of the Crown of Hungary' in the seventeenth and eighteenth centuries, and going on to acquire more South Slav populations. They already had the Slovenes in the southern part of their Austrian hereditary lands. Through the Hungarian connexion, they would rule Croatia. They were going to acquire the once Venetian Adriatic province of Dalmatia after the fall of Napoleon, in 1815, and the Turkish provinces of Bosnia and Herzegovina at the Congress of Berlin, in 1878.

In 1867 — twenty-five years before Josip Broz was born — the old family conglomerate ruled over by the House of Habsburg became the Dual Monarchy, or Austria-Hungary. It was

[1] His birthday was officially celebrated on 25 May as the Day of Youth. The date had been fixed during the war, before Tito's appointed biographer, Vladimir Dedijer, had been able to get his researchers to check the parish registers. Tito himself was not quite sure.

1

Epigraphs and opening of chapter 1 in S. Pavlowitch, *Tito* (Hurst, 1992), set in 'Bem' by Colset of Singapore. (56% of actual size)

THE PRELIMS, II

Pagination

The Prelims must be paginated with roman numerals. This is not a typographical conceit but an instrument of urgent practical necessity. A publisher who allows the pagination to be 'arabic' throughout, making the half-title 'page 1', will find himself in a straitjacket. Suppose that at the last minute, due to demands of space, he wants to omit a couple of pages from the Prelims or, due to editorial demands, add a couple, he will have to repaginate the whole book. In the age of computer setting this may seem a small matter, but it will not be if the book has already been indexed and/or contains cross-references. It is far worse if the book has to go into a new impression and, as often happens, a new Preface is required, running to several pages, for which nothing else in the Prelims can be sacrificed.

Can anyone be so foolish, the reader may ask? The answer is Yes. Not long before the time of writing, I was given camera-ready copy (CRC)—which I had paid for but not supervised—for a highly sophisticated book, and it had been paginated in this way. It was repaginated at my request with roman page-numbers* in the Prelims.

*On a question of terminology, I have thought it best in the book not to use the traditional printer's jargon word 'folio' for 'page-number' as being obscure and not indispensable.

Order

The order in which the key items in the Prelims appear is dictated by several factors, to be reviewed below. These items are (in random order) the Contents page; the lists of Illustrations, Maps, Figures and Tables; the author's Preface; the author's Acknowledgements; and a Foreword (this description implies something pretty short), Preface (a bit longer) or Introduction (much longer) written by an authority on the author's subject or (this will surely be no more than a Foreword) by a well-known personage. This list is far from exhaustive and further items will be dealt with below. There is no hard-and-fast rule; good sense must prevail.

We now consider each of these elements individually.

The contents lists

The main Contents list. This should always start on a recto, even if it is preceded by a single-page 'Acknowledgments' and thus faces a blank page. The words 'List of' or 'Table of' should never appear in the heading before 'Contents', 'Illustrations' etc.

In the listing, the Prelim items with roman pagination—e.g. *Acknowledgements*, *Preface, Acronyms, Note on Transliteration*—should be set in italic. (The lists of Illustrations etc. are sometimes included among these items by the author but should be struck out as not warranting inclusion—since they are no more than an extension of the main Contents itself.) A full line space should follow the Prelim items (a shoulder-heading on the left consisting of the word '*Chapters*' lends a sense of completeness).

After a very small extra space will follow the first chapter. I am against using roman numerals for chapters, decorative though they may be. If the number of chapters exceeds 9, care should be taken to indent numbers 1 to 9 by an 'en' space (i.e. a space equivalent to the letter 'n', a character of median width), so that they and the two-digit numerals that follow will range (typographical jargon for 'align') vertically on the right. A full-point after the numeral is neat and helps to give some vertical emphasis to counterbalance the mainly horizontal bias of the lines.

Should one include sub-chapters and sub-sub-chapters as well as chapters in the Contents listing? Some authors have a subdivision of some sort on almost every page, and in these cases it is advisable to include no more than the sub-chapters.

We prefer the chapter titles set in roman and the sub-chapter titles in italic; unlike the chapters, the sub-chapters and further sub-divisions should, without compelling reasons to the contrary, be unnumbered; an excess of numbering looks fussy. The sub-chapters should be ranged under the chapter titles, not under the chapter number. If it is deemed worthwhile to list sub-sub-chapters in the Contents listing (it is user-friendly to do so if they are not too numerous), they should also be in italic but preceded by an en-dash, ranged below the chapter and sub-chapter titles. Further division is likely to be user-unfriendly except in textbooks where aesthetics often have to be sacrificed to the 'greater good' of maximum comprehensibility. If any of these subordinate titles should over-run a single line, the second line should be indented 1 em, and in these cases the page-number must range horizontally with the *lower* line, not the upper one. This is something modern typesetters sometimes overlook if not given clear instructions, so the proof-reader should be watchful—ranging with the upper line is against nature.

Dotted lines linking the chapter titles with their page numbers—'leaders'—appear alien in modern British typography, and a mark of the amateur.

Type sizes should not be mixed within the body of the Contents list. If they are, the exigences of computer typesetting will result in some page-numbers being of different sizes from the rest, which severely upsets the typographical harmony. An exemption from this prohibition may be made for *Part titles*, which in our books are set in capitals and centred, and for which no page-number is shown for the aesthetic reasons already stated. They look well one size larger than the main matter.

How to divide the items vertically? Each chapter, plus all its 'subs', should be divided from its next neighbour by a half-line space; more looks odd, less looks mean. The chapter title should be divided from the first sub-chapter title by a wafer-thin space—0.5 mm. is enough—additional to the 1 pt 'leading' that should always divide one line of text from the following one. The sub-chapters should be divided from each other by the same 1 pt leading.

At the end of the chapters there may follow some Appendixes (*sic*—this spelling is a convention). These can be set out exactly like the chapters, with the shoulder-heading '*Appendixes*' preceding them. If the Appendixes are numerous and their titles lengthy, there will be danger of their outweighing the chapters; to help mitigate this, they can be set in a point-size lower than the chapters—or, an alternative worth considering, given a table of contents of their own on a half-title preceding the Appendixes section itself. If this is done, they need not be listed in the main Contents.

The Bibliography, if it is a general one, should not be categorised as an Appendix (setting rules for it will follow). Finally comes the Index—or indeed, possibly, the Indexes (*sic*): Index of Names, Index of Places, Index of Themes etc. Some authors, indeed some scholarly publishers, like to place Glossaries, lists of Acronyms, pronunciation guides for foreign words etc. at the end of the book. This seems to be abdicating the very purpose of having them in the book at all: i.e. to be available for quick and easy reference, which in my estimation will be quicker and easier at the front.

Setting of the Contents page should be in the same size as the book's main text, although if it is a particularly short one—e.g. with six chapters or less, and no 'subs'—one can go up a size.

List of Illustrations. If Illustrations are numerous—more than 12–15—their listing can be set one size smaller than the Contents. They should be unnumbered, unless they are of the kind where specific reference to them in the text by numbers is required. Authors often number them automatically without such references being present; one should check this point with the author, and omit the numbers if they serve no purpose. The term 'Plates' is old-fashioned; it can/could be justified for pictures separately printed on art paper, and can still be when they are of significant size and character and appear on the page solus, accompanied only by a caption. Scholarly publishers (other than those of art books) are unlikely to be printing photographs of Cecil Beaton or Cartier-Bresson quality, but neither will their photographic offerings be confined to amateur snapshots taken on anthropological field trips.

If the illustrations occur on unnumbered pages in a single block or several blocks placed strategically at intervals throughout the book, the list should be headed by (e.g.) the words '*between pages 102 and 103*', preferably two sizes of italic above that of the titles of the illustrations, and centred. If they are placed on unnumbered pages, mainly singly, throughout the book, they will all be '*facing*' a certain page, and this word by itself should be placed above the page numbers, in italic of the same size as the illustration titles, and ranged right.

Many authors like illustrations to occur on numbered text pages, cheek by jowl with the passage in the text that refers to them. This is eminently reasonable, but grouping them together, in one block or in several, can make a subtly greater aesthetic impact, in which the designer of the book should play a conscious part if this course is chosen. When, however, the pictures are specific and need to be 'dropped' into the text exactly where they are mentioned, the person who prepares the MS. for setting must take measurements to ensure that the amount of space left for each one and its accompanying caption is exactly right, neither too much nor too little. Every millimetre counts.

It may easily fall to the publisher to write the titles for the list of Illustrations, whereas the author is likely, at the publisher's request if not unbidden, to have supplied captions. The captions themselves have to be edited to achieve maximum succinctness, but the titles in the Illustrations list should be condensed to the barest essentials. E.g., in this list one would not name all the people portrayed in a group photo, but might name one of them if that person is likely to attract special attention in the context of the book.

List of Maps. Maps should be listed before the Tables—assuming that there are to be several. More compellingly than with illustrations, these should be placed through the book precisely where they are referred to. But a general map of the country or region which the book is about should fall at the very end of the Prelims, where the reader can consult it before plunging into the main text, and return to it for further consultation later without a tiresome hunt. If there is to be only one general map, it can be included among the Prelim items in the Contents list.

List of Tables. These are best numbered—by chapter and by their order within the chapter: 1.1, 1.2, 1.3, 2.1 etc. The (central) dots should be vertically ranged. Because of their strictly ancillary function, the list should be set in the type size below that of the main text and hence of the Contents. If a book contains a mere handful of not very prominent tables, listing them in the Prelims and indeed numbering them is unnecessary.

Ancillaries. There are certain ancillary items, presented more or less in tabular form—Glossary, list of Acronyms, Note on Transliteration/Pronunciation, Chronology, to cite the most common—which, as already mentioned, some publishers and some authors prefer to relegate to the end as Appendixes for fear of putting off the reader. All should have their ancillary status emphasised by being set in a size below the main text, and all—except a 'Note' on this or that, which will be in continuous prose—should be set in two columns: they are not like a dictionary, where all the information relating to a particular word is set in a continuum. The best style is to leave a small extra space (e.g. 2 points) between each item; this will improve legibility, especially if the full version of an acronym or a phrase in a glossary over-runs to more than a single line.

In a glossary foreign words should be italicised unless they are proper nouns (e.g. the name of a national assembly such as the Bundestag or the Duma) or 'proper phrases' (e.g. political parties, trade unions and institutions of all sorts). This applies equally to the full versions of acronyms.

A Chronology may run to several pages. Here too it should be set in (at least) two columns, the first a short one containing the date of the event, and then a broader one for the event itself. If there are several events that occur in a single year, they should form a group, with the year itself appearing only once, and displayed modestly as a shoulder-heading.

Acknowledgements

Here we come up against intangible matters of taste and instinct. For some authors it is natural, at the end of a Preface of 2–3 pages about the genesis and purpose of a book, to leave a space, and continue with specific acknowledgements to institutions that have financed research, mentors, personal sources of information, librarians, typists and, most important of all, spouses, children and even dogs and cats who have been deprived of the author's company but have not complained. This section can (but need not) carry the simple shoulder-heading '*Acknowledgements*'. In either case it is normal to have the author's name and the place and date of completion at the foot. Separated by a line space from the bottom line of text, the author's name looks nice set in large and small capitals ranged right, and the place and date in u.l.c. italic ranged left—the two ranged horizontally. The date is important. If perchance, due to the vicissitudes of production, the date already seems a bit ancient by the time the book is to be printed, it can be advanced to the time of going to press—but only with the permission of the author, who may have reasons for insisting on an earlier date. He should be asked at the same time if he wants to change or add anything.

But for some authors the Preface shades into an Introduction and is weightier altogether than the type of Preface adumbrated in the preceding paragraph. It might then seem less appropriate to tack on the Acknowledgements at the end, especially if this Preface runs to several pages. In these cases the Acknowledgements should immediately follow the title-verso, or the Dedication if there is one; almost certainly they will not run to more than two sides.

To bury the Contents page deeper inside the Prelims than after at most two sides of Acknowledgements smacks of pedantry. The reader wants to see it more than the Acknowledgements section, which he is likely to skip anyway if he is not mentioned in it, but the publisher must never underestimate the importance of these expressions of gratitude to the author, not only as a means of publicly discharging personal obligations but as a vehicle for self-expression. The publisher should be bold enough to carry out minor rephrasing—if only to seek variants to 'I should like to thank...'—if the author does not have a felicitous touch. He is bound to be pleased if there is a complimentary reference to himself; and if there is no such reference, complimentary or otherwise, *when the book has been commissioned by him*, he has at least the right and possibly a duty to ask for this bare fact, as part of the work's bibliographical history, to be recorded.

The Foreword

This designation usually belongs to an introductory piece by someone other than the author. Of the obvious categories, one is the short, bland puff by a well-known writer, politician or other public figure; this one hopes will not exceed, at most, two sides, and may well fit into a single side. The writer's name should appear at the top:

FOREWORD

*by Sir Florizel Glasspole**

It is helpful for reference to put the date at the foot, in italic, ranged left. As a flourish, a facsimile signature of the great person (if great enough) in exactly the correct size can be placed at the bottom (centre right).

Another category is the supporting essay, commentary, call it what one will, by an eminent authority in the same field as the author of the book. Sometimes this will accompany a work by a young and previously unknown scholar or, as in a recent experience of ours, the re-issue of a famous work by a well-known author who is too old—or unwilling for some other reason—to contribute a new preface himself. Here the writer's name should appear at the beginning, as in the other category, but it is helpful for the place as well as the date of composition to appear at the foot.

Out of courtesy to the writer, and because of its brevity, a Foreword in the first category should immediately follow the copyright page and precede the Contents page. If it is longer than two sides, it should follow the Contents and ancillary lists (Illustrations, Maps, Tables and suchlike only), and precede any Preface to this or a previous impression by the author himself. In such a case it is best to pack Acknowledgements in with the Preface.

*A genuine case and not an invention by the Marx Brothers: he was once Governor-General of Jamaica.

The author's Preface

(with or without Acknowledgements attached)

This, as already indicated, should not be confused with the Introduction, although it is sometimes difficult to distinguish precisely between the functions of the two. The author should be discouraged from making the Prelims too long, but it is legitimate for the preamble, apologia or however else one may describe this relatively intimate address to the reader to continue for up to about 10 pages.

Some authors like to set out the schema for the work to come, as if it were a thesis. I discourage this, unless it is done in the most general terms; a summary of the chapters is surely unnecessary, except in a multi-author 'edited' volume where it does make sense for the editor's Preface to include such a summary, since there is likely to be considerable variation in the content and character of the various chapters, and not every user of the book will necessarily want or need to read every chapter.

We will say a little more about Introductions when we have crossed the barrier from the end of the Prelims to page 1.

Map(s)

A general map is best placed as the last item in the Prelims. If there is to be just one map which can fit easily on a single page, the best place for it is a recto, followed by a blank. If space is too short to allow two pages to be allotted to one map, it can simply go on the last verso of the Prelims facing page 1. There can be two or more general maps: in one of the books by Pavlowitch already mentioned, there are three maps of Yugoslavia. The first contains rivers and mountains, towns and regions without regional boundaries; the second shows the country's political divisions before the First World War; and the third the same after the Second. All appear in the Prelims on two consecutive pairs of facing pages. On the preceding recto is the half-title 'MAPS' with an acknowledgment in small type at the foot to the mapmaker. The verso following the third map is blank.

It is obviously more appropriate to place maps showing (e.g.)

industries, movements of forces in a war, changes of frontiers, demography or a particular region of a country in the parts of the book to which they refer and which refer to them, and not in the Prelims.

With the general map of a country—I refer to this here because we are dealing at this point only with general maps—the question arises of whether, for the sake of the less knowledgeable, to include a thumbnail 'position map' showing the country in its regional setting, or the region in its continental setting. Europeans would disdain to 'place', say, Yugoslavia or Belgium in this way, but if the book were about a European region like Kosovo or the Basque country, a Central Asian republic or a state in tropical Africa, there would be a feeling that it might be useful if not indispensable. The next question that arises in this case is where to put it. If it can be inset in an 'empty quarter' of the first general map, well and good. If not it can go below the half-title already mentioned. In any case an acceptable solution will suggest itself.

There is more on Maps below (pp. 61–3).

Starting on rectos

The Acknowledgments (as a separate entity), the Contents, a Foreword by another person, and the Author's Preface must (not merely 'should') all start on rectos. The subsidiary 'Contents' items—lists of Illustrations etc.—simply follow without a page break from the Contents page(s). Each of these should ideally start on a new page, whether recto or verso; but if, say, the lists of Illustrations and Maps are short enough to fit together comfortably on a single page, they may do so. Or, if one of them is short, and there is space to spare on the final page of the main Contents, below the entry '*Index*', it can go there.

Those other characteristic Prelim items—Glossary, list of Acronyms, notes on orthography and/or pronunciation etc.—can, like the various 'Contents' items, be treated as a single group, each starting immediately following its predecessor, on either a recto or a verso. However, the first should start on a recto unless space is a severe problem.

Suppressed page numbers—right and wrong

No page number should appear anywhere on the opening half-title, the frontispiece, the title-page, the copyright page, a page containing solely a dedication or an epigraph, a half-title for the opening of a Part, or any blank. For one to do so offends against an unwritten rule of typographical etiquette.

Conversely, it is a widespread but (to this writer), incomprehensible custom to suppress the page number for the opening page of each chapter and each section of the Prelims, and to include it only on subsequent pages. Sometimes this is done as an affectation; but it also apparently arises from difficulties in some typesetters' computer programmes. Whatever the cause, it is a gratuitous inconvenience for the reader and must be avoided, if necessary by the use of scissors and paste. On chapter and section openers, the page number looks comfortable centred at the foot.

Section titles

(Contents, Tables, Preface, Glossary etc.)

These should be set a size smaller than the chapter titles in the main body of the book: either 12 pt roman caps, centred (compared to 14 pt for the chapter titles), or 14 pt roman u.l.c., ranged left (compared to 18 pt).

Running headlines

These should not at any point incorporate the title of the book. Both verso and recto headlines should simply read '*Contents*', '*Preface*' etc.

Farewell to the Prelims

It is a bonus if the final verso of the Prelims can be a blank, giving a breathing-space, but the way the succession of Prelim items falls may rule this out. A complete blank page (i.e. blank on both sides) at this point, even if one can be spared, looks affected—or as if someone has slipped up.

FORMAT AND TYPEFACE

These two all-important elements are arrived at by the publisher according to subjective criteria. Thus it is impossible to lay down firm rules. But, as with all aspects of the invisible art of book design, the right choice is not noticed but merely enjoyed, while a misjudged choice is noticeable and causes pain.

Format

A scholarly publisher in the social sciences or humanities is unlikely, without a compelling reason, to stray outside demy 8vo (octavo) or royal 8vo. The first has a trim size of 8.5 by 5.5 inches and a type area of 7 by 4 inches (42 by 24 pica ems); the second has a trim size of 9 by 6 inches and a type area of 7.5 by 4.5 inches (45 by 27 pica ems).* What should determine which one to choose?

The choice of royal 8vo, as the larger of the two, may be dictated simply by the presence of maps and illustrations which, if reduced to make them fit demy 8vo, would look too small. Even then, the less tangible criteria come into play—and may necessitate that extra squeeze required by demy. The book may simply not be suitable for royal. Some authors ask outright for

*Naturally what is suitable for demy 8vo or royal 8vo will be too big for 12mo and too small for folio. But we are concerned here with the 'human sciences' (to use the French term), where demy and royal 8vo are the standard sizes.

the larger size, or strongly hint that it would be more suitable for the book. Their usual reason is that it would somehow make the book more imposing and harder to ignore. This may be true or it may not be, and sometimes authors have to be gently persuaded that a smaller size is preferable. Our author contracts give us, the publishers, control over production, but, needless to say, this has to be exercised with tact and sometimes considerable patience.

Royal 8vo is most likely to be seen as desirable when the nature of the book requires the slightly but perceptibly grander format. We have used it for a two-volume history, a four-volume 19th-century scientific travelogue, a single-volume history of a famous German-Jewish merchant bank, and assorted biographies and autobiographies, most containing illustrations. With all these books we wanted to make a bit of an extra splash: if they had been in demy, we would have given the authors—and even more the republic of letters—less than they merited. For every book there is a right format, and it is one of the skills required of the publisher to know instinctively and automatically which it is. It may seem a minor skill, but it is a consequential one because a wrong decision, once put fully into effect, is obviously irreversible.* (Needless to say, the rules in trade publishing are different: a new bumper novel will be published in royal with a luxurious binding case, for no instrinsic reason but as part of a general marketing strategy, so that buyers will think they have got value for money, especially when they see the cheap paperback appearing a little later. It is all the more wasteful because quite a proportion of the print-run will end up as 'returns', destined for the junk-heap.)

In 1999 we had a disagreement over the format of a most distinguished literary book, of which the author's institute (also a publisher) supplied us with camera-ready setting, for which we paid. Because it contained numerous parallel headings in Chinese, it could have been set nowhere else in practice but in East Asia. When I learned that the setting was in royal 8vo format, every instinct told me that it should have been demy, as being

*It is not irreversible today until the page-proof stage is completed and the index has been set. With computer setting, the typeface and the format can be changed at the press of a button.

the natural, 'comfortable' format. The institute agreed to many small amendments I asked for, but insisted on sticking with royal, which was the format of a series of its own publications in which this was to be included.

Royal naturally costs more than demy, since it uses more paper and more binding material. There will be no saving on the extent (length) because a type-size suitable for the main text of a demy book with a 'measure' (line length) of 24 ems will appear attenuated if the measure is increased to 27 ems (the effect of generosity, which one strives to achieve by choosing the royal format, will be undermined with a vengeance if the type is too small). If one were to set the main text of a demy 8vo book in 10/11 pt Times or Baskerville, or in 11/12 pt Bembo, royal would require 11/12 pt Times or Baskerville, or 12/13 pt Bembo.

Typeface

The economy and flexibility publishers have achieved, and the relative ease of making corrections, by moving from metal to computer typesetting must put all other considerations in the shade. Those 'other' considerations are aesthetic ones—thus putting them in the shade is not a small matter. The Monotype Corporation's range of metal fonts might not have been wholly to the liking of Christophe Plantin, Giambattista Bodoni, Cardinal Pietro Bembo, Claude Garamond, William Caslon or John Baskerville, but compared to what has succeeded them—and especially to someone who worked with them every day (and thought nothing of it) and has seen their demise and the wonderful Monotype type-casting machines sold off for scrap—they represent Arcadia. Computer setting can produce fine types and layouts but the ultimate refinements of design of the characters themselves, and of spacing, have vanished like the snows of yesteryear.

There can be no purely objective standards for the choice of a book's typeface, but rules-of-thumb have to be made, and even if these are subjective in origin, they acquire in time an objective-seeming status. Using criteria which defy logic, my firm tends to choose the typeface according to the part of the world a book is about—for a list to which the label 'Area Studies' has become attached this perhaps has a logic of its own. We have a partiality for Bembo, but use Times, with its less literary and more 'workmanlike' character, when the subject is related to supranational organisations or to economics; for most multi-author volumes; and where textbook potential exists. We also occasionally use Baskerville and Garamond, but have never found a niche for Plantin. As a text face Caslon, though a classic, had already acquired an antiquarian flavour well before the demise of metal, and we have therefore never used it except in larger sizes for display on title-pages (see p.9) and covers—and once for an elderly author's new Introduction to our facsimile reprint of a book of his printed in that face many years earlier: the match, unsurprisingly, was perfect.* Today even finding two truly matching examples of computer-generated type, supposedly in the same typeface but obtained from different sources, can be difficult; variations—in which the degree of refinement is a significant factor—seem infinite. In recent years we have published several reprints of books first produced in the age of metal type, and, when setting new ancillary material, had to be content with an approximate matching. Yet in two of these we had to follow eccentric typographical design in the original—oddly placed chapter titles, running heads, folios etc. One had a jumbo-sized bold initial capital for the first word in each chapter, and of course we had to imitate this in our new Introduction—luckily the letter in question (W) could be photocopied from a later chapter. This same book, of some 1,000 pages, had 2 pt leading throughout, a fact we had overlooked until we received the proof of the new Introduction; of course we then had to increase the leading in it to match.

In another of these reprints we noticed that on the second page of main text King Haakon VII of Norway was referred to as a son of Christian IX of Denmark, and because he was actually

*That was in 1969 (the book was *Cyprus under the Turks* by Sir Harry Luke, original edn OUP, 1921), when Monotype Caslon was readily available (of all the classic faces Caslon has made the transition to computer-generation least successfully—testimony to the subtlety of the original). It was rather more of an achievement, in 1993, to get a perfect match—also for a new Introduction and a supplement to the old Bibliography—for Monotype Bembo, printed in 1970. It was supplied by Mould Type of Preston, Lancashire (the book was *Mannerheim: The Years of Preparation* by J.E.O. Screen, which had always been our publication). It was expensive but worth every penny.

a grandson this could not be allowed to stand. By a singularly fortunate chance the erroneous statement filled exactly one full line, so we took it out, dropped the preceding matter by a single-line space to fill the gap, and brought a line over from the previous page—because that was the opening page of the chapter, with a big 'drop', the sleight-of-hand was undetectable. The whole operation was done with a good photocopier, paste and scissors. Later in the book we also found a reference to 'Archduke Ferdinand of Austria' (see the 'Franz Ferdinand syndrome', p. 102) and by a more complicated piece of surgery inserted the missing 'Franz'. The same operation was performed in the Index, and in addition moving the entry down to below 'France' might not have overtaxed our skill, but in the end this did not seem worth the effort. However, in this process we did make the book, infinitesmally, a sounder work of historical scholarship than it had been before—which, added to the fact that the reprint has sold well, cannot be a bad thing.

Times is a 20th-century English face with—as suggested above—an open, accessible, non-arty character, designed for the eponymous newspaper by Stanley Morison, and of all accepted classics it seems to have lost least in the transition from metal.

Care has to be taken with Bembo for two reasons. The vital one is that compared to the other faces it has a small 'x-height', with correspondingly long ascenders and descenders. This means that it has to be set one size larger than they do in order to be read comfortably. In a demy 8vo book the text would therefore need to be in 11/12 pt (with Bibliography in 10/11 pt, and Notes and Index in 9/10 pt); in a royal 8vo book these sizes would be increased by one point-size. Also, because of the long ascenders and descenders, Bembo italic is especially liable to 'snagging' (see p. 50).

With all computer setting, lines are liable to be set too tight or too loose. In the former instance, the intrinsic nature of the typeface becomes distorted, and unrecognisable. In the latter, letterspacing within words occurs; wordspacing is far preferable; but probably neither is truly necessary. Letterspacing can achieve nice effects with words set in capitals, but should be avoided in lower case, which is not suited to it.

THE BOOK PROPER

Chapter opening

We are now at page 1, the beginning of the book. The chapter numbering should begin here. An Introduction, in the proper sense (i.e. as opposed to a preface), should be Chapter 1 (not Chapter I—romanised chapter numbers are a thing of the past*). It can be titled simply 'Introduction'; or, much better, it can be given a title like any subsequent chapter, but with the word 'Introduction' preceding it. A sufficiently elegant formula is:

1

INTRODUCTION

THE COUNTRY AND THE PEOPLE

Each line will be set in 14 pt, the word 'INTRODUCTION' in small capitals

(We need not bother about archaic flourishes like starting the text with a giant initial capital, occupying a depth of 3 lines or more, or setting the first word or two of the first line in capitals. These can look nice if well done, and if the subject-matter of the book does not appear to prohibit such a 'literary' convention, but a classic model should be consulted for guidance.)

*On the other hand, romanised Part or Volume numbers have a purpose, which is to provide a contrast with the 'arabic' chapter numbers. Contrast aids clarity.

The main text

In one of our demy 8vo books this will be set in 10/11 pt Times or Baskerville, or in 11/12 pt Bembo; in a royal 8vo one it will be in 11/12 pt Times or Baskerville, or in 12/13 pt Bembo (which we have successfully used in short books and attempt in this book).

The first line of the first paragraph of each new chapter or sub-chapter is 'full-out', i.e. not indented, but that of each subsequent paragraph in the chapter is indented by the space of 1 em *and no more*; excessive indentation bears the mark either of ignorance or of tiresome affectation.

The 1 point (one-seventy-second of an inch) of 'leading' between lines, signified by (say) '10/11pt'—i.e. 10 pt type on an 11 pt body, to use metal terminology—gives a necessary element of 'air' to a page. Without it, i.e. if set 'solid', the page will look over-dense and be wearisome to read. Setting type in a small size but with generous leading became a new fashion in literary publishing in the late 1990s. This needs, and has the mark of, skill and confidence, and is aesthetically appealing, but for scholarly texts it might be thought that form and content did not match, and that more conventional models should continue to be followed. In outlandishly bad setting one may encounter an extra space between paragraphs.

For 'widows' and 'orphans' see below, pp. 46–7.

The many elements of which the main text especially, but also other text, is made up are dealt with separately below.

Quoted extracts

Short quotations in the main text do not generally need to be extracted: they can be placed within quotation marks (hereafter 'quotes'), and 'run on', i.e. beginning on the same line as the immediately preceding matter. (Some authors—whimsically, one may think—prefer not to extract quotations of any length.) Where the dividing line comes between quotations which can be accommodated within the text and those that should be extracted is hard to say: 3 lines? 5 lines? The test should be whether a particular quotation needs, even demands, to be displayed by extraction. The assiduous reader will take it in just as well (or possibly better?) if it remains embedded within the main text, and there is no break.

The quoted extract can be treated typographically in one of two alternative basic styles to establish the necessary typographical contrast: (1) set in the same size as the main text but indented (1 em on the left is the norm); or (2) set in the next size smaller than the main text, but to the full measure, i.e. not indented.

In either case there should be a space equivalent to half a line above and below the extract. For a long quotation I prefer alternative (2), but of course the only firm rule is that the style chosen must be used consistently throughout the work. A quoted extract should only be placed within quotes when it consists of speech. To place quotes around an extracted quotation from, e.g., a book or a document is an error authors often fall into, and it must be corrected.

An interpolation by the author within a quotation of any length, whether the latter is extracted or run on, should be placed within square brackets. This can be, e.g., to supply a word missing in the original which is essential to convey the sense; the name of someone referred to by a pronoun; an explanatory observation by 'our' author including, e.g., 'emphasis added' or 'emphasis in original' (such observations should *not* be followed by the author's initials); the translation of a foreign word; or, conversely, a key word used in the original text of which the quotation is a translation.

A minor problem of style arises over the way one makes the transition from the main text to the extract. Often the extract is preceded by words to the effect that so-and-so said, argued or declared (the following:). Some writers put 'that' after 'said', 'argued' etc., but mostly this is not necessary and should be deleted. It is neater not to say (e.g.) 'said' at all but, e.g., to precede the quotation with a sentence such as 'X. conveys well the general shape of bourgeois society across the entire region:' or 'Much the same point is made by Y.:'. But sometimes a writer wants to establish what I would call an 'organic' link between the main text and the extract by making the beginning of the quotation (usually occurring in mid-sentence) the second part of a sentence of his own. It is effected by elision: the main text can be cut off without a punctuation mark, and the first word of the extract will not be capitalised—but it should preferably be preceded by four dots.

Quotation marks ('quotes')

Double quotes seem to me to be in the same category as the ending '-ize' (as opposed to '-ise'): as belonging to a slightly earlier period of English usage than the present, although, characteristically, they have remained the norm in the United States.

It is hardly necessary to remind the reader that quotes within quotes are differentiated by being double if the outer ones are single, and vice versa—just as brackets within brackets are 'square' ones, the outer ones (invariably) being round.* We need to consider here whether single or double quotes are preferable for 'primary' use (i.e. in the outer position). Our instinctive preference is for single ones, but we have usually fallen in with the preference of authors—and some clearly prefer double quotes, probably thinking them more 'natural'. I share this aesthetic preference where it comes to informal writing, e.g. of letters, but for our house-style we have come to the conclusion that we should urge our authors wherever possible to accept single ones. The reason is that, here as in other things, there has not been an easy transition from metal to computer-generated type. Double quotes seem particularly liable to snagging (see p. 50), which has to be corrected where it occurs—a laborious business. Also the twin inverted commas sometimes do not appear to lie very comfortably together, as if they really belong to each other.

A disadvantage of using single quotes is that if a plural word ending with an apostrophe occurs within a small quotation, it sets up a visual confusion. The same is liable to happen with transliterations of Arabic (also Persian and Urdu), where the

*Some authors accord a primary function to square brackets (e.g. in bibliographical notation) and to both single and double quotes in the same work. There is no convention governing either of these practices, and it is much better to use square brackets only within quotes or within parentheses (round brackets), a rare exception being their somewhat ornamental use in the running heads of endnotes (see p. 49)—and to decide at the outset whether single or double quotes will have primacy, and stick to that usage exclusively.

'*alif* and '*ain* occur. Momentarily one may wonder where the quotation actually ends. But this has to be borne.

Where a word or phrase in quotes occurs within a quotation but at the end of it (or, more rarely, at the beginning), care has to be taken *not* to show the neighbouring single and double quotes as three characters placed side by side without differentiation ("'). They must appear as follows: ' " or " '. The proof-corrector rather than the copy-editor has to be alert to this.

When should quotes and brackets be italicised and when not? The answer is that they should be italicised when they occur integrally *within* a piece of text setting which, for whatever reason, is in italic. They should be set in roman when they simply enclose a word, phrase or sentence in italic, of which the context is set in roman. This is a rather arcane rule, of which most typesetters today seem to be unaware, but it is necessary in order to avoid rampant inconsistency in these tiny details; the tendency of typesetters is to think that quotes or brackets (or both) must submit automatically to the typographic 'influence' of the matter they enclose.

Running headlines

These are commonly referred to in speech as 'running heads' and in writing as 'r/heads'. Here there are clear rules, as follows:

1. When the division is into chapters but there are no sub-chapters, put the book title on the verso and the chapter title on the recto.

2. Where there are sub-chapters, put the chapter title on the verso and the sub-chapter title on the recto. Note also:

   a. To create a visual distinction between the two, begin every significant word in the chapter title with a capital, but use lower case for the sub-chapter title except for the first word and proper names. (This assumes that u.l.c. italic is being used—see below.)

   b. On the electrical principle that like poles repel each other, a sub-chapter heading on a recto and the same words in a running head look horrible when too close together, and particularly when in direct proximity, i.e. when the heading occurs at the top of the page. How close is too close? Perhaps if the sub-chapter heading falls at least two-thirds of the way down the page, they are not too close. Otherwise the trick is to repeat on the recto the chapter title that appears on the verso.

3. In an 'edited' collection of contributions by different authors, put the author's name on the verso and the chapter title on the recto—the latter, if necessary, 'edited down' in length to fit.

4. The running head is automatically the same for both verso and recto in the following: lists of Contents, Illustrations or Tables running to more than one page each; in a Foreword by someone other than the author; in the author's Preface and Acknowledgments; in a Glossary, Chronology or any other Prelim item; in the Bibliography; in a block of Notes at the back of the book; and in the Index. The title of the book should not, in these cases, appear on the verso.

5. Where Notes are placed at the end of chapters, there is one solution for categories 1 and 3 above, and a different one for category 2. For 1 and 3, the r/heads should remain the same for the Notes as throughout the chapter. For 2, continue with the chapter title on the verso, but have '*Notes*' on the recto.

6. Appendixes. A reasonable solution would seem to be to have '*Appendixes*' or (e.g.) '*Appendix A*' on the verso and the title of the particular Appendix on the recto.

What is to be done when the r/head is longer than the space allowed for it, and is difficult to condense while still making sense? An obvious and quite elegant solution is to set it in two lines that are equidistant above and below the median line occupied by the page-number and by the one-line r/head on the facing page. The distance between that median line and the first line of the main text below it should not be increased. Computer setting often cannot deliver this refinement, but it should be kept in reserve until it no longer presents a problem to typesetters.

For the sake of differentiation, r/heads must be set in a manner that contrasts with the main text, yet is in harmony with it. An obvious way to achieve this is to use italic of the same font as the main text. This allows for a single line to be set without occupying an uncomfortably large space. If the author is economical in the use of words and has short chapter titles, u.l.c. italic may look less comfortable: then use a suitable size of capitals—one size smaller than the main text is probably ideal.

The r/head, in whatever style it is set, should be centred on the column of text below it. A horrible aberration into which typesetters have been known to fall is to centre the r/head between the page-number and the opposite margin; it looks so bad because it is nearly but not quite centred *vis-à-vis* the column of text. In classic (metal-based) typography it could never have happened, and should never be allowed to happen now.

Notes

Most of the books we publish contain notes, and some contain a lot. Wherever they are placed according to the criteria discussed below, they will ideally be set two sizes smaller than the main text; anything else makes them either too large or too small.

Notes fall into two basic types:

(1) supporting references to sources, with the minimum of comment or none, and

(2) narrative which supplements or, one could say, runs parallel with the main text, but would appear too diversionary if left within it.* A good copy-editor may suggest to the author transferring such a piece from the main text to a note, or, if an item in a footnote appears sufficiently important, vice versa.

Type (2) undoubtedly needs to be, literally, a footnote, so that it can be read in tandem with the main text without the need to search for it elsewhere in the book. Having Type (1) at the foot of the page gives a somewhat arid appearance.

If the author tends to confine notes mainly to unadorned source references, but occasionally to hold forth at some length, the two types can be split. The discursive notes can be placed at the foot of the page and flagged with an asterisk or, if more than one occur on a single page, with an asterisk, a dagger (†),

*Edward Gibbon must be the supreme exponent of this practice.

a double-cross (‡) and a paragraph sign (§), in that order, while the simple references can be numbered and grouped elsewhere.

Another use of divided notation is when a book, usually a biography or a history, contains references to a large number of persons, living or dead. Arguably more handy than a separate section of potted biographies is a series of footnotes giving a bare outline of the person's life-history, flagged with asterisks etc. Attaching even more slimmed-down versions of these notes to the index entries is another expedient.

To what other places should sets of references be relegated? There are two possibilities: (1) at the end of each chapter and (2) at the end of the book, after any Appendix but before the Bibliography. The latter system has the virtue of being more easily located. Certainly it should only be used if the notes are copious. More of this below (p. 49).

Let us deal briefly with the alternative forms of bibliographical references. The need for notes that consist solely of references can be obviated if, following the quotation in the text (or extracted), the Harvard system is used, viz. a parenthesis is inserted as follows: '(Brown, 1993a, 330–1)'. The work referred to can then be tracked down in the Bibliography. This also obviates the problem of how precisely to refer to works in notes if the traditional method is used. If that method is used, the first reference to a work is straightforward: author, title, number of volumes if more than one, place of publication, publisher, date of publication (mentioning date of first publication if a reprint has been published appreciably later), page number of location of source referred to. Some authors even include the number of pages in the work noted, but this is excessively zealous. In subsequent references to the same work, only the author, the shortest possible unmistakable rendering of the title and the location need be mentioned.

There was a time when it was customary, when employing footnotes, to number them afresh for each page. This, happily, now seems to be outdated, and I would over-rule any author's preference for this method (it last happened very recently) on the grounds of house-style. I can only recommend numbering right through the chapter (*never* right through the book), even if the number rises to 100 or more.

A possible advantage of not using the Harvard method is that if every work referred to is spelt out with its full bibliographical particulars in the footnotes, the absolute need for a bibliography is removed. But this only applies if the Bibliography does not contain works other than those which are specifically referred to. Where it is desired to present the sources, primary and secondary, in full, one cannot dispense with a bibliography—which is undoubtedly an asset to any book, however much it may be abbreviated.

We will return to endnotes and the Bibliography in their place below.

Now for the style of bibliographical entries in notes. First, in roman type, the author with forename or initials first, followed by the surname. Then, for a book, follows the title in italic, with (if the work is in English) a colon following it where there is a subtitle, the subtitle followed by a comma—which would follow the title if there is no subtitle. In all other languages than English, the title and subtitle are divided not by a colon but by a full-point. In French most notably, it seems to be the invariable rule that only the first word of the title and of the subtitle starts with a capital (proper nouns excepted), but in English-language works there is no fixed rule, and one has to improvise. One might go for each noun, verb and important adjective and adverb being capitalised in the title but follow the French style in the subtitle; or have capitals in these places throughout both title and subtitle. Or one could follow the French style—without, however, sacrificing our native colon in favour of the continental full-point. One could omit the capital following the mid-way colon (it clearly cannot be omitted after the continental full-point). The only absolute rule is, of course, consistency in the application of whatever style is chosen.

If the reference is to an *article* in a newspaper or journal, the title of that article follows the author's name, and is in roman type within quotes; it, in turn, is followed by a comma, followed by the title of the periodical in italic. With English-language periodicals it is generally safe, as well as desirable, to omit '*The*' wherever it occurs although, according to old custom, exceptions are made for *The Times* and *The Economist*. Where the title of a journal is rather long (e.g. the *British Journal of Middle East Studies*), and it occurs often, initials can be used after its first occurrence, where '(hereafter *BJMES*)' should be added. If the organ referred to is in a foreign language and the meaning of its title is not likely to be understood by the majority of readers (very well-known ones like *Pravda, Der Spiegel* or *Le Monde* are natural exceptions), an English translation can be inserted at its first occurrence, in parenthesis. A further minute qualification here is that this might be more desirable in footnotes, which may be seen by every reader, than in endnotes, which will only be sought out by specialists.

If the reference is to a *chapter* in an 'edited' (multi-author) work, the chapter title will again be in roman type within quotes, but followed not by a comma but by the word 'in' and the full apparatus for the work in which it appears, as

> ... in B.J. Smith (ed.), *The Agriculture of Siberia*, New York: Columbia University Press, 1997, pp. 131–55.
>
> ... in B.J. Smith and E. Murgatroyd (eds), ...
>
> ... in B.J. Smith, E. Murgatroyd *et al.* (eds), ...

Note that 'ed.', being cut off before the final letter of the word, has a full-point after the 'd', but 'eds', which includes the final letter of the word, does not (it is the same with 'vol.' and 'vols'). Parenthesising 'ed.' and 'eds' is optional; placing them between commas is just as good. Also note that the complete word '*et*', in '*et al.*', does not have a full-point whereas '*al.*', short for '*alii*', does.

There are various permutations for representing the co-ordinates of a journal article. It is usual to state the number of the volume, and of the 'number' within the volume, as well as the year, followed by the page reference. This can be done economically, as

> 23, 2 (1995), 250–71

or, more long-windedly, as

> vol. 23, no. 2 (1995), pp. 250–71.

The second gives instant clarity but the first is clear to those used to finding their way round bibliographies, and saves many key-strokes.

If the reference is to a book, the drill for setting out the author(s), title and subtitle is as for articles and chapters, but giving the publication details admits of some variation. The ideal is to name both the place of publication and the publisher, in the following manner:

London: Macmillan

Oxford: Blackwell

I refuse to give the name of the town where a university press has the same name, cutting down 'Princeton: Princeton University Press' to plain 'Princeton University Press'. It is the same with Oxford, Cambridge, Manchester and Edinburgh in Britain; although Oxford University Press was based in London for many decades of the 20th century, there is scarcely any need to put in 'London:' although strictly that might seem to be required. 'Oxford: Clarendon Press' for OUP's academic imprint has always been the correct form.

There is no objection to having 'Macmillan, London' instead of 'London: Macmillan', but 'London, Macmillan' is not acceptable.

While it helps to name the publisher, it should not be compulsory. The place has priority, and the publisher should not be named without it.

Some authors mistakenly give the name of an American state without the name of the town; this must be corrected, even if it means a little research.

Old-style 'Mass.', 'Calif.', 'Ill.' etc. for states are out. It is now 'MA', 'CA', 'IL' etc. without full-points. 'DC' for District of Columbia should also have no full-points.

If the place of publication is, e.g., a city on the European continent, use the English name for it if one exists, such as Cologne for Köln, Munich for München, Vienna for Wien, Zurich for Zürich, The Hague for Den Haag, Copenhagen for København. Where a book was published in Mumbai or Chennai when they were still called, respectively, Bombay and Madras, use the old forms.

Likewise, phrases like '*bearbeitet von*' and '*herausgegeben von*', both meaning 'edited by', should be translated. A slightly more moot point concerns 'Bd' and 'Tome', respectively German and French for 'volume': since they are invariably followed by a numeral, it is pretty obvious what they mean. But the former kind of phrase should be rooted out. We even had an Icelandic author putting relatively lengthy pieces of impenetrable Icelandic 'bibliographese' into his excellent Bibliography. He was sorry to see them go, but agreed with a good grace.

Some authors, again, will name more than one publisher if a book has been simultaneously co-published in different countries (notably Britain and America). This may help in tracing it in a library catalogue but is not necessary, and bound to be hit-and-miss because it is almost impossible to do it consistently. Therefore better state the place of original publication if that is easily ascertained; otherwise the only known place of publication. (Speaking for myself, a British publisher will feel piqued to see a book his firm originated attributed solely to the American co-publisher who imported it, and want this changed.)

If the edition (as distinct from the impression) cited is not the first, it should be stated which edition it is; there is no need to give the date of the original edition. If the title in question has been reprinted, probably with new apparatus, the original edition having been out of print, the date and place of first publication can be given, as

> ..., London: Frank Cass, 1967 (prev. publ. Oxford, 1898).

Where a citation is of a translated work, a parenthesis should be inserted immediately after the title, e.g.

> ... (transl. by R. Machetzki from the German *Die Ära Mao Tse-tung*, 1972)

The date must naturally precede that of English publication, and the length of the time-lag can be of some minor interest.

If the work consists of more than one volume, published at different dates, the information can be conflated thus:

> ... 3 vols, Oxford University Press, 1985, 1987 and 1990.

Where the reference is to a specific volume, the form is

... *Sahara and Sudan*, vol. IV: *Wadai and Darfur*, ...

Numbering of footnotes. What style should be adopted for this humble function? Of the possible alternatives I would opt for the numeral placed on and not above the line, followed by a full-point, and the full-point followed by an en-space before the matter begins. The second and subsequent lines to be vertically ranged on the beginning of the matter, as

72. Roger B. Porter, *Presidential Decision Making: The Economic Policy Board*, Cambridge University Press, 1980, p. 35.

Although it is neat, and practicable in a Contents list, to range the full-points following the key numerals vertically when the change from single- to double-digit occurs, it is virtually impracticable in Notes and not worth attempting.

Op. cit., ibid. What of those old standbys '*ibid.*' and '*op.cit.*', and, further, should they be italicised? To the latter question the answer is 'Better to do so'. To the former, it is 'Avoid them wherever possible'. I see a definite use for '*ibid.*': there is aesthetic offence in repeating in full a reference which has appeared in the previous line—this is equally true if the only change is a page number, where a notation such as '*Ibid.*, p. 35' is called for.

'*Op.cit.*', on the other hand, is beset with difficulty, and can be very confusing if more than one work by the author concerned is referred to in the course of the Notes. How much better to use the author's surname only and an abbreviated title, of which the reader can be warned by inserting, the first time the full title is cited, '(hereafter—)'—or give no such warning if the abbreviation is obvious, as in most cases it can be.

There are arguments as to whether '*op.cit.*' or an abbreviated title in lieu of it should be carried on from one chapter to the next. I would say that it can be, but only if there is a Bibliography for quick reference.

Making footnotes fit; widows

Compositional skill has always been needed by the typesetter to place every footnote correctly, i.e. on the same page as the superscript reference to it. If the latter falls too near the end of a page to allow both it and the related footnote to be carried over to the following page without disturbance to the general layout, the beginning of the note (assuming it consists of several lines) can be placed under the related superscript and the remaining lines placed at the foot of the next page with a light rule some 20 mm. long, ranged left, placed 2 mm. above it. This little rule performs a distinct and useful function and, in order that it can preserve that function, *rules should not be inserted above footnotes which do not over-run.*

There is only one situation where the disturbance to the layout referred to in the previous paragraph is permissible: viz. when a new sub-chapter or sub-sub-chapter begins at the top of the next page. To begin any new section low down on a page without a minimum of two lines of text below the section's title looks too skimpy. To begin it with the section's title alone, with the first line over-page, offends against every aesthetic and editorial principle.

Between the top line of the footnotes and the bottom line of main text there should ideally be a space at least equivalent to one line. It can be a little more, but not much more; large gaps in this position are ugly. However, the typesetter may conclude that leaving such a space has been made necessary when the alternative is to have a 'widow'—i.e. the last line of a paragraph, which in almost every instance consists of less than a complete line—as the top line on the next page. Widows are most troublesome when they consist of one or two words only; they offend the eye less when they occupy almost a complete line. But far better start the page with a *full line*, however short the one following it. (Sometimes, even well within the body of a page, the final line of a paragraph consisting of, say, one syllable of three letters has the disturbing effect of a widow and should be eliminated somehow.)

An 'orphan' is the first line of a paragraph occurring as the last line of a page. This is only mildly disturbing to the eye, and if unavoidable need cause no worry.

There are certain tricks to which the publisher can resort to eliminate widows and excessive gaps between text and footnote. One can look first to see whether the context permits the superscript reference to be moved up or down a line or two. Very likely it cannot, so one then looks to see if the widow can be removed by judicious cutting in the previous few lines without damaging the sense in order to absorb it into the preceding line—or by a judicious addition to enable a line to go over to the next page and thus make the short line a widow no longer. Often this is possible. Sometimes there is a need to cut a couple of lines on a page, and one immediately looks for very short lines to make this process easier. Conversely, when there is a need to add a line, or more than a line, to get rid of an unsightly gap, one looks for the longest lines at the end of paragraphs, where it may not be necessary to add more than a couple of words to run over. If neither adding nor subtracting a line or lines is possible on one page, one looks at neighbouring pages. An extra line can also be made by breaking a long paragraph at an editorially suitable point; there have to be enough characters in the bottom line of the paragraph to create the extra line when the break is made. Similarly a line can be lost by running two short paragraphs together.

There is another respectable way of slightly lengthening or shortening pages: this is by making a double-page spread longer or shorter than the norm by one line (but absolutely no more). It is unwise to tamper with spaces within pages where these are regulated by convention, viz. around sub-chapter titles and quoted extracts—not least because typesetters' computers often seem incapable of coping with these nuances. However, a practice which, convenient though it may seem, should be avoided like the plague is the fractional increasing or decreasing of leading to (respectively) fill and create space on a page. It offends against every canon of classical typography.

A widow of a different sort occurs if a chapter ends with a page containing so few lines as to appear barely viable. I would try to eliminate up to 4 lines in such an instance (but not before ensuring that the blank space cannot be used in some way, e.g. by inserting an illustration, or a map from the Prelims). Because the problem of an over-short page becomes clear at the first sight of page-proofs, the indexer can easily make the necessary adjustment if elimination of the short page is decided upon.

The last page of a chapter also has an uncomfortable look if it occupies the maximum space allowed and there is no blank space whatever at the foot. If the chapter is the last one in the book, the effect is still worse. I would always try to ease this if possible by one of the methods already described.

It sometimes happens that an author wishes to make a break within a chapter without inserting a shoulder-heading, and that this occurs at the foot of a page (which may or may not have a footnote or -notes). It will require great acuteness of observation in the reader to notice that the first line of the following paragraph—at the top of the next page—is full-out, thus marking the start of a new section. The only way round this problem is to insert a row of asterisks (three are enough) below the last line of the concluding section. But how does one do this if there is no space? A two-line space will suffice; therefore two lines have somehow to be saved—which means looking back to see either if there is a widow to be taken up by saving a word or two, or if there are two paragraphs that can be run together to save a line that way. How it is done is up to the publisher, but be done it must.

Some may object: is so much trouble worthwhile to avoid effects which will offend a seasoned typographical eye but pass most readers by? The self-respecting publisher, like the traditional printer for whom book printing was a time-honoured 'mystery' that required years of training, can only give one answer: yes, it is worthwhile. And it is ultimately the responsibility of the publisher, as the 'expert', and not that of the author—or even of the typesetter (many modern typesetters, however skilled they may be at carrying out their clients' instructions, are not trained or adept in the aesthetics of typography).

I would venture to claim that with ingenuity and literacy every one of the problems alluded to above can be solved.

Treatment of endnotes

Assuming it has been amicably decided between author and publisher that the Notes/References shall not be placed at the foot of the page, there remains the choice between placing them at the end of each chapter and at the end of the book.

Placing them at the end of the chapter makes them more accessible for readers of that particular chapter, and more user-friendly for them if they include any comment or additional factual material beyond the bare reference. But in non-academic scholarly books, e.g. biographies of famous personages, where they tend to be unaccompanied by any comment, they are almost always placed at the end of the book. We have placed the Notes together at the back where there is almost no comment, and—a subjective distinction one must be careful not to make invidious—where the book is of an intellectual substance which makes end-of-chapter Notes appear over-fussy. I emphasise that these are not easily definable or categorisable distinctions.

A few simple typographical rules:

1. For end-of-chapter Notes, a 2- or 3-line space should be left below the last line of the main text, then a heading—'NOTES' (centred) or 'Notes' (ranged left)—in, respectively, the next-lower size of capitals than the main text or a size larger in u.l.c.

2. For Notes running continuously at the end of the book, the introductory headings—'NOTES' or 'REFERENCES'—will be of the same size as for the Contents or Index, followed by a rubric where needed: this might include a list of abbreviations for frequently used references. On the succeeding pages the running head will consist of (e.g.)

INSIDE	*CENTRE*	*OUTSIDE*
[36–45]	*Notes*	365

I draw attention particularly to the 'inside' item—the span of pages in the book to which the notes on page 365 refer. Putting these in at page-proof stage is easy, and a boon to readers wishing to use the Notes, and therefore leaving them out seems gratuitously unhelpful. This exceptional 'primary' use of square brackets serves to distinguish them neatly.

In a continuous Notes section, insert a 2-line break between the end of one chapter's notes and the beginning of the next chapter's. The title of each chapter can be displayed in a variety of ways. Centring it, with the number of the chapter above it, is inappropriate, so why not settle for a shoulder-heading such as one of the two following examples:

Chapter 8 The Habsburg Period

Chapter 8 THE HABSBURG PERIOD

Where the first element and the second are distinguished typographically as above, no punctuation is needed between them. The word 'Chapter' should not be omitted.

Snagging

This is a term I use for a phenomenon which only manifested itself after the demise of hot-metal setting, and which indeed was physically impossible with metal type.

This is for characters to intersect. (It is the very opposite of the elegant erstwhile device of the ligature, viz. a character cunningly formed by two letters joined together.) It occurs in two main instances: (1) between a superscript reference number and a descender from the line above; and (2) when a word in italic occurs within roman parentheses. The descenders of '*p*' and especially of '*j*', '*y*' and '*f*', will snag the bottom of the opening bracket, and the ascender of '*f*' will snag not only a closing bracket but also a closing quotation mark. This will only be averted if the typesetter takes care to separate the snagged characters, and it should be assumed by the publisher that he will do so only when so instructed by the proof-reader. But separated they must be, even if the resulting space does not look altogether comfortable.

It is something similar in the minds of computers that results in a terminal roman 'f', which occurs overwhelmingly in 'of', being nearer to the first character of the succeeding word than it should be, so as virtually to close the word-space. This too needs to be corrected, but doing so on the scale necessary is tedious, and this anomaly may have to be accepted as a new convention. However, some instances are worse, and cry out for remedy more urgently, than others.

Word-breaks (hyphenation)

For me there is an internal logic in discussing this together with snagging. Judith Butcher, surprisingly, allows words to be broken virtually anywhere, but I disagree: clearly defined syllables and especially diphthongs and compound consonants should not be broken, although in English—unlike in Germanic languages—it is sometimes debatable where one syllable ends and the next begins. All the following examples occurred as shown in the left-hand column in a single page of setting:

es-tablished	est-
nu-merous	num-
cabi-net	cab-
broa-den	broad-
domes-tic	dom-
Jorda-nian	Jord- or Jordan-

I felt compelled to change them as shown in the right-hand column: simple aesthetics demanded it. A pitfall to be watched out for is where a word-break occurring on one set of proofs is carried over on to the subsequent set in which the word has moved to the middle of a line but without the hyphen being removed (e.g 'pheno-menon').

As to which forms of compound words are correct—e.g. war-time, war time or wartime—all authors have different preferences and I am not going to impose mine over an author's at the possible cost of doing so incompletely and thus lapsing into inconsistency.

The Bibliography

Should be scaled down overall from the main text by one type-size, including any shoulder-headings.

The style for presenting the details of published works has already been covered in connection with Notes, but some minor differences have to be observed:

Names of authors. These should start with the surname, unlike in Notes. Not to do so is not a total barrier to comprehension, but it stands to reason that it is more user-friendly to have the key word which the reader is looking for at the beginning of the entry. Thus 'Brown, J.C.,' but with works by more than one author, the normal order will be used for the second and subsequent name(s). It can look awkward to have, say, 'Brown, J.C., H.V. Robinson and T.F. White, but possible alternatives are worse.

More than one work by a single author (say J.C. Brown). These must appear in the order of date of first publication. Here we insert a dash—2 ems is a good length—in place of the author's name in the second and subsequent titles included.

It is possible, if a subsequent title is by Brown and a second author, to put '—— and T.F. White'. If, in the work concerned, White's name appears before Brown's, the title should of course appear under 'White'. A dash can only be put before the next title if it too is by Brown and White; it cannot if the work is by Brown only. But this eventuality is avoided by grouping works by Brown and those by him in conjunction with others separately, each group in date order.

Works which Brown has edited as well as those of which he is sole author can be included in a single group, for the sake of ease of reference.

Chinese, Japanese, Muslim and Indian names. Here the key name is often the one which occurs first. This is most obvious in Chinese: no one would ever think of listing Mao Tse-tung under 'Tung'—or Ho Chi-Minh under 'Minh'.

In Japanese the distinction is less obvious. Because the country is so westernised in many ways, it is easy for us to think of the first name as being the given name and the second one as being the family name. This is apparently not so, but it is an arcane area to most of us in the West. However, we must strive to get the nomenclature right, and to that end seek guidance from the author. If the author says 'Either way will do', the publisher must press for a firm ruling.

With Muslim names it would be nonsensical to list Muhammad Ali—either the Egyptian pasha or the boxer—under 'Ali', but on the same principle (of custom) one would not think of listing President Nasser under 'Gamal' or President Gaddafi under 'Muammar'. With names that are not well-known one should again demand a consistent approach, or at least a consistently logical one, from the author.

In India, personal names that may seem to an untutored westerner to be family names, because they are the ones most often used, may turn out to be given names; to that extent the family names in these instances are 'private'. Again, the author must be looked to for a ruling.

Division into sections. The most important division is between Primary and Secondary sources. This is not the same as that between unpublished and published: e.g., published collections of documents are primary sources, while unpublished dissertations are secondary.

I do not see any sense in making separate sections for books, chapters in books, articles and dissertations—it seems to be making unimportant distinctions, annoying to the reader eager to track down a source. Items that do need to be grouped separately *en masse* are Interviews, if the author chooses to list them in the Bibliography, and the titles of journals and newspapers consulted.

Because of the complexity of the subject and my inadequate knowledge of it, I will not attempt to set out any rules for archival sources: Butcher is the best authority. It is enough to say that it may be necessary to have sub- and sub-sub-headings, in which case the main heading 'Primary Sources' should be more commanding than a mere shoulder-heading in 11 pt italic. It—and 'Secondary Sources' where it comes—could be in, say, 10pt capitals, centred. The rule is to impose logic and order on the listings.

The index

For a scholarly publisher in the social sciences it is inconceivable to have a monograph, a collection of articles or, most of all, a biography (auto- or hetero-) which is without an index. This article of faith is not universally shared on the European continent—where a nuanced table of contents may be considered an adequate substitute.

For greatest ease of use, it should be in two columns, set two sizes smaller* than the main text, and with a channel between the columns of 1 em width—no more and no less. The minimum of show or affectation should be the rule. No displayed initial letter is needed to mark the transition from, say, the As to the Bs; a line space is enough. But before specifying the typography, a few more general comments.

The Index must be appropriate to the book. A sense of taste and propriety should guide the author and, since that sense may desert him, must without fail guide the publisher over what constitutes 'appropriateness'. It should not be over-elaborate, nor should it be too basic. What is 'too basic'? Certainly an index which consists of an undifferentiated, unqualified string of numerals after each key name/word is too basic. It may, strictly, fulfill its purpose, but a reader who can be expected to approach the work analytically should be aided by an index which subdivides and if necessary sub-subdivides aspects of the key items. This requires a careful indexer, sensitive to the author's intentions.

Naturally the ideal is for the author to create the index (although it is authors and not professional indexers who, through laziness, produce ones that are too basic and contrarily, through losing sight of the convenience of the reader, over-elaborate ones). There is one reason above all why the author should prepare the index, and should if possible be cajoled into doing so even if at first reluctant. This is that only the author knows the work from the inside, and will recognise those errors which he spots in the text in the course of indexing as not having been picked

*I have seen, in computer-set books, indexes in the same type-size as the main text and even, rarely, a size larger. Both show typographical insensitivity; the second is a monstrosity.

up before. This is only a subsidiary function of author-indexing, but self-evidently it is a useful one.

A skilled freelance indexer will not commit any of the stylistic errors into which an inexperienced author-indexer might fall. But it is the responsibility of the publisher to give adequate briefing, and to make clear the budgetary constraints. This publisher likes to be able to say 'Make the index exactly as elaborate as the work demands', but of course it is not always possible.

An integral part of the indexing process is the detection in the text of errors, typos and, most obviously, inconsistencies in nomenclature that escaped others who have read the proofs. For this reason it is an advantage to have the index made from the second, corrected proofs (even at some sacrifice of time) so that the indexer will not be distracted by errors that may have been picked up by someone else.

Now to style:

1. All key words other than proper names should start with lower-case.

2. A comma between the key word and the first page-number following it is generally better than no punctuation mark, although some authors and indexers opt for the latter. However, even a comma is only to be used with an entry of a sufficiently basic nature not to require any qualification, i.e. where the key word is indeed followed by only a few page-numbers. Where the key word is qualified once or more, it should be followed by a colon. For this reason especially it is better to follow key words with no subdivisions by a comma. Each sub-entry, except the last one, ends with a semi-colon. An illustration:

[without qualification] Major, John, 2, 199, 385
[with qualification] Churchill, Winston S.: early career, 23–35, 46–7, 85–8; service in Boer War, 99–103, 107, 110; as Home Secretary, 157–9, ...

3. Heavily qualified Indexes (*sic*—cf. 'Appendixes', p. 20) will probably be clearer with the column unjustified on the right, but where all the matter in an entry is run-on, a justified column looks neater.

4. Cross-referencing goes at the *end* of an entry—e.g. '...; *see also* Brezhnev, Gorbachev, Khrushchev'—not at the beginning.

5. Where dates have to occur in an entry, put them in parentheses, not between commas, to avoid visual confusion, as:

elections: (1953) 34–6, 39; (1958) 85–6; ...

6. If the last line of an entry comes out consisting of a single digit, try to eliminate it or, if that fails, to enlarge it a little. This is the widow problem occurring under a different guise. It also occurs if a line of only one or two characters falls at the top of a column.

7. Ensure that the two columns on the last page of the index (indeed on every page) range horizontally at the foot.

8. It is the rule to eliminate by elision all superfluous digits in linked pairs of years and of page numbers, e.g. not pages 123–124, or 123–24, but 123–4. Likewise, not 1906–1909, or 1906–09, but 1906–9. But there are exceptions. First, the teens: we always have pages 13–14 and 113–14, not 13–4 or 113–4; likewise we have 1914–18, not 1914–8. The second significant exception applies to pairs of days of the month, which should not be elided. It does not look right to have 26–7 May; 26–27 May does look right.

9. The order of personal names in certain non-European languages needs to be straightened out with the author at the start.

10. Omit strictly unnecessary entries. A book about, say, modern China might contain a stray reference to Julius Caesar or Napoleon, but in such a book an entry 'Julius Caesar, 3' looks forlorn. Also exclude: references in the Acknowledgements to the author's mentors and friends; references to the authors of works mentioned in the Notes if only the work and not the author as a distinct person is referred to; and, in multi-author volumes, references by one author to one or more of the others.

In sum, an Index should have a 'life of its own' and be self-evidently the product of intelligence and, in however modest a fashion, artistry.

Both the Index and the Bibliography should, ideally, start on rectos. It seems almost indecent, if the main text (especially of a fairly long book) has ended on a recto, to begin the Bibliography (or the Index if there is no Bibliography) on the immediately following verso without any breathing-space.

However, to avoid over-running an even working by one

page, some compromise with hallowed conventions may always be necessary. Sometimes the only way open to do this is by eliminating the final page of the Index if, by good luck, it is very short and falls on a recto; one then swiftly looks back to see if, by cutting out any unnecessary entries (i.e. ones not integral to the purpose of the book) or condensing the wording of others, one can save the requisite number of lines. Another way of accommodating the backward overspill is to lengthen a sufficient number of the preceding pages by one line per column. If there is only enough room for *either* the Bibliography *or* the Index to start on a recto, pride of place should be yielded to the Index, which must *always* start on a recto if possible. But if starting the Index on a recto were to necessitate losing the half-title at the beginning of the book, the half-title must be saved.

Appendixes

These would normally fall immediately following the end of the main text and before Notes, Bibliography and Index. In general, set the text and the heading each one size smaller than those used in the body of the book. To avoid any possible confusion with the main text, it seems a good idea to 'number' the Appendixes with letters of the alphabet.

Begin the first Appendix on a recto, with the word 'APPENDIXES' as an overall heading. If space permits and the publisher feels so inclined, this word can appear as a half-title, followed by a blank. The running head should read '*Appendixes*' on the verso and contain the title of the Appendix on the recto.

In rare instances an Appendix which consists of a document or letter of some importance can be reproduced facsimile if reducing it to fit on the page doesn't make it too small; it avoids the cost of typesetting and the possibility of new errors remaining undetected, and it greatly enhances the sense of authenticity. It should be combined with a standard running head.

Tables

'The matter looked dreary enough, with illustrative diagrams and repulsive tables of figures, ...' (Joseph Conrad, *Heart of Darkness*, Penguin edition, 1973, p. 71)

At first glance a somewhat 'dreary' area of typography, as Joseph Conrad implies, but one where typographical ingenuity can greatly aid clarity and lend a relatively pleasing appearance.

For visual differentiation, three type sizes can be used. We will assume that the main text of the book is in 10pt. In that case the *heading* can be set in 9 pt, e.g.

Table 2.1. NATIONAL INCOME [IN NIGERIA], 1960–87

'In Nigeria' is parenthesised because if the whole book is about Nigeria it is not needed. Use of u.l.c., capitals and punctuation looks well as shown.

The main matter will be set in 8/9 pt, with extra spacing to introduce 'air'.

	1960–9		*1970–9*		*1980–9*	
	× 1,000	*%*	*× 1,000*	*%*	*× 1,000*	*%*
Oil						
Engineering						
Agriculture						
Cattle raising						
etc.						
Total						

The *footnotes* and *sources* will be set in 7/8 pt. The footnotes come first, flagged by asterisks, daggers etc. or alternatively with lower-case italic letters. Numerals should be avoided. Rules for sources as for bibliographical footnotes.

An alternative formula, using the same setting rules, is as follows (GHIP etc. are imaginary political parties):

Table 8.3. ELECTION RESULTS, 1980–98

	GHIP		*SPP*		*JYP*		*NDPP*	
	Seats	*%*	*Seats*	*%*	*Seats*	*%*	*Seats*	*%*
1980								
1984 (Mar.)								
1984 (Nov.)								
1998								

Tables: simple rules

1. For differentiation, italicise column headings but not the key words (or, e.g. as in 'Table 8.3' above, the dates) down the left side.

2. Always delete '*Date*' at the top of the date column, if the author puts it in; nobody needs to be told that a date is a date.

3. Ensure that the column headings are centred *vis-à-vis* the columns.

4. If, as often happens, a column consists of numerals containing (a) decimal points or (b) digits separated by commas, ensure that the decimal point in (a) and the terminal digit in (b) range vertically with their companions above and below. It is so easy to do, but often neglected.

5. Note the words 'Cattle raising' on the left of the sample table above; other examples might be 'Castes and constituencies' or 'Water and electricity'. These come low in the hierarchy of headings/indicators, and therefore 'raising', 'constituencies' and 'electricity' should not have initial capitals. This is a fertile source of inconsistency, possibly barely noticeable to the untrained eye. But our main object, as well as consistency, is to preserve the hierarchy of non-proper words that should have initial capitals and those that should not have them.

6. If the table is too broad to place vertically on the page, place it horizontally (turning it 90° anti-clockwise). Then, if it is too deep to go on a single page, it must be begun on a verso and continued on the recto. In this case there is no need to repeat the general heading or the column headings in the lower part of the table on the recto page. If, however, a third page is called for, repeat the general heading, ranged left for differentiation, with '(*continued*)' following it. The column headings should be repeated too.

7. Where, as usually happens, an average-sized table occupies less than the depth of a full page but more than half a page, it should go either at the top with text below, or at the bottom with text above. Placed in the middle, it might orphan the text

below it. A small table can be placed anywhere, and will probably look more comfortable in the middle.

8. Authors sometimes conclude a paragraph with the words 'as shown in Table 8.3 below', followed by the table. The publisher should always alter this to 'as shown in Table 8.3', and have the next block of text running straight on from it. There is a risk otherwise that, as the pages fall, it may be impossible to have the table immediately following the word 'below'. But, whether this is the case or not, it is more elegant to adopt the style recommended.

9. Where, for example ('Table 8.3' above), a party wins no seats, merely insert an en-dash. If the author wants to show that a certain statistic was not available, insert '*n.a.*'.

10. Always check—it often proves to have been necessary—that the percentage column adds up to 100 (if it does not, ask the author to straighten the matter out), and that any other column where a total is given has been totalled correctly.

11. Where a book contains a large number of tables, the author sometimes suggests showing them all together in an appendix. If this is to spare the reader from frequent interruptions to the flow of the main text, I would suggest it is misguided. If all these tables occur in the text, readers can, after all, skip those they don't need to consult; whereas, if they are all at the end, readers will surely tire of having to turn frequently to the back of the book.

12. Vertical and horizontal rules, with which the copy submitted by the author may be replete, should be kept to the minimum. Vertical ones can be banished entirely unless there is a major division down the centre (e.g. if the tabular matter is to be set in two consecutive narrow columns). Horizontal ones can be used to good effect between the general heading and the column headings, between them and the columns themselves, and between the bottom of the tabular matter and the notes and/or source reference at the very bottom.

13. If a table has few columns, and therefore a fair amount of space, move the columns slightly towards each other, transferring

to the left and right sides some of the space saved. The horizontal rules should still extend for the full column width unless it is a truly small table with just two narrow columns, in which case it can be designed to a narrower format, with shorter rules. If a table is narrow but deep, the matter can be displayed consecutively in two columns, on the same principle as an index, as mentioned in 12 above.

I hope I have shown that the humble table requires considerable resourcefulness from the publisher.

Maps

These have been partly covered above (pp. 25–6). We looked in particular at the tendency to place a general map of the country or region with which the book is mainly concerned in the Prelims, with more specialised ones at the most relevant points in the subsequent text, and the need for a very small-scale, simplified position-map to locate the country or region within a wider geographical context. Sometimes a map is needed in a book which is not concerned with history, geography, politics or economics: for example, in a biography of a Turkish poet a number of places mostly unfamiliar to the average reader may be mentioned, and therefore a map of Turkey will be necessary (though not a position-map, because anyone reading such a book will know where Turkey is).

Some maps have to be to a large scale—e.g. one of a village or relatively small locality—or, while relatively small-scale, must cover a wide area, e.g. the Sahara, and it is impractical to force them on to a single page. One tries to avoid folding maps wherever possible (these were much favoured in books on military/naval campaigns or of scientific exploration in an earlier era), but may be obliged to settle for placing it across a double-page spread. To minimise the difficulty of this operation, it is advisable to choose the centre spread of a section (say one of 16 pages); then the map does not need to be cut down the centre, and if the book is laid right open, the whole of it can be seen together. Still, if one has any control over the mapmaking, one should ask for place-names down the vertical centre line to be displayed to the left or right of that line and not across it, to enable them to be read easily. This prescription assumes that the book will be bound in sewn sections and not by some form of 'perfect' binding, i.e. with the folds sheared off. In the latter case it does not matter whether the double-spread map is in the centre of a section or not; it will have to be cut down the middle anyway, and a channel of white space of 5 mm. allowed on either side of the gutter to enable everything on the map to be read.

If one *is* having sewn sections and it is important to position the double-spread map in the centre of a section, finding the ideal place can be tricky. In the Prelims it does not matter if it falls within a preface consisting of several pages of text, but it cannot break up any part of the lists of Contents, Illustrations and so on, and would cause disruption too if placed in the midst of an item such as the glossary. If the Prelims will not accommodate it, one must look to the centre of the next 16-page section, within the early pages of the first chapter.

Whereas a table naturally has its title above it, this is not the case with a map, where the caption, if set by the publisher, goes naturally at the bottom. Some mapmakers can produce very handsome titles within the framework of the map; where these can be provided, the publisher should not set them separately.

Maps will reach the publisher in reproducible form either directly from the author, or from a mapmaker to whom the publisher has sent rough originals produced by the author. In either case the publisher should make a number of spot-checks to ensure that place-names are spelt in the same way in the map as in the text of the book (and hence in the Index); inconsistencies will be rightly blamed on the carelessness of the publisher.

It is also important that in historical maps there are no anachronisms. Cities as well as countries change their names. The best-known examples must be Constantinople/Istanbul, St Petersburg/Petrograd/Leningrad/St Petersburg, Christiania/Oslo, Czechoslovakia/the Czech Republic/Slovakia, Ceylon/Sri Lanka, Bombay/Mumbai and Madras/Chennai. But throughout Central and Eastern Europe there have been many less well-known changes of nomenclature mainly brought about after the cataclysms of 1918 and 1945 by changes of overlords, e.g. Pressburg/Bratislava, Laibach/Ljubljana, Ragusa/Dubrovnik, Skutari/Shkoder, Fiume/Rijeka, Philippopolis/Plovdiv, Smyrna/Izmir, Adrianople/Edirne, Breslau/Wrocław, Lemberg/Lvov, Stettin/Szczecin, Königsberg/Kaliningrad, Reval/Tallinn, Dorpat/Tartu, Memel/Klaipeda, Kovno/Kaunas, Vilna/Vilnius, Stalingrad/Volgograd, to name only some of the less obscure. The pride of new states sometimes demands that the world abandons familiar spellings in favour of ones more correct phonetically, e.g. (in Ukraine) Kyiv for Kiev and Odesa for Odessa. The old and new names can be given together on the same (historical) map where this might help the reader. The odium in which the military regime of Burma is widely held has led to its preferred new style, 'Myanmar', often being ignored.

Maps should always contain a scale,* preferably in both miles and kilometres, and in large-scale maps, where the terrain is likely to appear unfamiliar to the reader, a north-point. Keys to different kinds of shading and to roads, railways and especially boundaries (international, regional and county) can be set up by the mapmaker, or these can be typeset by the publisher and inserted alongside the drawn items produced by the mapmaker, the latter especially when the map has been produced in a more amateur fashion.

Should a map always have a box-like border? Where the map covers a landmass which extends beyond the area shown, it should have one, but for an island, however large—or, at a stretch, a peninsula with a narrow isthmus—it is not needed. Obvious examples are Africa, South America, Australia, the British Isles, Japan, the Philippines, New Guinea and Iceland. A good reason for not having a border, and for removing one that the mapmaker has included, is to allow the map to be reduced slightly *less* (and thus be to a larger scale) than would be necessary if the border were left in and had to be accommodated within the available space. Here aesthetic considerations must be paramount; the map must look comfortable on the page whichever way is chosen.

*It might be thought that no competent mapmaker can produce an erroneous scale, and thus for the publisher to check a scale's accuracy indicates a wasteful excess of zeal. I assure the reader that this is an unsafe assumption.

Illustrations

By this I mean what used, in more spacious times, to be called 'Plates'. But whereas plates in a volume consisting mainly of text would be printed on special paper, possibly with a guard of fine tissue-paper tipped in to protect them, even pictures requiring quite high-quality reproduction can now be printed on the same paper as the text, provided the paper is receptive to halftones.

This gives the publisher flexibility in arranging the illustrations. For example, they can be arranged within the text, sometimes occupying a whole page, sometimes less, but always with a running head and page-number. But it may not always be suitable or necessary to integrate the pictures with the text so closely. Perhaps it is preferable to place them in a number of groups throughout the work. In this case, whereas in former days they would have been on art paper, they can now be decisively differentiated from the text by being on unnumbered pages; and flexibility comes from the freedom to place these groups of illustrations anywhere—not in the centre of text sections or wrapped around them.

Some may rebel at the idea of placing all the illustrations in a book together in one section, especially if there are a lot of them. But it can sometimes be effective. We did this in a book on Ukraine, where there were 40 photographs, many of them portraying ill-favoured Communist Party apparatchiks, occupying 16 pages. Massing them together gave them a power they would not have had if scattered throughout the book, and they seemed almost to form a chapter in themselves.

As for the distinction between halftone and line illustrations, of course the quality of line, unless it is very delicate, is hardly lessened by being printed on paper that would be unsuitable for halftones, but there may be a good 'editorial' reason for including some line illustrations in a section consisting mainly of halftones.

Clearly it is the nature and purpose of a book's illustrations that determine whether they should be slotted into the text precisely where they are referred to, or grouped in the general area of their greatest relevance. Groups may perform a more or less atmospheric function, as distinct from a directly illustrative one: to convey the flavour of a country, a period, a war, a political regime. Hence their effect will depend to some degree on how they are laid out. Should they be placed upon the page in pairs one above the other, reduced or enlarged to a uniform width—or should there be some give-and-take, some '*rubato*'?

Masking. Along with the consideration raised at the end of the previous paragraph goes the question: what is the ideal area of a picture to reproduce? Almost always a picture can do with some judicious 'masking' or 'cropping' on one, more than one, or all of its sides. This is caused by the fact that action photos, taken in the heat of the moment, and scenic ones are seldom carefully composed in the photographer's view-finder. But a basic reason for the need to crop is that if, say, the width of a photo is reduced, what remains can be reproduced to a larger scale and thus have greater 'punch'. But equally important is the desirability of cutting away 'dead' areas of the picture, which contribute nothing, and without which the area to be reproduced can have a better overall balance: this judgement is an aesthetic one. In a landscape it can be sky at the top of a picture; grass, water or pavement at the bottom; or a featureless field or wall at the side. In crowd scenes you have to make a fine judgement on how many of the bystanders at the far right and left can be cut away without blunting the character of the picture—the result must be to make the people who remain convey or express more than a larger assemblage would have done.

In a portrait, masking assumes special importance: it is desirable to reconcile the need to show the subject's face as clearly and hence as large as possible, but also to include significant parts of his attire (e.g. epaulettes and medals in the case of a military personage) and even his hands. In a group photo, in order to increase the scale, one looks for every millimetre that one can crop from either side, cutting into arms and shoulders. There may be a particular need to crop from the top and bottom to accommodate another picture on the same page or a longer caption than the average. There is always a safe limit to which cropping can be taken, and the author must of course approve of any major surgery one wants to carry out.

(The above, I hasten to add, cannot apply when the photographs provided are artistically composed and come from a high-grade professional photographer. Such pictures should be given solus positions and not mutilated.)

Out of the vertical. Too often one has the pain of seeing reproduced a photo in which the ground slopes at an angle it could clearly never have in real life, and vertical objects like walls and telegraph poles, and indeed people, appear to be keeling over. Amateur photographers often and professionals occasionally produce pictures like this, and the problem should be clear at first glance to the publisher, who needs to be aware that when the picture is reproduced on the printed page the fault, which may have been barely noticeable in the original, appears magnified and has become horribly noticeable. It is necessary to mask such a picture on all four sides to correct the tilt, taking as the new orientation a central vertical line (like a wall or a telegraph pole)—or a horizontal one like the sea or the horizon in a flat landscape. A solution is easy once the problem is grasped.

Layout. To return to this larger problem, let us assume it has been decided that the pictures are to be placed in a group or groups. When they are being printed on text paper, there is complete flexibility as to where they will fall and, above all, as to how many pages each group will occupy. If the pages are all unnumbered, they must, obviously, be in multiples of two (which may require one being backed by a blank). Every group should, as far as possible, be designed as a whole—to achieve, by positioning and masking, the maximum impact on the reader's senses. The limits for the deployment of the designer's skill are narrow, but they must be exploited to the full. The bounds of a single-page area can be broken by 'bleeding'—some printers charge extra for this, but not all do. One can pair together on the same page two pictures of which one has a horizontal emphasis and the other a vertical one; the first could, e.g., bleed off the fore-edge, and the second off the bottom.

The number of pages that may be available (within an even working) for illustrations may be slightly more than is strictly required to accommodate all that the book needs; in that case one can spread oneself a little, having two pages, each with a solus picture, instead of one with the two pictures paired. It will usually seem natural, for the sake of achieving the maximum scale, to position a solus picture with a horizontal bias over on its side (turned, as always, 90 degrees *anti*-clockwise). Often there is no alternative. But it can also achieve impact occupying the centre of a vertical page, bleeding left and right, with plenty of white space above and below.

Of course, if the minimum number of pages required to accommodate a particular set of illustrations is adhered to, this may cause the total extent to exceed an even working by a page or two. Then one has to look for other means of compression. If the illustration pages cannot be further compressed without suffering, one will search the Prelims and the end-matter to see if a saving can be made there. What is eventually decided will depend on a balance of desiderata, but just occasionally one may think 'To hell with scrimping and saving—if we have to go over an even working, we will do it properly, *adding* pages by loosening up the illustrations or even the Prelims.' This way the book will be enjoyed more.

In a book we published in 1999 confusion arose over the number of maps to be included, and it turned out at a late stage that there were two blank pages where there should have been text. Both were versos—the first was page 6 and the second page 192. We solved the problem by inserting on page 6 in black and white the photo reproduced on the cover in colour; and by starting the illustrations on page 192 and having the four planned unnumbered illustration pages directly following it, even though this was not the location we would have chosen for them under normal circumstances. In the latter instance it was easy to extend what had been planned as a 4-page picture section to cover 5 pages. Page 192 had to carry its normal page number, but we dispensed with a running head. A solution unquestionably had to be found without repaginating most of the book and thus unravelling the Index. This time we were lucky that it emerged so easily. It is an unchangeable axiom of book production that a solution has to be found to every problem in order to achieve 'invisibility', even if still more ingenious improvisation is necessary than on this occasion. (The book concerned was *Gao Village* by Mobo C.F. Gao.)

Captions. Should a caption consisting of less than one line be centred below the picture or should it be ranged on the left? What measure (width) should one adopt for a caption running to two or more lines? To justify (i.e. have each line running to a uniform length) or not to justify? What type size do we want?

On a demy 8vo page where a picture is placed upright, the measure should not exceed 24 ems (4 inches or 101 mm.)—the standard column width—*even if the width of the picture is greater.* When the picture is placed over on its side, it should not exceed 30 ems; if longer, it becomes difficult to read. If any caption *within a picture section* exceeds one line, then every caption, even when of less than one line, should be ranged left; this is a requirement of consistency. Where pictures are scattered through a book, I would suggest breaking this rule and centring short captions running to less than one line. This is especially the case when the frontispiece consists of a picture.

Where, say, two pictures are combined on a page, one with a horizontal and the other with a vertical emphasis, the caption will perforce be placed in the angle between the two, and have to be set to a narrow measure—unjustified (left or right as appropriate) to avoid distortion. This caption must include some of the words '*Above*', '*Below*', '*Left*' and '*Right*'.

Where two horizontal-shaped pictures are combined on a page, the captions should be placed separately, one under each picture—unless space is in short supply, in which case a combined one can be placed between the two, including the words '*Above*' and '*Below*'.

For the sake of differentiation, captions of any length should, whether within the text or in a separate section, be set one size smaller than the main text—or two sizes smaller if the text is set in a larger size than usual. They should never be set in the same size as the main text. Where a whole-page illustration showing a person or a place occurs within the text, the caption, if consisting of no more than a very few words, can actually be set to a size *larger* than the main text. Only the *same* size is taboo.

One cannot dictate what captions should say, except that, whatever they say, the amount of words should be the minimum possible. (A whimsical author may decide to treat a caption as a discursive author might treat a parallel footnote, including a minute description of what to anyone else might appear a rather ordinary scene, together with anecdotes etc. If this is done with panache, the publisher till want to encourage it.)

Where necessary, a credit to the photographer and the owner of the copyright will have to be added at the end of the caption—unless a collective credit is given elsewhere. These are very willingly given if a picture has been provided free. However, sometimes payment of a reproduction fee cannot be avoided, and consideration of economy may have to take precedence over ones of logic and aesthetics if the fee required by the owner seems exorbitant, as is often the case when the owner is a picture agency. The contract with the author is likely to say that all such payments are the author's responsibility, but in practice a compromise over this matter may be forced on the publisher. This publisher is always prepared to bear the full cost when the picture is wanted for the cover, i.e. for publicity—a decorative and not an editorial purpose.

THE MAIN TEXT

It is now time to turn to the parts of the book where continuous narrative or 'prose' occurs. It should be the publisher's endeavour, as it is his responsibility, to ensure that what the reader has to encounter is good English: as easy to understand as the subject-matter allows, and free from ambiguities. 'Good English' also means grammatical English, in no way slipshod, and shorn of dead phraseology. I have never felt that I have any obligation, as publisher, to seek an author's permission to correct constructions, phrases and words that are incorrect, insufficiently expressive, or inelegant (any more than a bookseller needs permission to return a book to a publisher which has a physical defect). The *mot juste* always exists, and merely needs to be found if it is not there already.

British publishers must allow American authors to write in American English and use American spellings, which are sometimes more authentic (e.g. labor, honor) than their British equivalents. (A degree of indulgence should be extended to foreign authors or translators writing in English—one would not want their productions to show no signs of their origins whatever.) I do, however, seek a mid-Atlantic compromise over punctuation, where some American usages seem to me perverse, e.g. 'bread, cheese, and pickles' in contrast to the British 'bread, cheese and pickles'. Americans put in what they call a 'serial' comma (after 'cheese') where to us in Britain it seems superfluous. However, with a series of clauses containing verbs I would definitely put in the comma to aid clarity, as in 'He likes bread, is exceptionally fond of cheese, and gets ecstatic about pickles'. British and American usages also differ over the placing of terminal quotation marks in relation to commas and full-points.

American usage	Asked what he liked best about English diet, he said 'Bread, cheese, and pickles.'
British usage	... he said 'Bread, cheese and pickles'.
American usage	Asked for his preference, he replied 'I would like bread, cheese, and pickles'.
British usage	... he replied 'I would like bread, cheese and pickles.'

In other words, the British would close the quotes on a short phrase not containing a verb before the terminal punctuation mark, but, in a sentence containing a verb, after it. The American usage is the opposite.

Ernest Gowers, in *Plain English*, inveighs against the obfuscatory style of government documents. This does not concern us directly, but his recommendation to cut out unnecessary words should be seriously heeded. Why say 'in large part', 'for the most part' or 'in the main' when you can say 'largely', 'mostly' or 'mainly'? Or 'in spite of the fact that' instead of 'although'?

Inclusive or non-sexist language

We had a woman author of progressive outlook who, when I altered the collective noun 'man' to 'humanity' in her text on African religion, insisted on 'man' being reinstated. She admitted that this was due to instinct rather than to cold logic. But whatever her reason, I agreed to her wish happily. Yet on the whole I would avoid 'man' in this sense, and would insist on suppressing 'men' in the sense of 'people'.

I admired the ingenuity of the phrase 'Comrade Chairperson' as a substitute for 'Mr/Madam Chairman' the first time I heard it at an international meeting, but in written material would not go further than 'chair' for 'chairman'.

But I draw the line at the singular 'they', strongly advocated on p. 1925 of *The New Oxford Dictionary of English* (Oxford University Press, 1998—hereafter *NODE**) as a means of avoiding the use of 'he or she', or of just 'he', to denote either sex. Two model usages of 'they' are cited: 'Anyone can join if they are a resident' or 'Ask a friend if they can help'. For the first there is nothing wrong with 'Anyone who is a resident can join' or 'Any resident can join'; and for the second 'See if you have a friend whom you could ask to help', 'See if a friend could help' or even 'Ask a friend to help'. Another way round is to make the subject plural. 'All residents may join' is workable, but this is not an option with the second example; 'friends' has different connotations from 'a friend'. But 'The reader may feel at this point that he is being imposed upon' can be changed to 'Readers may feel that they are. ...' The same goes for countless sentences of like construction. It is the job of lexicographers to sharpen, not to dull, distinctions of meaning. Only where there is precision can there be nuances.

If one doesn't wish to refer to God (where not referred to as 'God the Father') as 'He' (or 'he'), I recommend avoiding the pronoun and simply repeating 'God' as often as necessary.

Distinctions of spelling and distinctions of meaning

A number of alternative usages, where distinctions exist and have a long history of aiding maximum clarity, are today in an endangered state. Examples follow, in deliberately random sequence:

dependence, dependency. For me 'dependency' means only one thing: a country or province controlled by another. One should not talk of being in a state of dependency on, e.g., alcohol in the case of a person, or banana exports in the case of a state, but in a state of dependence. 'Dependency' in the latter sense is

*In the same entry there occurs the phrase 'has been used since at least the 16th century', which might have been written expressly to illustrate faulty syntax and hence imprecise expression: 'at least the 16th century' is devoid of meaning. If the *NODE*'s lexicographers had written 'at least as long ago as', 'as early as' or 'no later than' the 16th century, the sentence would have had form and precise meaning.

now common; but the very fact that the two words are not interchangeable, and that one cannot refer to a dependent country as a 'dependence', should confirm the need for the distinctions of meaning and spelling to be watertight. The *NODE* says that 'dependent' is an acceptable spelling for the noun 'dependant', i.e. a person dependent on another person. But this cannot be acceptable, any more than the noun 'confidant' could be spelled 'confident'. Incidentally, the *NODE* also extends the meaning of 'residency' to embrace what should be referred to only as 'residence', viz. the state of living somewhere. The *Shorter Oxford English Dictionary* (*SED*) in its first edition of 1933 has 'residency' meaning only the official residence of a governor. Why, notwithstanding the shortage of colonial governors today, could this clear and handy distinction not be maintained?

partly, partially. The meanings of these two words are closely intermingled. 'Partial' is the only adjectival form of 'part' other than, rarely, 'part' itself ('part genius and part criminal'). Therefore it appears natural to make 'partially' the adverb of 'partial'—until one recalls the specialised extended meaning of 'partial', of which 'partiality' is the noun, 'impartial' the opposite and, of course, 'partially' the adverb. So, since 'partly' is available to mean 'in part', why not use it exclusively in that sense and avoid the imputation of illiteracy? The *NODE* has a separate entry for 'partially sighted' but not for 'partly sighted' (what in unregenerate days used to be referred to as 'half-blind')—why?

orient(ed), orientate(d). The *SED* dates the first use of 'orientate' to 1849, but it is frequently used, most often metaphorically, in speech and writing. None the less it is an ugly usage, based on a vague sense that 'orient' used as a verb sounds hifalutin. This time on the side of the angels, the *NODE* does not accept the back-derivation 'orientate' as equal in validity to 'orient'.

importantly. By common usage this word has moved from being a simple adverb, which was all that the 1933 *SED* recognised, to something the *NODE* calls a 'sentence adverb'; the *NODE* goes further and gives this first place, relegating the simple adverbial use to second place. Its example of the simple use is 'Kruger strutted forward importantly', and of the 'sentence adverbial' use 'a non-drinking, non-smoking and, more importantly, non-political sportsman'. I have seen worse instances than this, but even here, a slight re-arrangement (e.g. ... and—more important—a non-political ...') would obviate any need for its use.

respectively. In Fowler, rev. 3rd edn 1998, Burchfield says that he had found no evidence in the 1990s of tautological use of this word, against which *Ur*-Fowler inveighed in the 1920s. Though without hard evidence to hand, I am not so sure, but will content myself with quoting one pellucidly correct use, dating from 1958: 'The revision [to the Prayer Book] was approved by the Synod ..., and accepted by the Houses of Commons and Lords respectively on 24 February and 17 March 1662.' Anyone who fully digests this example will be incapable of using the word incorrectly, i.e. other than to signify 'each separately or in turn, and in the order mentioned'. (It is also used correctly on page 77 below, under '*forcible, forceful*'.)

almost, practically, virtually. What are the precise distinctions between them? The 1933 *SED* says no more about 'practically' than that it is the adverb of 'practical', from which one can deduce the extended meaning 'for all practical purposes'. It gives the following definitions of 'virtually': 'as far as essential qualities and facts are concerned'; 'as good as'; 'to all intents'. 'Almost' means 'very nearly' or 'all but'. The implication here is that 'virtually' has a more exact meaning than 'almost'. But looking up 'practically' in the *NODE* confirms my hunch that for many non-literary writers today 'practically' and 'virtually' are mere (or 'virtual'?) synonyms of 'almost': its definition is 'virtually; almost'. The *NODE* defines 'virtually' as 'nearly; almost'—a considerable loss of precision since 1933.

publically. Not defended in any dictionary as an alternative to 'publicly', but written with amazing frequency. Likewise ...

dignatory for 'dignitary'; *ex-patriot* for 'expatriate'; *straightjacket* for 'straitjacket'.

intermediary. Means a go-between (n.) or, of a person or thing, acting as such (adj.). 'Through the intermediary of' has come into use, surely not by intention (it is a rare mid-19th-c. usage—see *SED*) but by default. 'Intermediation' or 'mediation' are correct and distinct.

pry, prise. 'Pry' means to put one's nose into other people's business, and 'prise' means to open by leverage. American English uses 'pry' for 'prise' and some users of English English do so too. Let us keep one spelling for each meaning.

The neuter plural. For someone who has never been taught Greek or Latin it can be hard to grasp that the plural of a noun in common English use that has been lifted from one of those languages should end in '-a'; and furthermore that every such plural form has its singular form ending in '-on' if Greek or '-um' if Latin. Thus one hears spoken, and sees written, 'a criteria', 'a phenomena', 'a desiderata' and 'an addenda'; not to mention 'criterias' and 'phenomenas'.

On the other hand, some such nouns have made the transition to the mainstream of English usage more completely than others. Thus it is rare for anyone to talk of 'premia' (certainly in connection with insurance). And if one talks of 'referenda', even some mild purists will argue that this signifies only the questions that are put to the vote in a referendum and not two or more referendums (*sic* in most cases, thus making a useful distinction). Other neuter plurals have truly achieved singular status, e.g. agenda; 'agendas' is conceivable, however much one might prefer to avoid it.

'Data', unmistakably a neuter plural (its singular form, 'datum', is much less common), is uneasily attracted towards each of the opposite poles of correct and incorrect usage. Unfortunately one feels slightly pedantic about writing 'the data are ...'; yet 'the data is ...', being incorrect, should surely be corrected.

etc., et al. It is sometimes forgotten that *'et cetera'* (the latter word a neuter plural) can only refer to inanimate things, or to impersonal 'bodies' even when those consist of human beings. Being thoroughly absorbed into both written and spoken

English, it is not italicised, but it is always followed by a full-point, and it should not be preceded by a comma, any more than 'and' is. Likewise it is sometimes forgotten that '*et al.*' (short for '*et alii*') can only refer to people. It is italicised; it is also (like 'etc.') not preceded by a comma; and it is a howler to put a full-point after the '*et*'.

as in its causal meaning (= 'since', 'because'). There has been an evolution here. In 1926 H.W. Fowler 'strongly objected' (Burchfield in Fowler, rev. 3rd edn 1998) to constructions where the 'as' clause follows the main clause, while accepting those where it precedes the main clause. Burchfield goes on to say that Fowler's objection now seems very dated. A MS. I worked on while this book was in production provided an example of each, cheek by jowl: 'Tan Zhen regretted the abolition of labour in exile in the new penal code, as he considered it particularly appropriate for a vast country... like China. As prisons suffered from overcrowding, labour in exile seemed a desirable alternative.' My own reaction against the causal 'as' in any position (in formal writing only—conversation is a different matter) comes from the gut. In this sense 'as' is a soft word, and the link it makes is weak, whereas 'since' and 'because' are strong words, used to the full extent of their meaning, and thus make the link strong. Might one not considerably improve the short passage above as follows: 'Tan Zhen regretted the abolition in the new penal code of labour in exile, which he considered particularly appropriate for a vast country like China. Because prisons suffered from overcrowding, labour in exile seemed a desirable alternative.'

debar, disbar. In the 1933 *SED* 'disbar' has only one meaning: to 'deprive someone of the status and privileges of a barrister'. The primary meaning in the *NODE* is the same (differently expressed), but the secondary meaning is given as 'exclude (someone) from something: *competitors wearing rings will be disbarred from competition*'. No hint is given that this is a malapropism based purely on the word's similarity to 'debar'. In short these two words have very different meanings and are in no case interchangeable.

testament, testimony. The prompting to investigate this one came from hearing, on BBC Radio's 'Today' programme, 'testament' used as in the following example from the *NODE* of what it cites as the word's secondary meaning: 'Growing attendance figures are a testament to the event's popularity.' Yet the following bizarre example, occurring in the *NODE* correctly under 'testimony', uses that word in exactly the same sense: 'His blackened finger was testimony to the fact that he had played in pain.' Nowhere does the *NODE* hint that the use of 'testament' in the sense of 'testimony' is so much as questionable. The 1933 *SED* treated the two words as totally distinct. Burchfield/Fowler, curiously, has no entry for either word. But we should surely sound a warning that here is yet another loss of expressiveness in the language which has come about virtually unnoticed.

convince, persuade. The use of 'convince' with an infinitive as a synonym for 'persuade' is said by the *NODE* to have come into use in the United States in the 1950s, and to be used now by 'well-established writers'. Also 10% of citations of 'convince' in the Oxford Reading Programme (ORP) are in this sense. Can there really be a justification for sanctioning the blurring of two words with distinct meanings?

masterly, masterful. The *NODE*, commenting on the usage of these two terms, says that '*some writers* maintain a distinction between them', using the first to mean 'with the skill of a master' and the second 'powerful and able to control others', but that 'in practice the words overlap considerably'. The *NODE* quotes the ORP not merely as evidence of this indisputable fact, but as authority for it. '*Some writers*' (my italics above) are surely right to maintain a necessary distinction, and the ORP is merely promoting an error which has arisen due to ignorance, leading to a loss of expressiveness in the written language.

forcible, forceful. The *SED* summarises their meanings, respectively, as 'done with force' and 'full of force', although in times long before the present there was overlapping of meaning. The *NODE* is sound on 'forceful' but cites without comment an instance of 'forcible' being used to mean 'forceful'. Let the two words retain their distinct meanings.

historic, historical; classic, classical. References to Yalta as a 'historical' conference, or that same event as a 'classical' case of great power politics are instances of erroneous usage. Confusion between these forms is not very common, but it does occur.

use, usage. The 1933 *SED* gives seven primary meanings of 'usage', all but one concerned with established or habitual use and custom. No. 7 deals with possibly its most frequent application today, the 'use of words, language, expressions etc.'. No. 5 alone is 'employment, use'. Yet the *NODE* elevates meaning No. 5 in the *SED* to first place, citing as examples 'a survey of water usage' and 'the usage of equipment'—a significant change since 1933. In both these examples I would replace 'usage' by 'use'.

comprise of (instead of 'consist of' or 'comprise'). This is recognised by the *NODE* as an error, but is stated to be fast becoming standard usage. In our opinion it should continue to be treated unequivocally as an error, and as a mark of illiteracy.

meet with, consult with. These Americanisms for 'meet' and 'consult' have only an insecure toehold in English English and should be corrected. (I cherish the folksy Americanism 'visit with', meaning to meet for a gossip without any actual 'visiting' as we understand it. It has so far not touched English English at all.)

early on and *later on* sound normal in conversation but look sloppy in narrative, where the 'on' should be omitted.

generally speaking, broadly speaking. As per previous entry. Omit 'speaking'.

perspective. The *NODE* manages once again to present sloppy usage as a model by citing 'Most guidebook history is written from the editor's perspective' (p. 1386). A more egregious use occurs in the dictionary's Preface: 'The [*NODE*] views the language *from* the perspective *that* English is a world language [my italics].' There is a dizzying syntactical leap in that sentence from '*from*' to '*that*'.

The *NODE*'s primary definition of the word itself is unexceptionable: 'the art of drawing solid objects ... so as to give the right impression of their height*, width, depth and position in relation to each other when viewed from a particular point'. A word of such importance is bound to spawn metaphors, e.g. the precise 'seeing matters in perspective'. But it should be clear that perspective is not in itself a point in space from which things can be seen, hence the incorrectness of 'from the editor's [or anyone else's] perspective'. What is meant is 'from the editor's viewpoint/point of view/angle', and that is what should be written. Or indeed, what is wrong with 'in' or 'within' the editor's perspective? This at least respects the meaning of 'perspective'.

A further point is that if 'perspective' is preceded by a qualifying adjective, e.g. 'Israeli' or 'Arab', the adjective in its turn should be preceded by the definite and not the indefinite article. Perspective is a physical concept (though one with no bulk), indivisible and unmultipliable. Hence it is impossible to have 'a' perspective.

as well as. This little phrase is not a synonym for 'and', as those who write a phrase such as 'bread, cheese as well as pickles' seem to assume. If one must have 'as well as', it is necessary to say 'bread and cheese as well as pickles'; or, by extension, 'bread, cheese and pickles as well as *pâté de foie gras*'.

'*evidence*' *as a verb*, e.g. 'as evidenced by', has a long history—its meaning, properly confined to legalese, is 'make evident, demonstrate, prove', and dates from 1807—but of all permitted usages it is one of the ugliest, and I would always want to change it.

unitary, Unitarian. In works of political science the phrase 'unitary state', i.e. a state that is not a federation, is quite common. Some writers use 'unitarian' as a synonym for 'unitary', seemingly unaware that the word is a proper noun coined to describe non-Trinitarian theology.

it. This word deserves the utmost respect for its many uses. However, I would always try to avoid using 'it' on the page in—as described by the *NODE*—'the normal subject or object

*I have known two builders of different generations who talked about 'heighth': how would this do as an alternative usage to put in a future edition of the *NODE*?

position when a more specific subject or object is given later in the sentence'. As an example of this it cites (p. 970): 'she found it interesting to learn about their strategy'. In the Preface the editors themselves write: 'The text design is ... accessible, making it easy to find the core meanings. ...' Why not say 'she found learning about their strategy interesting' and 'making the core meanings easy to find'?

or, nor. Frequently 'nor' is used incorrectly in place of 'or'. Today it is correct only after 'neither', whatever usages may have prevailed in the distant past. However, a sentence can begin with 'Nor'—e.g. 'Nor did the government increase public spending'—when following straight on from a related negative statement.

nation, state. Pace the 'United Nations' and the peculiar case of the United States, these words have entirely different meanings. The latter, due to its nature as a federation or union of states, cannot refer to itself as 'the State'; and, consisting as it does of immigrants from most of the world's nations (in the true sense) it has no indigenous nations other than those which had the misfortune to be trampled underfoot in the process of settlement; thus it, of all states, is entitled to refer to itself as 'the Nation', 'nation' here having a unique significance.

But in the Old World a nation is a people, which is rarely coterminous with the state or states it inhabits: this is equally true of stateless minority nations like the Kurds, the Copts, the Basques, the Sami, the Bretons and the Afrikaners, and of majority ones like the Russians, the Germans, the Serbs, the Hungarians and the Albanians. In sum, it is best to replace 'nation' with 'state' whenever the latter is meant.

meanwhile, in the mean time. 'Meanwhile' and 'mean time' are not interchangeable: it is impossible to use 'meantime' alone in the adverbial way that 'meanwhile' is used, and each has an individual feel to it that causes the two to be used in subtly different ways. 'In the mean while' is sanctified by citation in the *SED* as well as in the *NODE*, and it is in spoken use, but when writing why not make a distinction and avoid its use? It seems altogether neater for them to have distinct uses, which their non-interchangeability proves them to possess: 'meanwhile' on its own, as a single word, and 'in the mean time' as a four-word phrase.

principal, principle. I would not insult the reader of a work such as this by pointing out the difference between these two words, yet in the agreeably intelligent *Jordan, Syria & Lebanon Handbook* (Footprint, London 1998), each is routinely used in the sense of the other. 'With regards to' occurs more than once. Why did the *publisher* not notice?

forgo, forego; forbear (v.), forebear (n.). Even the *SED* of 1933 cites 'forego' as an alternative spelling for 'forgo', but the prefixes 'for-' and 'fore-' have very obviously distinct meanings, 'for-' being closely related to German '*ver-*'. Like '*ver-*', 'for-' often has a negative connotation, as in 'forgo', 'forget', 'forswear', 'forbid'. 'Forego' in its true meaning of 'go before' is rare, except in the phrase 'foregone conclusion'. 'Forgo' is often spelt 'forego', but this is surely to add to the sum of confusion in the world. 'Forebear' is a noun meaning 'ancestor' and 'forbear' a verb meaning to 'abstain' or 'refrain', and to 'tolerate', but I cannot forbear to mention that the two spellings are often confused.

In passing, it was surprising to find in the *Financial Times* in February 1999 the following: 'a sense of well-being borne [*sic*] of the strong economy ...' Conversely, an otherwise literate MS. referred to something having 'born [*sic*] witness' to something else.

among, amongst; while, whilst; amid, amidst. The *NODE* explains the strange origin of the '-st' suffix, but expresses no opinion on its usage. The '-st' form is often used in conversation, but I recommend excising it on the page, where it has an aura of archaism.

first, firstly. It is generally accepted that 'first', 'secondly', 'thirdly' etc. are the correct usages. I always feel that to insist on this differentiation borders on the pedantic, yet to say that 'firstly' is wrong is not pedantic: 'first' is not only an adjective but also an adverb (e.g. 'I will go first'), making 'firstly' a tautology. It seems entirely logical to render the other ordinal numbers as 'second', 'third' etc. to match.

marshal, marshall. Purely a question of spelling. The first is the noun, as in 'field-marshal', and the second is the verb ('to marshall one's forces') and a common surname (the Marshall Plan). Not even the *NODE* allows any seepage between the two, yet we find some of our authors not inadvertently spelling the noun as if it were the verb.

sobriquet, soubriquet. After the key-word 'sobriquet', the *NODE* adds, in parentheses, 'also soubriquet', giving no hint that the latter is totally incorrect and appears in no French dictionary.

homogeneous. Sometimes carelessly rendered as 'homogenous', a back-derivation from 'homogenise'. Equally offensive is 'odiferous' for 'odoriferous'—a word admittedly seldom used except in attempts at polysyllabic humour, and probably never encountered in works of social science. 'Odiferous' appeared in the *Guardian* on 25 April 2000.

render. In French one uses *rendre* and not *faire* for inducing a certain state in a person or thing (*faire* being used for making somebody do something). Among the examples cited in Harrap's French dictionary are '*Le homard me rend malade*' and '*Vous me rendez fou*'. Although this is a rule in French, it is not in English; Fowler ignores it completely. It is normal in English to use 'make' (*faire*) for both meanings. Yet 'render' in this particular French sense has a place is English—a very subsidiary one according to the 1933 *SED*, where it appears to be both archaic and rare. The *NODE* upgrades this meaning to second place out of five, citing 'The rains rendered his escape impossible'. For myself I regard this usage as poor style, comparable to 'prior to' for 'before' and 'commence' for 'begin', and change it to 'make' wherever I find it; 'made his escape impossible' would surely be preferable to the example given in the *NODE*.

low-key. One does not need to be learned in musical theory to understand that musical keys are neither high nor low: the key of A may be 'below' the key of B, but immediately below A is G. It is not unimaginable to use 'in a *minor* key' metaphorically, but a substitute has to be found for 'low-key'. This is difficult because 'low-profile', 'low-grade', 'low-intensity' are not synonyms for it; perhaps 'muted' conveys its intended sense most closely.

hopefully. The *NODE* contains a very intelligent short essay on how in the second half of the 20th century the 'sentence-adverbial' form of this word ('Hopefully it will not rain to-morrow') has far outstripped in frequency of use the simple adverbial form ('He strode forth hopefully, without an umbrella'), pointing out that the sentence-adverbial form—meaning 'It is to be hoped that'—is far removed from the word's original sense, and that the issue has become a shibboleth of 'correctness'. In this case I am inclined, for once, to yield to the *Zeitgeist*: the sentence-adverbial 'hopefully', exactly equivalent to German *hoffentlich*, is too useful to be disregarded.

The reader will by now be aware that an implicit purpose of this section, besides that of heightening linguistic precision on the page, is to heighten linguistic consciousness in the brain. This emboldens me to recommend two sets of usages which, while having that purpose, do not enjoy the sanction of any of the great Dictionaries.

till, until. The first should govern a noun or a verbless phrase only; the second a dependent clause containing a verb. E.g. 'I shall wait till evening'; 'I shall wait until she returns'. Although 'up till' is not a very euphonious combination, I would still use it for, e.g., 'from the Middle Ages up till the 19th century'.

though, although. Exactly as with '*till, until*'. 'I shall await her return, although I am not hopeful that she will come'; 'I shall await her return, though without much hope that she will come'. 'Albeit' is generally used, if at all, in the sense I have specified for 'though', but it is actually a shortening of 'although it be that' and thus has the meaning I have specified for 'although'. It now inevitably sounds rather precious in whatever way it is used.

Concerning dates

There are a number of refinements to be considered:

1. *the 1800s, the 1900s.* Used, as they frequently are, to mean respectively 'the 19th century' and 'the 20th century', they are grossly erroneous, and can never be allowed to stand. 'The 1800s' means only the years 1800–9 and 'the 1900s' the years 1900–9.

(This item, involving a distinction of meaning, belongs strictly in the previous section, but is placed here for convenience.)

2. '*from 1945–50*' is a slovenly usage, to be avoided always. One should write either 'from 1945 to 1950', 'between 1945 and 1950' or '*in* 1945–50'.

3. '*the 1940's*'. There is no justification whatever for inserting an apostrophe into what is merely a plural form, as is sometimes done. 'The 1940s' is plainly the neatest and most economical usage that I would always prefer to, say, 'the nineteen-forties' or, even more, 'the forties'. I would also not allow 'the '40s' to stand *on its own*, although this form is both neat and economical when immediately following the full form, as in 'the 1930s and '40s'.

4. How to write the date when it consists of day, month and year. Here the choice is substantially between what appear to be the European and American usages. The former I take to be, e.g., '10 February 1995' and the latter 'February 10, 1995'. As well as occurring in the text, it also has a place whenever a particular issue of a newspaper is referred to in a bibliographical note or the bibliography. We do not want a comma added in the first example (10 February, 1995) or omitted in the second (February 10 1995), as quite often happens. Likewise we do not want 'February, 1995' when only the month and not the day is referred to. But the American style requires that a comma should follow the year when it occurs in mid-sentence, as 'November 22, 1963, was a defining date'.

For the sake of neatness and economy, we should omit '-st', '-nd', '-rd' and '-th' when the date is set out in full.

5. *The season*. This quite often occurs in bibliographical contexts, when an issue of a quarterly journal is referred to. In these contexts its initial letter should always be l.c., as in 'vol. xx, no. 1 (spring 1999)'.

In narrative it should still be l.c., but expressed fully: 'in the spring of 1999'—*not* 'in spring 1999'.

Numerals

When to spell them out. The convention, now generally accepted as a basic rule, is that in straightforward narrative numerals are spelt out until you reach 100, and from there on they are represented by figures. An exception would be when a large number of quantities are mentioned together and spelling them out would be a barrier to rapid assimilation. Furthermore, it would appear absurd in such a group if quantities below 100 were spelt out and those above not.

Measurement are mostly exceptions to this rule, whether of distance, area, weight, speed, money, percentage or any other. Here numerals are the general rule. However, an author might reasonably prefer a low number of units of distance spelt out, as in 'two miles' or 'six feet [tall]', and one could not but agree, but if these occur in a context of other similar distances, then it would look neater if they were all in figures. Also, (all) metric measurements lend themselves more naturally to being in figures than to being spelt out (e.g. '2 km.' rather than 'two kilometres').

There are other contexts where spelling-out looks laboured and pedantic, and figures are in every way more convenient. These are when a number of different quantities are grouped close together. An example is a non-tabular review of election results: the numbers of votes cast for the various parties are likely anyway to be much too high to warrant being spelt out, but this is not the case with the numbers of seats won. The latter, however low the quantities, should be shown in figures.

Parallel instances might be numbers of casualties in a battle, of different kinds of livestock in farms, of occupational, gender and other groups in a census, and of gender and ethnic groups in individual schools and colleges.

Time needs to be considered separately. Numbers of minutes, hours, days, months and (under 100) years, and a person's age, should be spelt out in straightforward narratives. However, as with the instances cited above, this will appear clumsy if a number of different times or persons' ages are grouped together in a passage of statistical information, where figures are preferable.

Percentage. Our usual practice is to spell out 'per cent' (not percent), but never to spell out the figures. One will avoid repetition as much as possible by such devices as '... respectively 4, 16 and 25 per cent', but where wearisome repetition cannot be avoided, I would always opt instead for the entirely innocuous '%'.

The rule is: having decided on a rule, stick to it whenever possible, but be flexible.

Hyphenation

Centuries. Most people (though not all) would never dream of hyphenating the substantive phrase 'the 19th century', but in its adjectival sense it acquires a hyphen: '19th-century art'. This is a rule without exceptions. It extends to, e.g., 'late-19th-century art'.

Class. The correct usages are 'the middle class' and 'the upper middle class'; and 'middle-class' or 'upper-middle-class values/ prejudices'.

Examples of these forms are very numerous, and the copy-editor needs to remember that they are fertile fields for author error and inconsistency.

Over-punctuation

In sentences beginning in a similar way to the following—'On 5 December they were instructed by the General....'; 'Ten days later the General....'—many authors insert a comma after the time element. This is not required because the time element and the main statement form a single, organic, uninterrupted whole. To reinforce the point, there would be no question of inserting a comma if the time element were placed *after* the main statement.

Similarly a comma is not required after 'Thus', 'Also', 'Similarly', 'Likewise', 'Otherwise' and a legion of other such expressions when they begin a sentence. This is because there is no break in the sentence structure, as there is (albeit a slight one) after interjections such as 'However', 'Therefore' etc. (see p. 91).

In bibliographies some authors are prone to writing 'see:' or 'in': when 'see' or 'in' alone would meet the case.

This merges with the question of apposition which is extensively covered in Burchfield/Fowler.

The general rule, as with paired numerals, is to *omit* punctuation where the sense is not merely unharmed but actually enhanced, even slightly, by doing so. Complementarily, it should be *added*, or strengthened if already present, to meet the same criterion.

For the highly literate, which I assume every editor to be, the most reliable guidance comes from gut feeling—which may not be the same in every person, but which should at least ensure consistent treatment in a single job.

Tautology

A tautology should be identifiable by a publisher at sight, but some take a few moments to sink in. Saying that X. 'went on to add' something in a speech is one. So is 'further exacerbated'. So too are 'the most pre-eminent case', 'the surrounding environment', and '*it is possible* that this *may* become more important'.

The *NODE* contains a textbook example on page xvii of its Introduction: 'Compared with other European languages, English has comparatively few inflections.' I wondered about the *NODE*'s secondary definition of the noun 'cock' as 'a man's penis': if it says 'a man's' to distinguish it from, say, a giraffe's, it is not tautological, but if the implied distinction is from the feminine gender (which I suspect), then it is.

It is tautological to introduce a string of objects with 'e.g.' and, having done so, then to end it with 'etc.'.

A common tautological form, in speech and in writing, is the belt-and-braces 'double past', e.g. 'He would have liked to have been present'. Surely the past-conditional main verb is enough to determine the whole sentence, and should be followed by the present infinitive: 'He would have liked to be present'.

Mixed metaphors

A rich source of belly-laughs—Fowler cites *inter alia*, from published sources, lions and tigers coming home to roost, and digesting the nuts and bolts of a matter.

But we should be on the look-out for the less dramatic mixing of images in a fundamentally absurd manner, e.g. 'Separation of powers is still a goal pursued by modernisers'. Goalposts do not move except in one of the more cliché'd metaphors, and therefore goals should be sought rather than pursued.

Agreement of number

It is far from uncommon to meet sentences like 'The constitution was abrogated, the national and provincial legislatures dissolved.' One of the basic skills of sophisticated writing is not to include unnecessary words, and the writer here has omitted the auxiliary verb 'was' from the second part of the sentence, leaving it to be 'understood'. The only problem is that the subject of the first part is singular and that of the second part is plural, so that in our minds we form the words '... legislatures *was* dissolved'. To avoid this, it is simply necessary to insert 'were' before 'dissolved'.

This concatenation is reversed in the sentence 'Steamships were small and their consumption of coal heavy.'

The memory of some writers is short, cf. the sentence 'the importance of rich symbols *have* been recognised'.

It is quite common to encounter phrases like 'one or several modern languages'. Because of the presence of 'or', 'one' directly governs 'languages' and therefore the sentence is faulty. This can be got round by saying instead 'one or more than one modern language'. There is always a way round.

Are collective nouns singular or plural in effect?

I refer to 'population', 'family', 'group'; and 'the government', 'the cabinet', 'the board', 'Parliament'.

There is no clear-cut rule as to whether these words, used in the singular, govern a singular or a plural verb. This is clear from the following examples: 'The population is the largest in the Balkan region'; but 'The population are largely engaged in agriculture'. Consider also 'The family is the bedrock of society'; but 'My family are very fond of board games'.

It is probably impossible in any circumstances to say 'The group are...', but it is not unusual to get the feeling that 'The group is...' does not sound quite right. The way round this is to say 'Members of the group are...'

Disjunction due to change of subject in mid-sentence

Careless writers quite often lose sight of the subject with which they started a sentence, as in 'By emphasising growth at the expense of income distribution, the inequalities of society had been exacerbated'. Of course we understand what is meant, but that is not enough: the sentence reads as if the inequalities emphasised growth. The simplest way to get round the disjunction here is to open the sentence with something like 'Because of the emphasis on growth ...' Similar real-life cases follow: 'A committed communist since before the war, X's writing exceeds ...' 'The daughter of a boiler-maker, Hunter's first lessons came from ...' (obituary of Rita Hunter, *Guardian*, 2 May 2001). 'It was only by getting Tito to over-ride the ministry that work on the plan could continue.' 'The bleakness of the future cannot be attributed only to nationalism but also to ...'.

The Bookseller of 10 August 2001 contained two fine examples: 'Described as "a focused manager, able to galvanise people without meddling", Ms Fraser's first priority will be to...' and 'Dressed in a soiled green polo shirt and combat trousers..., street trader Ronald Jordan's arrival... could hardly have been more unprepossessing'.

Non sequitur

According to the *SED* (and the *NODE* defines it almost in the same words), this is 'an inference or conclusion that does not follow from the premisses'. The dictionary definition here is rather narrow, and it is surprising that neither *Ur*-Fowler nor Burchfield-Fowler mentions what, in the writings of some scholars, is a recurring problem and can only be called non sequitur. It usually occurs in narrative that is densely packed with factual statements, and when encountered is unmistakable. Put simply, the sentence you are contemplating stands in isolation from the one preceding it. And the one that follows may likewise be isolated from the present one. Reading prose that has this character is like walking over boulders.

However important the facts presented, to write in this non-sequent manner is self-defeating. The reader may be conscious of no more than fatigue, but the good editor is galvanised into action at once, and gets to work linking sentences where they can be linked and, where they cannot, introducing small modifications so that the transition from one capsule of thinking to the next is never made too abrupt by clumsy phrasing.

Around 1980 we commissioned a book later published with the title *Antarctic Law and Politics*. It became a standard work in its time, but was written in just such a staccato fashion as I have tried to convey. The chapters had several hundred footnotes apiece, each one attached to a discrete statement, immediately following and followed by another. I sweated blood moulding the book into some semblance of a sequent narrative—only to have a lot of it stetted by the author in proof. However, I stood my ground and my changes largely prevailed.

This experience has heightened my sensitivity to the problem when it occurs in less rebarbative texts. Non sequiturs require no special training or knowledge to detect; they make their presence known by the equivalent of the bleep of a metal detector in the brain.

Whatever the subject, the language must *flow*.

Where to place 'both' and 'not only'

This is similar in 'feel' to the error cited under '*Agreement of number*'. Take the sentence 'This proved to be both costly and marked a further shift in policy'. The only correct place for 'both' is between 'This' and 'proved'.

Consider also 'This not only jeopardised its fighting ability but such routine tasks as. ...' The only correct place for 'not only' is after 'jeopardised'.

Here is a case of multiple misplacement: 'Not only did the French forces fight fiercely and suffer heavy losses on the — front, but also for the land where they lived.'

'Both' and 'not only ... but also' are quite often used when there is no need for them to achieve the sense intended.

If altering an author's word-order will produce more subtle shades of emphasis and greater expressiveness, the editor should inhesitatingly do it to the extent necessary, while at the same time trying to avoid an excess of intrusion.

Where to place 'however' and similar words

Similar words include 'therefore', 'moreover', 'nevertheless', 'nonetheless' or the more old-fashioned 'none the less', 'for instance/example', 'in short', 'no doubt/doubtless', 'finally'. There are no rules about placing such words, and rhetorical effect can be gained by dropping them into a sentence at its perceived fulcrum. But in the great majority of instances I would opt for placing them at the beginning of the sentence. This results in greater vigour and directness—putting them in the middle often seems a shade precious.

Punctuation in relation to abbreviations, acronyms etc.

Abbreviated words. The rule for abbreviated words is to complete them with a full-point if the final letter of the abbreviation is different from that of the word itself. Examples are

etc., m., km., cm., mm., ml., in., cu., sq., kg.*
Prof., Rev. ('Revd' is a more Catholic usage—see below), Hon., M. (for Monsieur)
Gen., Brig., Col., Maj., Capt., Lieut., Div., Batt.
(*in bibliographies*) publ., diss. (dissertation), transl., ed., repr., vol., no., p., ff.,
viz., etc.

If the final letter is the same as that of the word itself, no full-point is needed, e.g.

Mr, Mrs, Mme, Dr, Rt, St, Mgr, Revd
Adml, Sgt, Cpl, Pte, Bde,
ft, Ltd
(*in bibliographies*) edn, eds, vols, nos

Points of the compass in geopolitical expressions

Whether to use capitals for them is a more complex issue than may appear at first sight. I may feel that my decision on each

*'Kilo' is now preferable, having become a word in its own right and of course not requiring a terminal full-point in spite of being an abbreviation.

point is subjective and instinctive, but more often than not one finds general agreement.

Let us start with

Europe. We will indisputably capitalise the compass-point in Western, Central and Eastern Europe. But I would not do the same for northern and southern Europe, which have a less *geopolitical* identity. The adjectival forms of Western Europe and Eastern Europe are 'West European' and 'East European'.

Asia. None of us has problems about 'East Asia', 'South Asia', 'Southeast Asia' and 'Central Asia', except:

— Do we spell the third of these 'Southeast', 'South-east' or 'South-East'? I do not venture an opinion, except that consistency be maintained.

— Is Burma in South Asia, as it would have been considered in the days of British India, or in Southeast Asia? Again I don't venture an answer, although the present-day consensus tends towards the latter.

— Central Asia is generally taken to mean the former Soviet Islamic republics of Kazakhstan, Uzbekistan, Tadjikistan, Turkmenistan and Kyrghyzstan. But probably Afghanistan should be added, so fulfilling the old tsarist* dream.

— The term West Asia is less often used than perhaps it should be; it is difficult to see how else one should describe Iran, which cannot be included in 'the Arab World', 'the Middle East' or (almost certainly) Central Asia.

— This raises the question of whether the terms 'Near East', 'Middle East' and 'Far East' are truly legitimate. For the last of these there is no problem: it is East Asia or, at a pinch, Southeast Asia. But for all of them one should ask 'east of where?' Then their dubious nature becomes apparent, because they clearly

*'Tsar', transliterated directly from Russian, is now the standard spelling in British-English, whether referring to a Russian emperor or to a public official with sweeping powers, e.g. 'drugs tsar'. 'Czar', still cited in dictionaries as an alternative, now looks old-fashioned.

mean 'east of London' (or Paris or Washington). It seems both absurd and pathetic for both Arab and Israeli politicians to talk of their home region as 'the Middle East', as they often do in press conferences etc. The Australians started a welcome revolt by referring to the 'Far East' as the 'Near North'. This is where 'West Asia' comes in useful—or, for greater precision, 'the Gulf', 'Arabia', 'the Levant' or plain 'Turkey'.

Africa. North, East, West, Sub-Saharan, Central and Southern Africa. All have definite geopolitical identities.

India. North and South India are capitalised, but northern and southern India are not. West India and East India are not standard terms in relation to the Indian subcontinent, although 'East India' is the precise translation of the old term (Oost-Indië) for the Dutch Indies, now Indonesia.

Nigeria. Northern, Western and Eastern Nigeria are all capitalised.

The points of the compass have various other significations:

— 'The West' – meaning the rich capitalist world as opposed to the Communist East, when it existed, and the developing world, wherever it is located – must always be capitalised, as should 'Western' used in this sense.

— 'The East' likewise, though it has a rather different spectrum of meanings from 'the West'.

— 'The North' serves to describe the whole sub-Arctic region, merging into the 'Far North'. And for many countries it has a local meaning. In England it means the area starting from Yorkshire and Lancashire and ending at the Scottish border. In the United States it means the side that won the War between the States; in Nigeria the 'holy and undivided [Muslim] North'.

— 'The South' had a rich resonance for the northern European poets of the Romantic period. For Goethe it was the land where the lemons grow, and Keats wrote of 'a beaker full of the warm South'. In North America and Italy 'the South' contains undertones of oppressive heat, poverty and violence. The 'South of France' has almost the opposite connotations. In Sudan 'the South' has a poignant significance.

The political wings

For clarity's sake—as a 'marker'—we should write 'the Left' and 'the Right' with capitals. But forget about 'the Far East'; 'the far Right' and 'the far Left' have the adjective in lower case. In compounds like 'left-wing' or 'right-inclined' the sense is instantly understood and the capital is not necessary.

Positions and titles

My inclination is to be generous with capitals, and include them when talking of 'the President', 'the 'Prime Minister', and equally the 'Deputy Minister of Communications'. I would also capitalise 'the Chairman' and 'the General Secretary' of a political party as a trade union, but not 'the chairman', 'the president' or 'a/ the director' of a corporation or other institution.

—When referring to 'the Presidency' of a state, theoretically or in a specific case, it should have a capital; but I would not be so categoric about 'the prime ministership', since 'prime minister' can only mean one thing whereas conceptually 'presidency' has wider applications.

—Lower case should be used for 'presidential', 'prime-ministerial' (*sic*, with hyphen) etc.

—Ministries should have initial capitals throughout.

—'Foreign Ministry'. This is the usual shortened form of 'Ministry of Foreign Affairs'. In Britain alone 'Foreign Office', which should be used when the relatively recent title 'Foreign and Commonwealth Office' is not appropriate, is the invariable sobriquet; some writers use it generically when referring to other countries, but this should be corrected. 'Department of State' refers only to the United States, and is the only term that can be used for that institution; to refer to it as the US Foreign Ministry, as is sometimes done, is wrong.

— 'government'. There is no reason to capitalise it, even when the reference is to a specific one.

— 'state'. Up to a point the same rule applies as for 'government'. The exception would be in works of political theory or philosophy: the author could make a case that 'the State' as a concept should be capitalised.

— 'church'. When used as part of a title, like 'Catholic Church', 'Orthodox Church' etc, it is normally capitalised. Doubt arises when, to avoid repetition, it is used on its own to refer to the institution or, in the religious sense, to the body of believers. Writers are often inconsistent in this, but we should not be and, I submit, should opt for the 'secular' usage of lower case, as with 'state' and 'government'. 'Catholic', 'Orthodox', 'Anglican', 'Islamic' and similar terms, when used adjectivally, should be capitalised.

Sets of initials

When do we insert full-points in these? The answer is logical: whenever they are written in lower case, as a.m., p.m., m.p.h., r.p.m., e.g., i.e.

This avoids any possible visual confusion. Such confusion is not likely to arise when they are written in capitals, so all institutions, political parties, decorations etc. represented by initials can have full-points omitted. An exception, significant for publishers, is 'MS.' and 'MSS.'.

We can live comfortably with acronyms which form short, relatively euphonious words being always spelt in capitals, such as NATO and ASEAN. But when they exceed a certain (indeterminate) length there comes a point where for visual comfort one would prefer to have them in l.c., e.g. Unicef, Unesco, Unifil, Ecomog, Ecowas, Aslef, Sogat (the last two being once-powerful British trade unions).

When initials are used in personal names, they *should* have full points: E.M. Forster, not EM Forster; P.D. James, not PD James. Leaving them out, as some designers do, strikes me as perverse.

The rules concerning AD and BC are that they do not have full-points and are set in small capitals, 'AD' before the date and

'BC' after it. However, for those who, for whatever reason, wish to take a secular approach, other styles are available: 'CE' (Common Era) and 'BCE' (Before the Common Era). 'AH' (*anno Hegirae*, the Hegira being the Prophet Muhammad's departure from Mecca in 622 CE) should be remembered by those who are culturally Christian.

With the USA, the UK, the UN and the USSR the question is usage, not punctuation.

When referring to the United States of America, I recommend the following rules:

1. As a noun, use 'the United States' only. Do not say 'the USA'. It somehow looks inelegant in a book. Even more definitely, do not say 'the US'.

2. As an adjective, do use 'US', as in 'US foreign policy', 'US troops' etc.

3. Care is needed with the use of 'America' and 'American', which cannot be a US monopoly, since Latin and Native Americans, and Canadians, are Americans too. 'North American' is a useful expression with a specific meaning. In the language of US politicians and officials, 'American' is undoubtedly synonymous with 'US', but for many its connotation is much wider, encompassing the cultural, the ethical and the sociological.

We only refer to the USSR now historically, and will continue doing so for some time, but aesthetically 'the Soviet Union', with its associated adjective 'Soviet', is preferable on the page.

In certain contexts, where a semi-colloquial usage is desirable, 'the UK' can be acceptable, but 'the United Kingdom' sounds very official and artificial in ordinary narrative, and 'Britain' (*not* 'Great Britain') is preferable.*

I believe, on the other hand, that 'the UN' and 'UN' are fully acceptable in writing, respectively as noun and adjective, by a long-drawn-out process of familiarisation. But, for good order, at the organisation's first mention in the book the words 'United Nations' should still be spelt out in full.

*Technically, and thus in legislation, the United Kingdom includes Northern Ireland, and Great Britain does not. 'Britain' can thus be used more confidently in a general sense.

Other established usages include 'the Netherlands' rather than 'Holland', if the whole country and not the particular part of it called Holland is referred to.* 'Romania' should be used rather than 'Rumania' or 'Roumania'; it is, after all, the version used in the country itself. This is not the place to discuss the relative merits of the acronym 'FYROM' and 'Macedonia' *tout court* to refer to the independent state that was formerly the Yugoslav Republic of Macedonia. These are likely to be determined by Balkan *Realpolitik*.

Use of foreign accents and diacritics

When foreign words are taken out of their native linguistic context, there is a choice as to whether one uses the original accents or not. Whether one should or should not italicise foreign words and phrases that have become indigenised in English is discussed by both Hart and Butcher, so I will not offer a list of my own, but merely repeat that whatever course is chosen must be followed consistently. But, among such words, the question whether or not to accent arises with differing degrees of force, and each must be considered separately. What is certain is that no two authors or editors will entirely agree, but a publisher should aim for a house-style. Here are some common examples:

élite: accent present in the 1933 *SED* but absent in the *NODE*. Indeed it is often left out, but because it makes some difference to the pronunciation it ought to be left in, even if doing so seems élitist to some.

regime: has been used in English without an accent since the 18th century; but when the word appears in italics, as in *ancien régime*, it must have the accent.

émigré: having two accents on an English word seems rather a lot, but the final one is essential (as in 'fiancée'), which means that the first has to stay in too. This also applies to 'protégé'; which is often misspelt with the final accent only. (It can be argued,

*Note the different rendering of the definite articles in 'the Netherlands' (l.c.) and 'The Hague' (capital 'T').

incidentally, that 'émigré' is only a snob form of 'emigrant': that Russian aristocrats and Viennese Jewish professors were émigrés and the huddled masses emigrants.)

débâcle: the *NODE* omits both accents entirely, and the *SED* shows the word with and without them. To have a circumflex in English seems excessive, so it is probably better to omit both.

role: with or without the original circumflex on the 'o' it is pronounced the same (as is 'hotel'), so omit it: it looks precious.

dénouement: has the accent in the 1933 *SED* but not in the *NODE*; it should be retained because of the clear difference it makes to the pronunciation.

attaché, chargé d'affaires, communiqué: no one has yet sought to remove the accent from these, since it adds a syllable.

matériel: always with the accent, which helps to reinforce the word's distinct meaning (military hardware).

résumé: the *NODE* confuses us by leaving out the first accent in the key entry set in bold type, but including it in the only example of the word's use that follows. Few of us, I imagine, pronounce it precisely in the French way in everyday English speech, but since the second accent is always voiced and is therefore indispensable, the first one must stay.

étatism: always with the accent.

cortège: always with the accent.

naive, *naïveté* (to mention only the forms of this common expression that one is most likely to encounter). Burchfield/Fowler states the problem with admirable clarity: 'This most useful French word [the feminine form of the adjective *naïf*] is still at an imperfectly naturalised stage in English....' Some will spell the adjective with the diaeresis (naïve), but more commonly it is left off. To use the masculine form on its own in normal narrative, whether in roman (with or without the diaeresis) or italic (in which the diaeresis would be obligatory), would seem affected—except in a specialised French form such as '*faux naïf*'.

As for the noun, a completely Gallic rendering, italic and all, seems best if one is going to have both accents (as in other instances we have cited, if you have the essential one [*é*] you must have the other too). But why should one be forced to italicise, i.e. to render as foreign, a word that has been used in English since the 17th century? My reluctant preference, for serviceability and consistency, is for 'naive' and 'naivety'.

Three other French expressions that have a firm foothold in English usage are *raison d'être*, *cause célèbre* and *vis-à-vis*, but in spite of their familiarity they have not, in this writer's opinion, truly made the transition to being used without italic and without their accents, nor are likely to do so. The first two are more truly indigenised in so far as they have no elegant English synonyms. The third is paraphraseable (e.g. by 'in relation to') but yet is often used. Worse, it is often used in roman type and without the accent.

We must now move on to accents and diacritical marks used in their native context, where the question of anglicisation does not arise: in names of people and places, straight quotations, and the titles of books and other literary works, published or unpublished. A scholarly publisher who allows any omissions or errors in this area to get into print is falling down on the job.

The one instance where even someone unfamiliar with the language should not be able to slip up is the French cedilla: in *ca*-, *co*-, *cu*- the *c* is hard; in *ce*-, *ci*- and *cy*- it is soft. So for the former to become soft, one has to add the cedilla, *comma ça*. In the commonest example—'*français*'—it is often left out.

Likewise the basic rule for *grave* accents is simple: when an *e* is followed by a single consonant, followed by another *e*, it invariably becomes *è*. This can also occur with double consonants, as in *siècle* (century): because this word occurs in the titles of many scholarly works, publishers should bear it particularly in mind.

As for German umlauts and French circumflexes, and spelling generally (usually far more logical than in English), a fair knowledge of those languages is needed to give one confidence in dealing with them, but a grasp of rules of spelling can be acquired with only a superficial grasp of vocabulary and syntax. But no scholarly publisher's office can afford to be without substantial French and German dictionaries (Spanish, Italian and Latin ones are scarcely less useful), and these should be consulted if one is in any doubt—as one may well be, even with some familiarity.

If one is ignorant of any language which occurs in a work under one's hand, the only thing to do is to ask someone familiar with it to go through and check every item.

The *tilde* in Spanish (ñ) and Portuguese (ão), the Italian final *à* (Università and *L'Unità*, the communist newspaper, are frequently encountered in our kind of book and *Pietà* in certain art books), the Nordic å and ø, the Finnish ää and the Hungarian ő are traps for the unwary. Icelandic and Faroese preserve the useful ð and þ, equivalent to respectively voiced and unvoiced 'th'. All these characters are indispensable and have to be obtained when needed.

In Serbian and Croatian, the native orthography is now used in Western scholarly works where westernised forms were once standard: č, š and ž have replaced, respectively, *ch*, *sh* and *zh*. The 'inverted circumflex' is easy to obtain from a typesetter; the Romanian 'inverted pudding basin', ş̆, less so (here the inverted circumflex is no substitute). I draw the line at the Serbian đ for dj, and the unpronounceable Polish ł, not so much because they are difficult to obtain (which they are) but because they trip up the non-expert reader.

In Turkish the dotted capital İ and the dotless l.c. ı occur frequently and cannot be avoided. Turkish has the character 'ş' with a cedilla, and it is important to note that Romanian has it too, notably in Ceauşescu; that villain's name cannot be spelt correctly without it.

Whether to go the whole hog with Arabic transliteration, beyond the easy *'ain* (as in *shari'a*, Shi'a, Ba'th) and *'alif* (as in the Qu'ran), and incorporate every dot under certain consonants and macron (a dash over long vowels), as required by the rigorist, must be a matter for earnest discussion between publisher and author. If the author can agree that the integrity of his work will not suffer if a simplified system is used, the publisher's and the typesetter's tasks will be made much less arduous.

There is only one fixed rule: once a standard for consistency has been agreed upon, conformity to it must be absolute.

German borrowings

A small problem arises when German common (not proper) nouns are used in English, as borrowings, in italic. Because all German nouns are spelt with an initial capital, should the same practice be carried over when they are used in English? The answer has to be Yes. But other German nouns have jumped the language barrier and become absorbed, with their original spelling, into English, but without italic or initial capital, e.g. angst, leitmotiv, the semi-slang 'Blitz' referring in particular to the German aerial bombing of London in 1940–1 (in its extended colloquial uses, such as 'I'm having a blitz in the office today', the capital is dropped), and ersatz (surprisingly in common use in Britain during the Second World War*, but seemingly abandoned without trace since then). Examples of those which have not made the transition in spite of being in occasional use are *Blitzkrieg* (when spelt in full), *Doppelgänger, Ewigkeit, Gemütlichkeit, Lebensraum, Liebestod, Realpolitik, Schadenfreude, Schwärmerei, Weltanschauung, Weltschmerz, Zeitgeist.*

Names commonly mis-spelt

However prominent or obscure the role an individual has played in history, spelling and otherwise rendering that individual's name correctly continues to matter long after he or she is dead and gone. It continues to matter for ever.

It is almost impossible to mis-spell the English transliterations of such Russian names as Brezhnev, Andropov and Gorbachev, but we find Krushchev mis-spelt 'Kruschev', which does not take account of the presence of two distinctly pronounced consonants in the middle of the word.

* *Sic.* I have never seen or heard an opinion expressed on whether 'the First [or Second] World War' or 'World War I [or II]' is preferable, but my preference is definitely for the former as being more dignified and hence more appropriate.

The surname of François Mitterrand, late President of France, is often mis-spelt with only one 'r'.

As a touchstone let us consider Sir Nevile Henderson, British ambassador in Berlin at the outbreak of the Second World War. He was not a great or even a particularly admirable figure, but because of where he was and when he was there, he figures in many historical works. But he is important to the copy-editor out of all proportion to his importance in history because of the spelling of his first name—with only one el, unlike his contemporary Neville Chamberlain and most other bearers of that moniker. I have had to correct it, when spelt with two els, more than once. Some will say: what could be more unimportant? What does it matter how he spelt his name, and who will even notice if it is spelt wrong except a few troglodytic pedants? The 'Nevile Henderson syndrome' should keep our profession for ever on its toes.

A variant of it is the 'Franz Ferdinand' syndrome. The Austrian archduke of that name, whose assassination triggered the start of the First World War, is sometimes referred to even by Balkanologists as 'Archduke Ferdinand' *tout court*, which is of course incorrect. A warning here against the error of spelling the famous dynastic name 'Habsburg' as it is pronounced, viz. 'Hapsburg'. Further, the Habsburg empire was termed 'Austria' up till the *Ausgleich* of 1867, and only thereafter 'Austria-Hungary', of which the adjectival form is 'Austro-Hungarian'. However the Dual Monarchy was never termed 'Austro-Hungary', another common error. A related error is to refer to 'Austria-Hungary' as if it existed before 1867.

Possibly more worrying are relatively *unfamiliar* names that are mis-spelt, since the chance of their being corrected is that much smaller. On finding the German military commander of 1914–18, Ludendorff, spelt 'Luddendorf' in a MS. by a military expert, I felt rage mixed with despair: if I, a mere labourer in the vineyard, had not been able to spot it, who else would have prevented it from getting into print and inviting the scorn of *cognoscenti*? Wide general knowledge is not a virtue—indeed it can characterise an obsessive personality—but it is an indispensable attribute of the scholarly publisher.

We cannot deal here with the huge number of variant spellings of many surnames and forenames, except to say that the greatest care should be taken *in every case* (i.e. not only with the likes of Sir Nevile Henderson and Archduke Franz Ferdinand) to be sure that only the correct spellings of personal names get into print.

Transliteration

This is a major subject, the rules for which could easily occupy several chapters. Suffice it to say here that there are standard systems for transliterating Chinese and Russian in English, which differ from those in use that apply in the other major European languages. With Chinese, the Pinyin and Wade-Giles systems are used with total consistency by the devotees of each. With Russian, although there is a constant style favoured by rigorous purists, there tends to be slippage between that style and the 'popular' forms with which most of us have been familiar all our lives for names such as Tolstoy and Dostoievsky. The 'rigorous' style will be used in direct quotations and in the titles of books, articles etc., even for very well-known names such as these.

For Greek there appears to be no standard system of phonetic transliteration into English; in an earlier generation (as in the 1933 *SED*) the well-educated English reader was assumed to be familiar with the Greek alphabet, and this saved a lot of bother. No such assumption has ever been possible for the Cyrillic alphabet.

Part II. THE SCHOLARLY PUBLISHER

'... Book publishing is not such a simple task as is usually thought. Despite the current impression to the contrary, neither an honours degree at a university* nor even literary ability is a sufficient qualification. Manifold technical knowledge and commercial acumen are essential. Furthermore, it will usually be found that the most able and successful publishers have been right through the business from start to finish, and can therefore, from personal knowledge, check and follow all the work, including the various processes of production. The knowledge that is needed cannot be acquired in a day or even a year.' (Sir Stanley Unwin, *The Truth about Publishing*, London: Geo. Allen & Unwin, 1960 edn, p. 319)

*I would maintain that Britain produced just three publishers of undoubted genius in the 19th and 20th centuries: George Smith (1824–1901) of Smith, Elder & Co., publisher of *Jane Eyre* and many other great contemporary works of literature, and only begetter of the *Dictionary of National Biography*; the exemplary Sir Stanley Unwin himself (1884–1968); and Sir Allen Lane (1902–70), founder of Penguin Books. Not one of them had a university education. Smith was apprenticed at the age of fourteen, Unwin had to cut short his schooling and enter a shipping office aged fifteen at a time when his father's printing business was in difficulties, and Lane entered the publishing office of John Lane the Bodley Head, which belonged to a distant relative of his mother, at sixteen. Furthermore they were not intellectuals or men of great learning, although they revered and promoted learning and literature.

PREPARATION

However many rules one propounds, the scholarly publisher—the editorial head—has ultimately to be the source of the high standards of the house. Unless one is the heir to an established family publishing business,* one has to prepare over a long period to practise the publishing profession. (Of course one has to prepare even if one is the heir to an established publishing business, but the chances are that by the time of entering upon one's inheritance one will have long been in a symbiotic relationship with experienced and well-disposed mentors.)†

*One by one, since the 1960s, the families that once bestrode the publishing world in Britain have sold out: Longman, Macmillan, Hodder-Williams/Attenborough, Collins, Unwin, Franklin, Dent. This has happened for reasons ranging from exhaustion of talent and energy to internecine feuding. The only historic firm which has remained in the control of its founding family is John Murray (A. & C. Black was sold by the Black family in 2000 after I had drafted this passage): significantly it is of medium size, and has kept out of the rat-race of paying crazy advances and seeking salvation through expansion. Once-great operators—Jonathan Cape, Ian Parsons (Chatto and Windus), Frederic Warburg, Hamish Hamilton, Michael Joseph and Max Reinhardt (the Bodley Head)—left no publishing heirs, and without their personal flair and magnetism their imprints, even when nominally surviving, ceased to mean very much.

†The relative value of, on the one hand, training through structured courses in Publishing—either long-term ones at universities or short-term ones organised by the Book Trade itself—and, on the other, of learning on the job will always be a subject of hot debate. I recall, at a meeting held by the Publishers Association to promote the concept of National Vocational Qualifications (NVQs) for publishing staff, the derision expressed by Dag Smith, their chief proponent, for 'learning from

The preparation I am seeking to describe is in a sense negative; it involves much less specialised knowledge than would be required in order to become an adept of almost any other profession—I am thinking not of medicine, law and architecture but of the academic professions of history, economics, political science, anthropology or 'religious studies' (as distinct from theology). But it requires more general knowledge in the latter fields than many practitioners of a particular one of them would feel they needed to possess of the others. Also, as already mentioned, it requires a grasp of the basic rules of spelling and syntax—by no means the same as fluency of expression—in a number of European languages other than English. But if it is possible to rank linguistic abilities in order of importance, pride of place must go to mastery of English.

A person who acquires extensive general knowledge of this kind, and feels no intellectual or atavistic compulsion to enter a learned profession, is well qualified to become a scholarly publisher. But such a person will know enough to know how little he knows, and will therefore acknowledge as a golden rule the necessity of checking everything. A learned work must be read by a specialist in the author's own field. If the work contains the names of places, people, institutions and published works in, say, Hungarian, clearly the hired reader in this case must know that language also, since it will be beyond the publisher's competence to check their accuracy even with a dictionary. A knowledgeable publisher can correct a fact or name he knows to be incorrect, but must have at hand dictionaries and encyclopaedias to check those he suspects of being so.

Nellie'. By this he meant picking up skills from experienced colleagues. It would be wrong to represent NVQs and 'learning from Nellie' as being the only alternatives open to the aspiring publisher, who can benefit from attending classes and seminars dealing with certain specific skills, but I felt then, and do now with equal conviction, that learning from more experienced colleagues in one's own firm, and on occasions in other firms as well, is the sovereign way to learn about publishing. The choice of the name 'Nellie' was just a bit of psychological warfare. As it turned out, NVQs signally failed to catch on in the Trade.

PUBLISHER AND AUTHOR: THE EDITORIAL PROCESS

Vetting the work

Publishers give rein to their own principles and prejudices when agreeing to sign a contract to publish a work not yet written or only partly written, but when it comes to accepting the finished work, they will do well to disengage from their prejudices and fancies, and submit wholly or largely to the judgement of others. This means obtaining outside reviews, however much in-house reading may be done.

Co-publication of our books in North America is essential for our economic survival;* the great majority of our partners are university presses, and most of these are obliged by their constitutions to obtain 'peer reviews'—reports by experts in the author's own discipline—before the press can propose the work to its publication committee (of academics), which must give final approval. Sometimes their rules require two such reviews, but one may be enough. We, the originating publisher, will send a copy of our review to our American partner, which

*The alternative would be to have a single 'distributor'—probably a well-established publishing house—in the United States, which would promote and sell our books there. Several firms comparable in size and scope to C. Hurst & Co. have chosen this way, but for various reasons we have not done so. The endless pursuit of co-publishers lends an element of anxiety to our activity, but the scrutiny to which it subjects, severally, every one of our books is a vital quality check. Also, very important, it is more fun.

should concentrate minds at the other end, even if it does not greatly speed up the review process.

It is unlikely that the originating publisher is going to reject the work on the say-so of a would-be co-publisher's negative review, although if this is devastating it will certainly concentrate his mind. Rejection is most likely after the publisher has received his own review, and he will of course send the rejected author a copy of it. Almost every such review is anonymous, and only submitted on that understanding (which does not prevent the 'victim' from sometimes guessing the identity of the reviewer from internal evidence). If the reviews are encouraging, with the result that publication will go ahead, but contain some criticism, detailed or general, the anonymity rule may be dropped with the consent of the reviewer—a dialogue between the latter and the author may be welcomed by both parties, and certainly should be by the publisher.

The author is thus in danger of being overwhelmed and possibly confused by the sheer volume of advice, help, criticism etc., some of it possibly contradictory. The publisher, as the mediator, has to handle this process with sensitivity—and must warn the author at this point too that, when the copy-editing has been completed, a much more detailed inquisition will be on its way, in the form of the copy-editor's queries.

The more constructive criticism a review contains, the more useful it is and the more welcome it should be. Egotistical reviewers sometimes in effect say that the author should have written a different book, as the reviewer would have written it; such reviews can be demoralising and should be treated with caution. But one should closely heed advice to add or expand a chapter here; cut or prune one there; give greater emphasis to this and less to that; ease up on the conceptual aspects, or give them more prominence. The review may remark on a tendency to repetition, or criticise the author's style as jargon-ridden. It may, if the reviewer has done his job positively and conscientiously, contain a list of points relating to fact or interpretation.

The last-mentioned item—a list of points— is the easiest to deal with, because the author must attend to it. The publisher has to use discretion over the extent to which the author should act upon broader criticisms; at least the author should consider them fully and answer them. The potential co-publisher may insist on certain amendments; and I knew one US press director, now long retired, who simply assumed that every one of his reviewer's suggestions should be carried out; he was a man of little imagination or tact. It has to be the originating publisher's task to strike a just balance over how much or how little should be done: the sole object of course should be to produce a better book. At the same time the author has to preserve his integrity. I have never known an American press complain after publication that changes recommended by a reviewer had not been carried out, even when such a complaint might have been justified. Some ask to see the revised MS., which is reasonable if the revision has needed to be extensive.

Lastly, if one of the reviewers is eminent enough in his field and says something nice enough about the work, permission may be asked for a nugget from the review to be printed, along with the blurb, in the publisher's catalogue and on the cover.

Copy-editing

This process is at the very heart of what publishing is 'about'. Its purpose is to produce a text as nearly flawless in both matter and presentation as human limitations allow, which will bring glory to the author and to the publishing house. What else can be the point of publishing books?

No one can manage a publishing house who does not have a flair for trading and take a delight in it. But no less important is the relentless pursuit of quality. We all sometimes fail at it, and if this were a textbook it would highlight, in order, every weak link along the production chain where things can go wrong. Had he 'but world enough, and time', the head of the publishing house would copy-edit and proofread every MS. himself, but however desirable that might be, it is not possible, and therefore work has to be delegated to assistants and freelance workers.

The publisher cannot expect those people either (1) to do what they have not been trained or educated to do, or (2) to read his mind. For both those reasons, briefing has to be very precise. Going on courses and reading books on editorial functions are all very well, but there is no education like immersion in a MS.—doing it for real, and knowing what one should look out for. The more you do, the more skilled you become until it is second nature.

Now that so many Ph.D. students need to supplement their grants, it is not difficult to engage someone to copy-edit a specialised MS. who has some expert knowledge of the subject-matter. But this can be a snare: such a person may get so absorbed in the subjectmatter that simpler things like house-style and common comprehensibility get neglected.

Expert eyes have already feasted themselves on the MS. by the time the copy-editor gets to work, and the latter's task is to ensure not that the scholarship is superior but that the intelligent non-expert reader, such as he ideally is, can understand every statement, every exposition however complicated, and every expression of opinion, and will not stumble over them because they are ill-expressed, or suffer an emotional shock because the author's use of English is incorrect. It is part of the copy-editor's responsibility to improve the author's style where this proves desirable—in consultation with the head of the firm; it is not fair on the part of the latter to expose the copy-editor to the possible ire of the author at having his work messed about. A MS. can be made much more readable by the elimination of superfluous words and phrases, simplifying tortuous constructions, and re-arranging phrases within a sentence, sentences within a paragraph, and paragraphs or parts thereof within a chapter to achieve greater cogency and a more logical progression of thought. Needless repetitions should be got rid of. One ought not to *look* for things to correct, but merely be alert and respond as soon as they present themselves.

One should put the work aside if one feels that one is becoming too tired to concentrate fully. A related point: the copy-editor will not immediately feel familiar with an author's way of thinking and style of writing, with the result that his editing may not get into top gear until he has been at it for quite a number of pages (speaking for myself, this is certainly the case). Therefore, on reaching the end, he should go back and start again, only stopping when he knows that the point where he got into top gear has been reached.

A scholarly publisher is likely to have to handle many MSS. which have been written in English, or translated into English, by people whose mother-tongue is not English. What one will want to do is not render the language of such MSS. into impeccable Augustan prose, but merely eliminate what is not correct or clear.

The converse of this is the English writer who, usually as a form of exhibitionism, indulges in idiomatic, slangy or jokey expressions which, however inappropriate in their context, are readily understood by fellow-Anglos but would deeply mystify a foreigner who had not lived in Britain for many years and absorbed our argot. One reason why publishers like ourselves do not often sell translation rights in our books to publishers in Germany, France, Spain and Italy, not to mention smaller language groups, is that the people in those countries who need to read the books can usually do so in English; all the more reason to avoid expressions that would mystify them, even at the risk of our appearing to the authors narrow-minded killjoys. The use of chatty, long-winded language tends to occur when the author's usual vehicle for academic communication is the lecture or the tutorial—the recipients being students, who need to be entertained as well as instructed.

Along with over-relaxed writing one should bracket excessive use of the first person singular. Two books we produced in the same season about the same country—one by an anthropologist on a particular region and the other by a sociologist on the country as a whole—exemplifyied the proper and the dubious use of the first person. The anthropologist described intimate scenes of cultural and religious significance at which he had been present: how could he do justice to them without presenting himself as a witness-cum-participant? The sociologist continually used such constructions as: 'In reply to such images ... I insist here upon the need ...'; 'as I have already suggested in the quotation from [name] above'; 'whereas in this account I do not need to address the question ..., I do need to explain ...'; 'the kind of contextual discussion I have in mind'; and so on. This writer is no egoist; on the contrary, although he is a confident and expert scholar, he is modest. But he does a lot of teaching, which perhaps explains his use of this style. One could not root out the extremely numerous uses of 'I' in this book without endless inventiveness in rephrasing, and without altering its essential character; we just have to live with it. But where it occurs infrequently, and without the justification adduced above in the case of the anthropologist, I would always remove it, either by turning the construction into the passive; or, in the case of 'in my opinion', which does not imply certainty, by substituting 'perhaps'; and, in the case of 'I believe', simply deleting it—it should be assumed that every unqualified general statement by the author represents his beliefs.

Where the first person occurs only in a very few places in a scholarly work, and its presence may bring the reader up short, one can always resort to the old circumlocution 'this author' or 'the present author'—which some authors understandably think smacks of pomposity. In other instances the 'authorial we' can be an acceptable substitute for 'I' (e.g. 'we will now consider ...'), with the additional advantage that it can appear to reach out to the reader.

To return to the copy-editor skipping or hacking a way through the MS. Important though style is, substance must at no point be ignored: therefore, the moment he stumbles upon a crux—anything suggesting the slightest doubt over a matter of fact or interpretation—which cannot be resolved on the spot with the help of a reference work or a phone call to a source of bibliographical information, it must be noted for submission to the author. Primitive as it may seem in the age of computers, a simple drill is to mark the locus of each query with a question-mark in the margin and a cross at the top of the page, the page-number being noted on a separate sheet. When the reading has been completed, one goes through the MS., consolidating the queries, and if one feels at the moment of identifying the query that there is any danger, when one returns to it later, of not being able to recapture the exact perceptions one had at the time, one must write a short explanatory marginal note to aid the memory. Such a failure of recollection does not mean that one's first instinct to raise a query was groundless; it may simply mean that one's brain is exhausted.

Authors have been known to submit long MSS. which are completely unpaginated; and relatively frequent for them to number each chapter separately but not the whole ms. straight through. In either case the first thing to be done in the office is to number the pages consecutively through from beginning to end—not least to avoid a disaster should the MS. accidentally slide off the table and scatter on the floor. It should in fact be routine for the author to be asked, before submitting the MS., to do this himself with the help of his computer.

The computer has imported possible complications into the editing process, which the publisher should guard against. When the author has received the copy-editor's queries, it is all too easy for him to think that by incorporating the copy-editor's comments, and possibly some other amendments that occur to him at the same time, into the MS. via his disk and thereby producing a new clean MS., he is saving the publisher time and trouble. The reverse is often the case.

My practice—and it is one that I would still recommend—is always to copy-edit by hand on to the hard copy, and I therefore want to write the author's responses to all the queries on to the ms. by the same method. The typesetter, working with the original disk and my marked hard copy, will produce a set of proofs incorporating all the corrections. We have once or twice been left by obstinate authors with no choice but to copy-edit the new 'clean' text, which almost always proves to be less clean than appears at first sight. For the publisher this is an infuriating thing to happen (it can be mitigated if the author faithfully highlights every altered passage in his new version). It goes without saying that the publisher must cultivate handwriting of the utmost legibility for copy-editing and proof-correcting.

I do not deny that a copy-editor may be able to copy-edit a MS. effectively on a computer, although I will always doubt if it is more effective than working with pen on paper, with the wide angle of vision that this affords. But such a copy-editor may still fall victim to the author who sends a new disk, incorporating changes, after his copy-editing has been done.

Apart from everything else, there is one thing that a publisher should do with every MS. and later every set of proofs. That is to re-read, closely, the introductory and concluding sections. By the former I mean all prefatory narrative in the Prelims, the Introduction and the opening pages of the first chapter of the main narrative. Some works have a chapter actually called—or in some other way earmarked as—a Conclusion.* Others do not, but in every case the final few pages, and most particularly the final few sentences, need to be scrutinised. The object of these re-readings is to ensure that they fulfill their functions in a worthy fashion, and are well written, and to remove, even at this late stage, any ambiguities or infelicities. If the Conclusion does not appear truly to conclude the book, the author should be asked to strengthen it.

These parts of the book make a special impression on the reader, solely by virtue of their location, and for this reason should receive special attention.

Can a sow's ear ever be turned into a silk purse? Every publisher must sometimes feel that making a particular work publishable is taking up more time, skill and expense than it is worth. In the world of car insurance, the would-be repairer of damage resulting from an accident sends an estimate to the insurance company, and if the cost of repair exceeds the write-off value, the car is written off and the repair does not go ahead. Likewise, when confronted by a hopelessly ill-written MS., however good the material intrinsically, the publisher should try to summon the resolution to ditch the project. If that involves writing off an advance paid to the author—and in these circumstances asking for its repayment is probably best not attempted—it is cheap at the price. But if the publisher is too closely wedded to the project to be able to abandon it, that is his funeral: just as the

*It is not uncommon for academic writers who divide chapters into sub-chapters, and give each one a title, to designate the concluding one '*Conclusion*', even if this occurs *seriatim* at the end of every chapter. In the opinion of this writer, such a practice gives the book an unsophisticated air and should be avoided. Sometimes the section in question occupies only a page or two, in which case a 2-line break is all that is needed to distinguish it from the foregoing matter; a title is unnecessary. If it runs to several pages, the author should be asked to give it an alternative title.

owner of the damaged car who cannot bear to part with it must pay the cost of repairs in excess of the write-off value himself.

Checking for errors: proofs and proof-reading

It is axiomatic that every scholarly book must go through two proof stages. The passing of the second proofs should be followed by the production of camera-ready copy (CRC), and most printers in Asian countries will submit, as a matter of course, ozalid proofs—blueprints—of the CRC before finally going to press.

The second proofs must be checked against the corrected first proofs, and the CRC must be checked against the corrected second proofs. The ozalids do not need to be checked for the accuracy of the text, but they give the opportunity to ensure finally that everything is in its right place.

The first proofs. This is where one hopes to catch every 'literal' or 'typo'. It is also where flaws which have escaped the attention of the copy-editor come to light: a MS., as we have seen, may have to be wrestled with to get it into decent order, and inevitably some loose ends will be left dangling when it goes to the type-setter. Every one of these must be tied up. It is also very likely that total consistency, e.g. in the use of capitals or italic and in biblio-graphical notation, will not have been achieved, and this must be dealt with.

The proof-reader should not expect, or attempt, to complete the reading of the first proofs in a single, albeit complete, read through the work. One reading—whether it is the first or not is for the reader to choose—should be devoted to the main text alone, excluding footnotes and such details as punctuation and numerals that require standardisation. As well as looking out for errors, the reader will be aware of whether it reads smoothly or not and, where it does not, will give a further polish. Another run-through can concentrate exclusively on footnotes; another on tables and captions; another on the running heads; and another on ensuring that the sub-headings are reflected correctly in the running heads, and are precisely as listed in the Contents list as regards wording, punctuation and use of capitals. The same of course goes for chapter and part titles. Yet another discrete operation which must be performed no later than the first proof stage is—with illustrated books—ensuring that no more and no less space than necessary has been left in the text for all illustrations, of whatever kind, and their captions.

One should seek the maximum involvement of the author in the first proof stage: some authors are very good proof-readers, while others are hopeless at it. However well one knows the author, it is a good idea to ask him to enlist at least one other person—colleague, spouse, friend—to read the proofs too. It is legitimate for the publisher to emphasise to the author, in asking for this kind of co-operation, that the emergence at the end of a virtually error-free book is in everyone's interest, but in every case it is with the publisher that the final responsibility lies. A tendency has grown for publishers explicitly to abdicate that responsibility, placing it on the author and decreeing that there shall be no more than one proof stage. This is alien to all our traditions and seems, in the most literal sense, counter-productive.

Normally one does not send second proofs to the author, unless they differ in pagination from the first ones and he must have them in order to prepare the index. Some authors simply want to see the second proofs for their own peace of mind, and this should be welcomed by the publisher.

First proofs in galley form. In the days of metal type it was common to have the first proofs in galley—the word then had actual meaning (the tray that held type that had been composed). This meant that the text had not yet been broken up into pages, with page-numbers, running heads etc., and one thus had greater freedom in making changes. A second, paged set had inevitably to follow. The best reason for ordering galley proofs today is if one wishes to retain some freedom about placing of illustrative matter, while pressing forward with setting and correcting the text. The computer has removed the difficulty of making extensive changes to proofs that have already been paged up—provided the index is not yet in being.

The second proofs. The essential purpose of the second proofs is to check that all the corrections marked on the first proofs have been correctly carried out. This sounds like an almost mechanical job that can be done by a relatively inexperienced person, but a watch also has to be kept for new errors that have been introduced independently of corrections made on the first proofs. Obviously this can only be discovered if the whole proof is read again, and I am not recommending that; the problem is usually manifested by the appearance of 'glitches' such as strange characters, words and characters that have merged, and other unmistakable flaws. But it is advisable when checking the correctness of each correction to look at the whole line in which it occurs. If the problem of new errors is clearly serious, the whole second proof must indeed be re-read, and compensation sought from the typesetter.

It is likely that by the time the book is in its second proof stage, its final form will have stabilised. It is therefore time to check whether all the Prelim items, chapters, sub-chapters, appendixes, tables etc., and the Bibliography and Index, actually begin on the page which the Contents page would lead the reader to expect: in other words, that the Contents page is accurate in every detail. I suggested in the preceding section on the first proof stage that that was a time when a check should be run to ensure that there is exact correspondence between the wording and use of capitals of every chapter, sub-chapter etc. as they occur in the body of the book and on the Contents page, and that the running heads are all correct. There is no harm in checking these again at the second proof stage, even if they have been checked once before.

Revisiting the title page. Strangers to publishing might think that, of all things, the title and subtitle of the book and the author's name do not need to be checked on the title page and the cover—either in themselves or against each other, but they would be wrong. If the title or subtitle includes dates, are they represented in the same way in both places? Has a letter been left out of the author's name? A serious discrepancy would almost certainly require correction if it appeared in the printed book, and this can be very expensive. Checking takes only a few minutes. Similarly, the blurb on the jacket or paperback cover cannot be read too many times before going to press. And does the barcode on the outside of the book correspond with the ISBN on the copyright page? A good printer will check this, but it is rather shaming for the publisher to have his own sloppiness pointed out, however politely, by the printer.

The camera-ready copy (CRC). The vital task here is to ensure that every paragraph in the book follows on in the correct sequence from every other; this is done by looking at the end of one and the beginning of the next. Combined with this is ensuring that each page truly follows on in the correct sequence from the preceding one. Very strange things can happen in typesetters' computers, and it was one such occurrence that led to the disaster related in numbered section 6 on pp. 122–3. We were caught napping, and learned a harsh lesson—irreparable damage having been done meanwhile to an excellent publication and to our reputation in the eyes of its editor, who was clearly traumatised by the experience.

But there will also be the routine matter of checking that the (hopefully*) few corrections marked on the second proofs have been carried out. If only a very small number of errors remain, I dare to say that these can be corrected by the use of the house computer (to produce a substitute word or line), paste and scissors. Primitive though this may seem, it can produce total accuracy, and refinement of detail.

Of course the publisher will finally check, before sending the CRC to the printer, that every page is present.

The ozalids. As already mentioned, it can be assumed that, by the time the ozalids appear, the pages are correct in themselves if the two stages of proof-reading have been gone through efficiently, and especially if the CRC has also been properly checked. If this has not been done, now is the time to do it. So what should one look for?

The first thing to do is to go right through, checking that every page is present and in its right place. This is not difficult, and is vitally important.

One should also ensure that the imposition—the positioning

*See above, p. 83.

of the type on the page—is as it should be: that the text pages are not imposed either too high or too low, and that the 'display' pages—the half-title(s), the title-page, the copyright page, the dedication page—are all as one wishes them to be. One should look at the chapter openings, which some printers have a tendency to 'sky', ignoring the 'drop' and leaving an unsightly gap at the bottom.

If one has left to the printer the task of reducing or enlarging and positioning the halftone illustrations, it is vital to check that they have not been muddled up (i.e. that each one still has the correct caption under it—if in the slightest doubt, seek the author's help), are straight, and generally look right on the page. This is the last chance to make corrections that might avoid disaster, and—at the other end of the scale—to make minor adjustments for the sake of a more aesthetically pleasing effect. The author will feel reassured by being consulted at this stage, and the publisher will feel more secure with the author's imprimatur.

Disasters—potential and actual

I always take the first advance copy of a newly-printed book into my hands with a feeling of apprehension. Looking straight at the title-page, the cover, the blurb, the Contents—the places where an error is most obvious and where the publisher's reputation for competence is most exposed—calls for an effort of will. If there is an error, I know that it will immediately jump out at me. If it does jump out, why did it not do so when we last looked at those things, and still had time to correct it? How does one explain the mysterious occlusion of the faculties that publishers are prone to at this most important moment in the publishing process?

No amount of checking can achieve total success; we can be sure that somewhere in the book an error or two will have escaped scrutiny, and can derive a crumb of comfort by recalling the dictum of our one-time author Yasmine Gooneratne that any product of man that is without blemish angers the gods, since they alone are perfect. There is a shred of comfort too in the assurance that typos discovered after publication can be corrected in the next impression, if there is one. But we must not be complacent. Errors that pass into print are of differing orders of gravity. Some are venial but others are mortal. The test of which are which (the answer is likely to occur to one instinctively) can perhaps be narrowed down to three questions. If the error is not corrected, whatever the cost, can I face the author? Can I face the book's American co-publisher? And can I face the world with the firm's reputation intact?

Some disasters which I have experienced, and for which as publisher I was responsible, are recounted below.

1. In the 1970s we printed a large multi-author volume, important for us at the time, in which the Contents page contained no page-numbers. I saw this the moment I opened the first copy we received from the binders, and it remains a mystery to me how everyone had failed to see it earlier. Without further ado we ordered corrected cancel pages to be printed and tipped in.

2. In 1999 we were alerted by our Indian printer (for which we shall always bless her name) that in the jacket blurb the Italian author's name was mis-spelt at a crucial point, viz. the beginning of the short résumé of his career. Only one letter was missing, but this omission changed the pronunciation. The jacket was already printed: would we let this error pass? The author, whose first book this was, had already been patient, and I could imagine this modest man's distress at seeing his name travestied, which would have been compounded if he had thought we didn't care. So we corrected the error and reprinted the jackets. It was unfortunate, but once again there was no way out.

3. In the 1980s the title of a book was slightly changed at the proof stage, and we changed it on the title page and the jacket, but not in the verso running heads throughout. I only discovered this when the book was well and truly in the market-place, but did not think that the error was more than venial, despite the painful jolt it gave me and the evidence it provided of poor standards of control in our house (i.e. by myself). So it was allowed to stand: we really had no option.

4. In the mid-1990s my partner and I were both looking at newly-arrived advance copies of a historical work which had recently become topical; and he asked me if my copy—like his—had a certain page blank. It had. We immediately looked at the ozalids, in which it was also blank, so there was no doubt that every copy was the same, and the fault was entirely ours. The books had not been shipped from the printer in Hong Kong, and a new page was quickly printed and tipped in by hand—the only way. But it was expensive, and taught us for all time the importance of looking at every page of the ozalids, and furthermore to rely only on ourselves for all essential checking.

5. In the mid-1990s we had another book whose title the author decided to change at a late point in the production process. The title-page was changed but not the paperback cover, with the result that the whole paperback run had to have the covers stripped off and replaced with reprinted ones. Purely in terms of cost, this was probably the most expensive of these disasters.

6. The worst printing error ever committed in our name occurred in a collective volume, written and edited by Scandinavian scholars, which we published in 1999. A few months after publication the author of one of the chapters phoned from his home country and told me, quite good-humouredly, that in his chapter four pages were repeated, and the material which should have occupied the space thus colonised by the repetition was completely missing. Had the same thing happened, he asked, in other copies? Of course it had. The page-numbers on the offending pages were correct—if they too had been repeated, we could not have failed to spot the misplacement—and the pages themselves had been correct when the proofs were read and the Index prepared. A convulsion had taken place in the typesetter's computer after the second proofs were returned, which could simply not have been foreseen; one cannot go on checking proofs indefinitely. But we are now wiser as the result of this experience, and have now adopted the exhaustive checking procedure described on page 111 above.

As a result of this disaster we sacked the typesetter, with whom we had collaborated successfully for several years, but this in no way mitigated my unrelieved sense of defeat. I felt so stunned and ashamed that I could not bring myself immediately to compose a suitable letter to the editor of the work. What could I say? While I havered, he wrote to me saying that in his view the book was a complete failure, and I had compounded the crime by not writing to confess it. This was a terrible moment, made worse by the fact that we could offer no palliative (the extreme but logical one being withdrawal of the publication): months had passed since the book had reached the market, hence withdrawal was out of the question.

If the Indian printer in instance no. 2 noticed the mis-spelt name on a jacket, why did no one in the printing house notice the far more glaring errors in instances 1, 4, 5 and 6? There is no answer to that question. I think each time that the expense, or the blow to our professional *amour-propre*, can be written off to experience if it has taught us never to commit such an error again—until we do. It is no excuse, but it is worth others bearing in mind, that we and publishers like us are not OUP, with a many-layered editorial infrastructure. This may be part of our appeal to authors, but the risk of disasters occurring is greater; and when they do occur, the chief offender—the head of the house—cannot be removed, demoted or moved sideways. He can always find a way out by committing *hara-kiri*, but that will neither solve this enduring problem nor greatly advance the cause of good scholarly publishing. Instead he should repeat to himself every day: what can go wrong will go wrong.

Which errors are venial and which are mortal must never concern us while there is still the possibility of correcting them—i.e. before the book has gone to press. Once it has gone to press, the tests adumbrated above have to be applied.

'Second impression, corrected'

Every author should be urged to keep aside one copy of the work in which to note typos and any other errors that have come to light after publication, and asked, when a new impression is in view, to list them—not for inclusion in an Errata page, but for incorporation into the text. The pages concerned will be returned to the typesetter for emendation, but if the book is of some age, the disk may no longer exist. In this case the amendments, hopefully small and few, will have to be set (preferably in the office) in a font of the same face that matches the original as closely as possible, and incorporated on the pages of a clean copy of the book using paste and scissors. This procedure requires completely accurate co-ordination of eye and hand, but need not be excessively laborious. The line which forms the sub-heading of the present section should then appear in the copyright information. Every new impression, with its date, must be noted—with the addition of 'corrected' where appropriate (see above, p. 14).

It goes without saying that the author should only be invited to make corrections that can be accommodated with the minimum of disruption.

SENDING SIGNALS, I

The title

The managing editor in a large publishing combine would say that we invited trouble by allowing the author in instance 5 on page 122 to change the title of his book so late. Clearly this is something one should avoid if possible, but a book evolves in the making, as does the thinking of both the author and the publisher about it. This can make a late change seem a small price to pay for having a title which is as near right as possible.

Traditionally one refused to change a title once it had been announced, and had appeared in booksellers' catalogues and generated orders; a change was an invitation to customers to order the same book twice under different titles. Changing only the sub-title was less serious and could sometimes do the trick. However, the advent of the computer and the Internet has lessened the force of the old prohibition against late changes.

On the other hand, the title is one of the most important things that one should discuss with an author when plans for a book are first being mooted and the contract has not yet been signed. It can never be premature. One should ask: 'What do you think this book should be called?' Finding the right title is part of the publisher's invisible art, and sometimes calls for intense thought, not to mention flashes of inspiration. It may become necessary to use strong and subtle persuasion to talk an author out of his preference for a title that is either outrightly unsuitable or merely uninspiring, but the publisher can at least claim the benefit of experience, and to be motivated by concern for public reception of the book, and hence sales—factors to which the author cannot be indifferent.

Many authors in the social sciences, and not only inexperienced ones, are attracted by titles with a generally abstract flavour, which are deeply meaningful to them, and which they believe will attract the readers they seek. If the book is concerned with, say, political philosophy, such a title may be justified, but in this case a more explicit subtitle should be added to tether it in time and place. The title of a book is a signal: it should have a single, clear message.

In 1999 we replaced the uninspiring title of one book by a more catchy one, and added a sub-title to another where none had been previously but the title seemed too enigmatic to stand on its own. Both had already been announced in our catalogue, and we had obtained good US co-publication deals for them, each with a different university press. In neither case would our US co-publisher follow suit, but this did not deter us from obeying our instinct.

The cover design

From 'the title' it is a short step to 'the jacket' or, in the case of paperbacks, 'the cover'. Here too we are dealing with signals and unspoken messages (the physical aspects are dealt with in the next chapter). What precise blend of words and images to put on the packaging of a product is a question that exercises every seller of finished goods, whether they be breakfast foods, slug pellets or books. The thought-processes involved for both seller and buyer are in essence the same, and publishers wear themselves out in concentrating their faculties on the problem with every new title they produce.

The cover design, no less than the title, should start to figure in the publisher's thoughts at an early stage in the book's gestation. Should it include a picture, and if so what sort of picture? Or should typography suffice? If a picture is considered desirable, there is every chance that the author has the one that will suit the book, or at least knows of it and is able to obtain it. If some illustrations are to be included in the book, again there is a good chance that one of them will be suitable for the cover, and they should be looked at closely with this in mind. Here, however, a distinction has to be made. A cover picture is not in itself an illustration and should not be treated as such (although a caption describing what it is and, if necessary, acknowledging its provenance must appear on the back of the cover). It is used because it contains certain qualities that transcend its illustrative function. In some way it conveys the theme of the book.

Whereas for most social science publishers, and certainly for us, it is inconceivable to have colour illustrations inside a book, it is relatively affordable to use on the cover up to four colours (the minimum necessary for a colour halftone). Thus to reproduce in colour on the cover one of a set of illustrations which appear inside in black and white acts as both a supplement and an appetiser. This is not to say that a black and white photo can not be used effectively in a cover design; most certainly it can. But the difference from using a colour photo is that more daring use of background colour is desirable in order to set it off, whereas a colour photo is likely to look better against a black, grey, white or otherwise subdued background.

It may be important to avoid cliché (which can occur in various forms), but the effectiveness of a cover design is far more likely to suffer if somehow the message is confused or over-subtle. I recall one author, a man of considerable intellect, who sketched on the back of an envelope a highly complicated abstract design (he had no pretensions to being an artist), which in his view summarised the themes of the book, and which he thought an artist could work up. Commissioning works of art to be reproduced on jackets is far beyond our means, but this author's scheme could only have caused puzzlement and perplexity, whereas the photo that we eventually used conveyed a clear message. Other authors have suggested montages of two or more photos, each conveying some of the essence of the book; but here one should recall the adage 'The better is the enemy of the good'. One picture that conveys part of the essence of the book beats several which together convey all of it. The punter may only look at the cover for an instant, and if the single message the one picture conveys gets across in that instant, the design has been successful.

Sometimes a single photo can be reduced to a quite small size if that seems to serve a larger design incorporating strong typematter and possibly a national (or other) symbol.

Bookstores continuously display bestsellers where the author's name appears in huge letters and the book title is relatively small. We have never handled that kind of merchandise, but even for us the relative weight of title, subtitle and author's name can vary according to a similar criterion. For example, a short subtitle can be given much more weight than a relatively long one.

Sometimes the difficulty of finding a suitable picture finally defeats us and we opt for typography. In a history of Croatia which we published in 1999 I long resisted urgings to use a photo of Dubrovnik, an idea which seemed the epitome of a visual cliché, and the Croatian author's wish to show a Meštrović sculpture of heavy but far from obvious symbolism. However I lighted by chance on a splendid coloured lithograph of the walled city by the artist Paul Hogarth, and with his permission we used that. It did not then seem like a cliché at all.

The back panel (*paperback*). While the spine should be an extension of the front cover design, the back is left to the publisher to treat according to normal house-style. I would only say that while the blurb may occupy the width of a column of text inside the book (24 pica ems [4 inches] on a demy 8vo page), and be centred, the margin thus established should be broken at the bottom right by the barcode, which looks much better positioned near to the spine fold (a space of about 7 mm. works well), and close to the bottom trim, than ranged vertically with the blurb; likewise a caption for the cover picture (if there is one) can break the left margin. This is a delicate matter of balance.

SENDING SIGNALS, II

The catalogue

By emphasising the importance of aesthetics and literacy in the production of books, I have not in the least sought to downplay the publisher's entrepreneurial role. What are we if not merchants selling goods? (Perhaps '*marchands de livres*' sounds better.) The two aspects—the intangible and the material—must be evenly balanced.

Nowhere does this appear more self-evident than in the publisher's catalogue. Here a middle way has to be found between several pairs of opposed demands—exactly where will doubtless vary from one catalogue to the next.

1. (a) to give a feeling of substance, and (b) not to incur excessive postage costs.

Like exceeding an even working by a whisker, so bringing out a catalogue that tips the scale at a weight fractionally over the key postal threshholds of 100 or 150 grams suggests carelessness. A method that is economical in weight is the 'self-cover'—i.e. a cover printed on the same sheet of paper as the text, or part of it, and hence integral with it. Assuming that ordinary text paper is used, it will not be suitable for 4-colour halftones, and only solid colour can be used—but, needless to say, solid colour can be used to great effect. Viewed in this light, the self-cover's limitation can become an advantage. It might also be thought more cosy and unpretentious, less aggressive and less attuned to marketing imperatives.

So what are the advantages of a cover separately printed on stock heavier than the text paper, with a coating that is hospitable to 4-colour halftones? Clearly there is more flexibility in presentation, and there can be just that subliminal sense of expectancy as one turns from the polished exterior to what lies within. Inevitably the publisher's self-image is involved; even though we publish specialised books, he may think, we would not like the people out there to think that we don't take a certain pride in what we do. Putting on a bit of a show is a sign of respect for our clientele. And so on.

One's commission reps inevitably like to be able to present to booksellers something for which they, the reps, will not feel any need to apologise. Whether this consideration nets any extra sales to balance the extra cost of printing an alluring cover and the possible extra postage cost is a perpetually unresolved question.

2. (a) to say enough about each book to arouse interest as well as inform, and (b) not to say too much.

This applies in almost equal measure to the blurb on the exterior of the individual book, but the description in the catalogue should aim to be more concise; after all, there are a lot of other blurbs in competition with it.

The blurb in its typographical context is discussed elsewhere, but here seems to be the place to enunciate a few ideal aims in its composition.

There are three elements that need to be kept in balance (not the same as saying they should be of equal weight). First, the general principles need to be stated: the objective factual background to the book, which could include a reference to, though not a discourse on, the present state of knowledge on the subject. This could be the longest section. Then should follow a brief synopsis of what the book sets out to do. The final section should state, with fitting modesty, in what ways this book is superior to its competitors—e.g. that it is the first comprehensive study of the subject, or that it is based on recently opened archival material. One frequent usage in blurbs—that the book increases 'our' understanding of whatever-it-is—smacks of condescension and is best avoided.

Clearly it is easy for the publisher to err on the side of prolixity, forgetting that the reader/user is in search of no more than the essentials. Yet too little information is frustrating.

The scholarly publisher may think that listing the chapters is a service to the user, but it is so only if done with discretion. If the chapter titles are truly informative (chapters entitled 'Introduction' or 'Conclusion' should be routinely omitted), then the 'prose' of the blurb can be correspondingly reduced. If they are not, there is no point in listing them.

In a multi-author volume, of course the titles of the chapters and the authors' names should be listed (the titles can be shortened).

Truly positive—and at the same time informative—quotes from recognised authorities on the subject who have read the MS. are a gift. The best place for them is directly below the title information (author, title, subtitle), but a nugget which the publisher feels will be irresistible can be placed above it.

Last comes a note about the author. Too short a one is barely helpful. Too long, and again the publisher appears to be overestimating the user's attention-span. If one is itemising some of the author's previous books, the date of publication should be inserted in parentheses; if any of them happen to have been published by 'us', then we can add our name in the catalogue, but this can only be done on the jacket or cover if the latter is not also going to be used for the American co-edition; the American co-publisher will not want the British publication details.

In a translated work, the translator's name should occupy a line to itself below the author's biographical note and before the bibliographical particulars (the 'biblios'), with a half-line space separating each of these items, and preferably in a distinguishing face like small capitals.

The biblios themselves should be in standard format, in the following order:

— the format *if not demy 8vo* (this convention can be spelt out in a rubric at the beginning of the catalogue);

— the page extent if known, giving both the roman of the Prelims and the arabic of the main text—if it is not known, give an *approximate* extent (a round figure) in arabic only;

— the numbers of illustrations and maps, if known—if they are not known, approximate numbers should be attempted, since they are selling points;

— the approximate date of publication, taking the most conservative estimate (even this may ultimately prove to have been over-optimistic)—the temptation to be knowingly over-optimistic because it is an exciting book and one cannot wait to announce it should be resisted;

— the price: this should be given adequate thought in every case—announcing a book in a casebound edition only and then issuing a paperback also on its first publication may justifiably be thought disingenuous;

— the International Standard Book Number (ISBN), which should be double-checked, since an error (one digit too few, too many or misplaced is enough) can disable the distribution process later.

3. (a) to give the most important books suitable prominence without (b) making the others seem downgraded.

I state this problem in order to highlight its existence, rather than to prescribe a solution—which will always be elusive. Giving a small number of books special prominence by placing them first and/or calibrating their typography and layout in a distinctive, attention-seeking way must send a signal to the catalogue users and to the authors of the other books that the latter are regarded by the publisher as the foot-sloggers and not the standard-bearers.

A large scholarly publisher will no doubt produce separate catalogues for different categories, but for a smaller house this is scarcely practical; hence the categories must themselves be placed in a certain order within a single catalogue. This at least imposes an over-arching imperative on the disposition of the books which is not directly related to individual titles and authors; but here again the publisher will think 'Surely we cannot put X. on page 11 when he should be at the very beginning?' So will certain titles be treated as transcending their categories because of their importance? Also, amoeba-like, the question of precedence will have multiplied—from 'within the catalogue as a whole' to 'within a category'.

A possibly far-fetched but beautifully logical scheme might be to determine the placing of the new books throughout by lot—taking names out of a hat. That this had been done would need to be stated at the beginning in large type. Then, to be consistent, the presentation of every book would have to be treated in, as nearly as possible, a uniform manner. Would the big books suffer and the others get more than their due? This would be a real test of the blurb-writer's art. A similarly impartial method might be to place the books in alphabetical order by author, but I suspect that this would go down less well than a genuinely random order; after all, the author whose name begins with Z starts without a chance.

Should new books announced for the first time (As) be differentiated from new books that have been announced before but then delayed (Bs)? For the purpose of providing the maximum of data to professional catalogue-users—librarians and booksellers—the answer has to be 'yes'. The simplest way to do it is with colour, e.g. printing the titles of the As in a second colour and those of the Bs in black.

4. to choose a cover design that delivers a single clear message, even if it is about just one characteristic new book, which avoids being either (a) banal or vulgar, or (b) too tasteful and subtle.

This is at one short remove from choosing a cover design for a book, only with the catalogue one has to think generically: does the design we want to use fairly represent the list as a whole?

It is very likely that one will make the choice from among current book-cover pictures (I avoid the term 'illustrations' where covers are concerned, because the purpose here is not to illustrate anything, but to send a signal). These have already been chosen—as cover pictures—for their symbolic or semiotic quality, and there must be one or two among them which will adapt easily for the catalogue. The picture must stimulate the mind and the senses, without necessarily yielding up its precise significance (in that case a caption needs to be printed on the inside front cover).

Illustrated here is one happy example. The problem of finding the right picture for the cover of this book bothered us for a long time: a group of fighters? a distant view of Algiers with smoke rising after an explosion? Then we leafed through a run of an old magazine which had ceased publication, and came upon this shot of a voter in the election which the Islamists

July 2000-February 2001 Hurst

New books and select backlist

History, politics, sociology and religion

won but the government annulled, thus sparking off the civil war. To me the composition, in spite of being obviously accidental, has a classical, restrained intensity which gives it great power. It was a natural choice for the cover of our catalogue.

5. (a) to allow some expression of individuality, and (b) not to lapse into self-importance and self-advertisement.

If it is an artist's or a poet's work and not his life-history that should engage the attention of posterity, how much more is this true of the publisher. Publishers who start their own imprints are typically egoists and, apart from setting their stamp on the lists that come out over their names, may be tempted to seek other, more visible vehicles of self-expression. I will confine my examples to two of the older, now departed generation, both of whom I knew.

André Deutsch, among the best general publishers of his time, was the supreme egoist, as *Stet*, Diana Athill's memoirs (Granta, 2000), testifies, but his books were always handsomely produced in a conservative style, and the firm's catalogues and publicity were similarly restrained, just as he himself always dressed with style and taste. Fred Praeger was a specialist in contemporary history and international affairs, who also imported art books, and his authors were largely academics and members of the Washington establishment. One might have expected from him an academic demeanour, but not a bit of it. He expressed one side of his complex personality by wearing lumberjack shirts and adopting a hail-fellow-well-met manner, while another face appeared in his corporate publicity. Every catalogue he ever produced, first at Praeger in New York and later at Westview Press in Boulder, Colorado, carried at its masthead the well-known saying of Spinoza: '*Sedula curavi, humanas actiones non ridere, non lugere, neque detestare, sed intellegere*' (I have striven not to laugh at human actions, not to weep at them, not to hate them, but to understand them). As if that were not enough, he borrowed from Sir Stanley Unwin the motto 'Books that Matter'. During his fruitful later years at the helm of his new firm, Westview, he would preface his catalogue with a letter, headed 'Dear Friends', weaving variations on the general theme that Westview was doing a uniquely important job. The tone was at once folksy and high-minded. Fred was a proud and sensitive man, but he evidently could not see that all this solemnity about his books, which were no better and no worse than those found in many other similar lists, served little purpose. He evidently had to do it. My view is that the publisher should resist any temptation to address his clientele directly in this way, but instead make sure that the front of his catalogue contains a rubric, simply expressed and laid out, with all the factual information needed by its users.

THE EXTERNALS

This is not a manual on 'how to do it' in book production. Such manuals exist, and 'how to do it' is just what young aspirants can expect to learn on publishing courses: about paper, binding and presentation generally. As must already be clear, this book enunciates, *inter alia*, what I see as objective standards for the editing and design of scholarly books, and in the use of English—some may regard them as mere prejudices. What I have to say about the physical aspect of the book may also be dismissed as just one person's opinion. My knowledge, such as it is, springs from producing my firm's books over a long period, during which time my production self has crystallised—giving it a certain organic consistency, if not, *per se*, any claim to rightness.*

Let us start on the outside and work inwards. We will take hardcover with jacket; hardcover without jacket; hardcover with the equivalent of a paperback cover glued to the outside of the

*I emphasise further that my experience has been with books mainly in the social sciences, but also in the humanities, and thus I do not see my kind of production as generically different from that of biographies and historical books aimed at a wide readership, or indeed novels. However, the gulf separating people like me from *textbook* publishers is like that between small mammals and the lepidoptera. Our books are sometimes recommended for class use in relatively specialised areas; but they are still leagues away from A4 and Cr 4to student teaching manuals.

A comprehensive introduction to the material aspects of book making, which I recommend for its accessibility, deep knowledge and pertinent illustrations, is Anthony Rota's *Apart from the Text* (Pinner, Middx: Private Libraries Association, 1998).

binding case* in place of plain cloth† or cloth substitute; and paperback.

The loose jacket

In its history the jacket has evolved from a mere protective wrapper to an entity with some artistic pretensions—and beyond (of which more shortly). A question asked not only by every jacket designer but by every publisher from time to time is: how long will the book retain the jacket once it has been bought? If it goes into a large library the jacket will, almost routinely, be discarded. Some private buyers may do the same; in the past, when spine blocking was a self-contained mini-art and the binding material was usually real cloth fortified by a discreet glaze, there was an aesthetic justification for doing so.‡ But the utilitarian function gradually came to be overlaid as the jacket became a promotional tool. Even a book not destined for a popular readership will be spurned by reps if its jacket is not punchy.

Pictorial jackets incorporating photos have always been printed on 'art' (coated) paper, although formerly this was lighter in weight, and hence flimsier and more liable to tear, than is the custom now. The heavier jacket has come about with lamination. Unlaminated jackets could be permanently spoiled by the pressure, however brief, of a warm finger or thumb on solid colour. With laminated ones you can even wipe off coffee, butter etc. without leaving a blemish. More recently a new choice has opened up: between glossy and matt lamination. The latter has gained ground

*I mention this type of binding here for the sake of completeness, but do not propose to discuss it here. Its virtues—economy and a brightness of appearance—are obvious, but for me it lacks a sense of permanence, of being liveable-with in the long term.

†The American book trade uses 'cloth' as a generic term to describe any material in a single colour that is wrapped over, and glued to binding case—whether it is actually cloth or, much more common today, a plastic substitute, usually stamped to give the appearance, if not the texture, of a woven material. Insistence on real cloth survived longer in US publishing houses than in British ones.

‡But a financial disincentive if book buyers could have seen into the distant future, to the time when a jacketed volume—especially the first edition of a work that went on to become famous—would have a much greater value in the antiquarian market than a bare one.

and is almost certainly subtler in effect. But just occasionally the less subtle effect delivers the goods better.

Jackets that only contained type, whether of traditional design with perhaps the addition of ornamental rules and borders, or trend-setting like Gollancz's, were usually printed on cartridge paper, which could take additional solid or line colour. But these, like the old-fashioned art paper jackets, were vulnerable to staining and easily torn, but if they survived these hazards could add character and possessibility.

Spine setting has undergone an evolution along with other features of the jacket. Formerly the setting on the spine of the binding case was treated in complete isolation from any aspect of the jacket design—a legacy from the time before jackets existed. It almost invariably ran across the spine, to be easily read when on the shelf, and this was so even with the slimmest volumes, thus testing the typographer's art. Today horizontal spine setting is rare, even on relatively bulky volumes.

The same, roughly, applied to jackets, but—again probably influenced by sales considerations—the vertical positioning of the title and, often though not invariably, of the author's name became the norm. Even if one had to turn one's head around to see them, the vertically set co-ordinates could be set to a relatively large size (how large depending on the quantity of words and the area available) and thus be visible from a distance. (It seems strange now that some publishers favoured, or tolerated, the vertical setting running upwards, so that when the book was laid flat with the front panel uppermost, it would be upside-down. This is now a rarity.)

Today, instead of having primacy, the spine setting on the binding-case is subordinate to that on the jacket—the brass for the spine blocking being made from the latter photographically.

Needless to say, spine setting requires typographical sensitivity. In each case the following questions arise:

— Will the author's full name be displayed or the surname only? If space permits (as it may do if the title happens to be short) there is no physical impediment to having the full name. If there are two authors, aesthetic considerations are likely to dictate having surnames only. If the volume is a collective one, it looks better not to include the word 'editor' on the spine, although it should certainly go on the front of the jacket.

— What will be the difference in weight between the author and the title, and how will it be conveyed? The title may be long enough to require that it be set in two lines, but any possibility that the author's name (if it is not, *per se*, a selling point) will outweigh it can be overcome by, e.g., setting the title in a bold sans-serif face and the author in a lighter serif face.

— Assuming the absence of a colophon, how will the imprint at the foot be set? My preference is to use the text face of the book, in a size of capitals that is dictated by the number of characters to be set. Horizontal is best, but for a long name vertical may be necessary. 9 pt capitals is a nice size for demy and royal 8vo books, letterspaced if the name is short. A rather larger size in u.l.c. can look nice with some names but not all ('HURST' looks better in capitals).

— Spacing. There is always an ideal apportionment of space between the items of type (and between them and the top and bottom trims), and there are many that are not ideal, possibly missing it by a millimetre or two either way. Similarly there is an ideal size for each item, which can be attained by trial and error—either on the computer or, perhaps better, with the aid of a good photocopier that enlarges and reduces; an initial rough pencil sketch helps to attain the ideal dimensions. If asked to prescribe a rule to achieve ideal spacing in a particular instance, I would say: do it by instinct. Look long and hard at the total space and the elements, and move them around till they come right; immerse yourself in the problem. An aid to such contemplation is the classical Golden Section.

Next, the *flaps**—traditionally 3.5 inches wide, with a margin for the typematter of 0.5 inch either side of the blurb, which of course has a measure of 2.5 inches (15 ems, 63 mm.). The

*The idea of having paperbacks with flaps has never caught on in Britain, but it is possible, and well worth considering as an amphibian solution for a book that also does not fit easily into any category—like this book.

type-size is determined by the length of the piece but within narrow limits. Too small risks being difficult to read, but it should at the very least be one size smaller than the main text size.

If the text runs over to the back flap, set the following:

[continued on back flap

continued from front flap]

There should then be a single-line space between the end of the blurb and the first line of the biographical note about the author, which must be full-out. The author's name should not be in plain roman u.l.c., but italic may lose its effect if a number of his/her publications follow, also in italic. Large and small capitals—or, in a light face, large capitals—can be a pleasant alternative. If the blurb ends on the front flap and there is no room for the author-bio below it, one can insert

For a note on the author(s) see back flap

ranged left. It is a refinement and not strictly necessary.

Prices are not printed nowadays except on editions expected to sell quickly. Booksellers' price stickers have become standard.

One item which should not be forgotten is the line at the bottom of the back flap stating where the book has been printed. This is a legal requirement in the United States and, even if it were not, it is a harmless flourish.

The *back panel* must carry, at the very minimum,

— the publisher's imprint, with or without address (postal and/or electronic) added;

— the barcode (it works perfectly well if only a few millimetres high, so this relatively unobtrusive format—a barcode is hardly a thing of beauty, even when small—should be preferred to the sometimes grotesquely deep one);

— a caption for the front cover picture if there is one and it requires explanation, and, very important, a credit to the copyright owner and/or the photographer or artist who created it. This should be set very small (7/8 pt Times, 8/9 pt Bembo) under a shoulder heading simply saying '*Cover*'.

My preference is to centre the imprint with its centre of gravity 61.8% of the way down the panel (see reference works on the Golden Section); place the barcode in the bottom-right corner about 7 mm. from the spine and 10 mm. from the bottom trim; and place the caption 7 mm. from the left edge, its first line ranged with the top of the barcode. If the caption has to be rather lengthy, it may well look better in a similar position at the top left.

The back panel is also often used to promote the publisher's recent books on related subjects, and particularly any other works by the author of the 'present' work which the publisher has in print. An elegant layout is easily achieved by clearly differentiating, by size and typographical style, the properties of each book listed—author, title, subtitle, possibly a short gobbet from a favourable review, and the bibliographical details; a heading saying '*Of related interest*' or '*By the same author*'—appealing to tidy minds, if not strictly necessary—should be ranged left and set at least one and possibly two point sizes larger than the largest elements in the matter below. Italic usually works well.

Getting the horizontal dimensions correct to within an infinitesimal tolerance is necessary if the jacket is to look comfortable on the book. The vital dimension on which the others depend is the spine width. If this has been incorrectly calculated, either the spine of the jacket, with its carefully laid-out setting, will be off-centre while the front panel has the dimensions which the designer intended for it, or the latter will appear to have moved to the right or left of its proper position while the spine setting is in the correct position. Either way, the designer's intentions will have been frustrated, and even passive enjoyment of the result marred.

Smaller publishers who may follow the usually prudent course of relying on the printer to act as the paper-buyer cannot rely on the bulk of a previously printed book as a measure for a job currently in preparation. The paper thickness may change from one purchase by the printer to the next. Asking him for the spine width each time and, as an additional precaution, for the dimensions of the binding boards to be used is a necessary chore.

Mutatis mutandis, this applies equally to paperbacks.

The binding

Just as a barber and a shoemaker look at, respectively, a man's hair and feet before anything else, so on being handed a finished casebound book I will immediately fold back the jacket and appraise the binding. This may seem to the fastidious rather like lifting up a woman's skirt to look at her legs, but the binding's cardinal importance overcomes all scruples. It should be treated by the publisher with an eye to the (probably jacketless) long term. I have already referred to the spine setting. Copied, as it now so often is, from the jacket, does it look good when divorced from the jacket? Since the book will spend most of its life on the shelf, is it as legible (not to say pleasing to the eye) as it could possibly be?

Legal and medical tomes are usually unjacketed (often with a stout transparent loose cover), and because they tend to be of great length and hence bulk, there is no problem about setting the title and author's name horizontally; often, too, a second colour is incorporated as a background to the setting in imitation of the separate label—in earlier times of wafer-thin leather and from *circa* the early 19th century onwards of stout paper—which used to be glued to the binding. The publication of unjacketed casebound books is normal for publishers of any sort when the main concentration is upon the paperback; they will be produced in a small edition of from a few hundred down to barely 100 copies to satisfy library or other special orders.

It is thought by some that an unjacketed book should be blocked on the front panel as well as the spine (the 'brass' for this too will simply be reproduced photographically from the jacket). But one need only examine this assumption to see that it is unfounded. The book, as we keep on saying, will spend most of its life on the shelf, where the front panel is invisible.

For the reader front blocking is not needed because he knows the book's identity. The book will not be displayed face-outwards or face-upwards in a bookshop. So that leaves—what? Front blocking also costs extra because binders' brasses are priced by overall area.

In a different category is front blocking that serves a purely decorative, unfunctional purpose—like a symbol associated with the subject of the book or an ornament. Gold might seem over-emphatic—so what about blind embossing? In this case it has to be fairly large to be fully legible and achieve impact. Oxford University Press have traditionally done this on their Standard Authors and World's Classics series, and Thames and Hudson too use their logo effectively in this way.

We now look beyond the blocking to the binding material itself. Real cloth covering of the boards long ago ceased to be obtainable in Britain at a reasonable cost. Until 1989 books that one imported from, or had printed, east of the Iron Curtain often had real cloth, and still today it is common in India. Good plastic substitutes are obtainable in all countries with a modern printing industry.

What should the colour be? Judgement on this can ultimately only be subjective, but it is assisted by a few objective considerations, such as: what is the dominant colour of the jacket? Is a particular colour suggested, even in somewhat cliché'd form, by the content—e.g. medium-dark green for Islam or an Islamic country; red for China; sandy brown for the Indian subcontinent and Africa; dark blue for Britain, France and the United States; medium blue for the Nordic countries? If both these questions produce dusty answers, there is always black. For the blocking, gold is the standard, but white looks bolder—artistry in design can impose its own rules.

It is not uncommon in some continental European countries to find a preference for square-backed case-binding, whereas in Britain we definitely prefer the rounded back. I have had square backs sprung on me from time to time by Indian printers, and although I cannot say I dislike them, I prefer the rounded ones, which are physically more flexible and thus, I surmise, less liable to split through constant use of the volume.

The cotton *headband* and tailband are almost extinct in the West, but still flourish in Asian countries where the technology of book production is advanced, as in Hong Kong and Malaysia, and where it is less widely so, as in India. Its presence gives comfort, and it should be used where the extra cost is modest, which it would not be in Europe. However, a plastic headband, which an Indian printer once foisted on us, looks and feels cheap, and is worse than no headband at all.

We now open the book and are confronted by the *endpapers*. These, I am convinced, should be regarded as a medium for giving the reader pleasure rather than information. Having white ones is simplest and safest. As soon as you move into colour, you are creating a mood—a very subjective thing. Is it the right mood for the book, or only for the designer at the moment the book crosses his desk? Light grey cannot offend anybody, but blue? green? red? brown? (Think of wallpaper, a not inappropriate touchstone for comparison.) Yet even light grey might be thought of as 'making a statement'—either about the book or about the publisher's ego.

A favourite use of endpapers is for maps; but, to be *used*, maps should surely be inside the book—spatially limited or special-purpose ones near the place where they are referred to, and general ones at the beginning of the book. The sovereign objection to using the front endpaper to impart information available nowhere else in the book is the hazard that a book plate and/or a record of loans will be stuck there and thus obliterate it.

One can run that risk with a thematic picture—a landscape, a cityscape, a historic building, a battle, a *conversazione*, an autograph—intended purely for aesthetic effect to gratify the reader. Not to be obtrusive, it should be printed in a single colour and a blended one, avoiding primary colours or black, and neither too dark nor too light. The rear endpaper can repeat the front one, so that the picture will still be enjoyed in its entirety if the front endpaper is defaced.

Paper

The paper the book is printed on will have a considerable effect on the reader's sensations in handling and reading it. But it is not my task (nor is it within my competence) to enter into a technical discussion of its chemical properties and various 'grammages'—except to state, uncontroversially, that 80–90 grams per square metre (gsm) defines the ballpark for text paper. For one thing, this is a subject with which an aspiring publisher can become fully conversant through courses at various colleges, universities and institutes. For another, I have nearly always relied on printers to obtain suitable paper; as with wine, so with paper, I enjoy it when it is good and recoil from it when it is bad, but am not an expert, nor do I feel any need to become one. Undoubtedly relying on printers does not always work satisfactorily; they have been known to cut corners. The question of whether one should invariably use acid-free paper is one which, again, I would rather not tackle. In the 1980s the battle for it was on, and one heard about it all the time. Today the battle is either won, or it has been abandoned. One obvious fact is that some books are more 'monumental', and destined for a longer shelf-life, than others. Thus the publisher has a responsibility to take their durability seriously.

But certain criteria can safely be advanced. The bulk must be sufficient; an ordinary text paper must not feel unsubstantial or flimsy, nor must it be too thick. The most important consideration here is the avoidance of showthrough. This can be seen starkly when the reverse of the title page is clearly visible underlying the copyright information on the title verso, but it is worse when the reverse image of the copyright information mars the title page, which is, or should be, the fruit of careful design or even of inspiration. It is also regrettable when a table, map or other diagram such as a graph or pie-chart interferes with the text backing it.

Halftone illustrations present a slightly different problem. We have left behind the era when halftones *had* to be printed on art paper and either sewn in as extra sections, wrapped round text sections, or 'tipped in' singly. Of course they still can be, but text paper is obtainable of a quality that enables halftones to have depth and sparkle. To be sure, we are not talking of faithful reproductions of works of art, which are outside our purview. With halftones special care has to be taken about showthrough, although this can be a worse problem when they are scattered throughout the book, each one occupying part or all of a text page, and backed by, and itself backing, text. Much is gained, and nothing lost (except possibly an even working, and this cannot be calculated in advance), by allotting each a page to itself backed by a blank—or, as a lesser evil than interference by and of text, by another halftone. Then we come back to traditional sections of halftones not on art but on text paper (see pp. 63ff.).

The one hard-and-fast remedy against showthrough—and acid deterioration—is to print on lightly coated paper, preferably matt (viz. 'matt art'), which assures the best reproduction of halftones with text. This kind of paper is heavier, and generally less bulky, than conventional text paper—the heaviness has the economic consequence of added postage costs. Generally a book printed on matt art paper needs to have intrinsic, qualitative weight to match the physical weight.*

It is of course possible to bulk up a relatively slender volume—say, one of under 200 pages—by printing on paper bulkier, though not heavier, than the norm. Within a very narrow tolerance this is harmless, but there is something almost meretricious about book paper that has a fluffy, inflated feel to it.

As to the vital aspect of *colour*, matt art is dead white, but there

*I would stoutly deny that this is a fanciful consideration. It was brought home to me in a succession of annual meetings of the Association of American University Presses, at which a 'Book Show' is a standard feature. The show is actually the aftermath of a competition in which various aspects of book design, and general excellence, are in play. Some of the exhibits wonderfully marry content and design, but there are too many books which are patently 'over-designed', with a conspicuous quality of typography, paper, binding etc. embarrassingly disproportionate to their importance—a symptom of academic self-aggrandisement. Every university press is governed by a committee of academics, who no doubt are responsible for this mismatch. These pundits clearly do not anticipate a time when heaps of these lovingly crafted volumes will adorn the remainder tables or be pulped.

is a wide choice in ordinary text papers between dead white and cream—neither of which seems to me ideal: dead white can dazzle; cream is not historically or aesthetically correct. Off-white is the answer, unobtrusive and, as such, easy on the eye.

Before leaving paper, we should go back to one of the integral factors in binding: namely, whether to bind in *sewn sections* or go for '*perfect*' or '*notched*' binding. In the latter the folded and gathered section has its folded, inner side sliced off, and thus in effect becomes 8 or 16 separate page-sized leaves. These are glued in. When 'perfect' binding was first introduced as a cost-saving alternative to sewing, individual pages not infrequently came loose and escaped, and the term 'perfect' became a mockery. Today 'notching' is preferred as giving near-total security.

This is purely a matter of economy; by no stretch of imagination can it be argued that 'perfect' or even 'notched' binding is in any way superior to sewn, aesthetically or practically. As one reads, the ideal is for the book to lie open, even when one is not holding it. This is manifestly impossible when there is nothing holding one page to its neighbours except glue. With sewn sections it becomes at least theoretically possible, and with casebound books a little coaxing may achieve this end and not an alarming splitting sound and the beginning of disintegration. Sewn sections furthermore make possible the use of the centre spread of a section to accommodate an illustration or map that spans it entirely without a vertical break in the centre. My printers in Asia, who achieve superb quality at reasonable cost, have never indicated to me that 'perfect' binding is an option. It simply represents cheapness at the expense of quality—quality here being co-terminous with user-friendliness.

LEGAL AND GENERAL

Plagiarism and libel are seen primarily as legal problems. They are specifically covered in publisher-author contracts, with a warranty by the author to the publisher that the work 'is original, ... is in no way whatever a violation of existing copyright, and contains nothing ... libellous' (the quotation is from my firm's author contract). Lawyers may become involved at any stage where libel is concerned. Libel insurance is obtainable by publishers, and no doubt one could in theory insure against the legal consequences of plagiarism of which the publisher was unaware. But the full responsibility for both libel and plagiarism—their commission and their detection—has to be borne by the publisher in his editorial capacity, and their detection depends on editorial skills.

Qualitatively the two things are utterly different. The consequences of libel can destroy a publishing house financially, but unless the libel is the result of a malicious conspiracy between publisher and author, it cannot be said to have any moral/ethical component, whatever may be alleged by a claimant and his lawyers to the contrary. The case is very different with plagiarism.

Plagiarism

The detection of plagiarism is not at any point a task for lawyers. Any scholar familiar with a particular subject (such as should be invited to vet the MS.) can be assumed also to be familiar with the literature about it, and should be brought up short on encountering the views—and, even more, the actual words—of someone other than the author of the MS. in question.

Guidelines exist for what constitutes 'fair dealing' in the direct quotation of copyright sources, and, whatever they are, it will be understood that such direct quotations must be marked as such with the utmost clarity. Either they will be extracted from the main text and set in a smaller size or to a narrower measure, or they will be placed in quotes; either way, the author of the quotation will be mentioned by name, and a reference to the source will be given.

Any publisher who has inadvertently published a book containing plagiarism will not need to be told how painful and shocking its discovery is. How did it happen? Was the author knowingly and deliberately committing a crime against all scholarly and legal canons and conventions, or was it an astonishing case of naivety, with no 'criminal' intent? How did we, the publishers, fail to find out the truth in the course of having the book vetted? These are the 'academic' questions. Of more urgent concern is what to do next. If the presence of plagarism has not come to light before publication, it is unlikely to do so immediately afterwards—some time can be expected to pass before the book comes into the hands of individuals whose works have been plagiarised in it.

In the only case we have experienced hitherto, it did so after the book had been in circulation for several months, and a good number of copies of both our original edition and the American co-edition had been sold. Several reviews, some of them highly favourable, had appeared. Both we and our co-publishers still had copies in stock. Strictly we should have withdrawn these from sale, but over this we compromised; we both let our editions sell out, which they did rapidly, while it was left to us as the originating publishers to cancel our contract with the author—who could in theory, though scarcely in practice, have issued a new edition somehow under another imprint. We briefly considered carrying out a surgical operation on the text, but this would have been too drastic in its effect and appeared impractical.

We were lucky that the plagiarised author(s), while outraged by what had happened, on the whole showed more sympathy for us in our plight than desire for retribution. It has to be said, at the risk of immodesty, that our good reputation in the relevant area of knowledge helped us. We forfeited thousands of pounds' worth of potential sales—as did our co-publisher, who never demurred over the need to make the book out-of-print with us as quickly as possible.

If I have one piece of advice, it is to be resolute and act quickly before one starts to have second thoughts.

Libel

The publisher who is successfully sued for libel, probably—and the one who publishes a book containing plagiarism, certainly—have both taken insufficient precautions. But libel in a book is an infinitely more complex issue than plagiarism.

Because libel damages may be heavy, and the services of good libel lawyers are expensive, a small publisher can be wiped out of existence by losing—or even by having to defend—a libel suit. Even if damages are light, the costs, if awarded to the complainant, will be punitive. The impecunious defendant may go into court without a lawyer, but the saving in case of failure will not be significant. Even if the suit fails, the strain on the defendant and the loss of productive time and energy are tremendous.

The factors to be considered here are (1) prevention; (2) libel insurance; and (3) the ethical dimension.

(1) Only an irresponsible author will not alert the publisher in advance to any possible libel dangers in his MS., and for the publisher to know that the author is aware of the pitfalls is reassuring. But it is for the publisher to investigate these dangers for himself; he must carry out his own tests. Is there any statement or suggestion in the book that a named or clearly identified individual has acted dishonestly, corruptly, criminally or in any other way shamefully or even embarrassingly? If so, is there any way that the said statement or suggestion can be so hedged around with disclaimers as to make it impossible for the person in question to complain of a libel? The publisher who turns a

blind eye to any obvious danger-spot is inviting trouble and deserves no sympathy. But what to do if danger is perceived is a weighty question. The publisher may use his discretion whether to (a) ignore the danger and make no changes; (b) re-phrase possible offending passages to make them inoffensive—something which the publisher and author can do together and, one hopes, without disagreement; (c) excise all offending passages completely; or (d) refuse publication if the author proves obdurate.

The conventional method whereby a publisher can be satisfied that publication will be 'safe' is to commission a report from a solicitor specialising in libel. I paid £100 each for opinions from recognised experts on two MSS. in the early 1970s, but legal fees have rocketed since then, and it would be unimaginable today to get a complete report and detailed recommendations for less than a sum that would appreciably add to the production cost of the book.

(2) Obtaining a legal opinion may be a self-contained exercise, designed solely to help the publisher—most likely, confirming impressions he had formed already. Or it may be connected with insurance.

Companies that specialise in publishers' libel insurance assert that they do not need to have a report on every one of the client publisher's books in order to provide cover for the whole list—and it is only a whole list, never a single risky title, that they will insure. But it would be a very unwise publisher who, knowing that a particular book contains libel risks, relies on this disclaimer and fails to obtain a report on it. It is inconceivable that a claim will be met if no report has been obtained. For some large publishing houses libel insurance is axiomatic. These firms may be expected to be those which do sometimes publish the sort of books which are the subject of newsworthy lawsuits, and attract swingeing damages. For that reason the 'excess' they are required to bear in the event of a claim can be spectacularly high; for Macmillan, I was reliably informed not many years ago by a senior director of that firm, it is £100,000. But we are talking here of a different world from that inhabited by the likes of C. Hurst & Co.

I return to the obvious fact that to obtain cover for risky books a firm must, apart from insuring the safe ones as well, have a report on those risky ones from a libel lawyer of note—who will list all the passages in the MS. which he thinks contain the slightest risk. The lawyer, if uncertain on any point, will recommend obtaining a counsel's opinion. And the resulting recommendations will have to be carried out to the letter; failure to have done so if a claim arises will of course result in the claim being rejected. And the lawyer who gives the report is not likely to err on the side of liberality; if a passage which he has passed as innocuous is found by a court to be libellous, his reputation will be in tatters.

So what is the publisher, faced with a MS. over which he feels certain doubts, to do?

(3) An independent publisher, while fully aware of the risks of libel, may not wish for ever to steer clear of controversial material. Insurance will seem to him expensive in more ways than one. First there are the premiums and especially the legal fees he will have to pay out at intervals to guarantee safety. But there is also the firm's integrity to consider. Is its publishing policy going to be dictated perpetually by legal and actuarial demands?

Whatever other attributes a publisher may possess (for example, a desire for justice in the world), analytical power is indispensable. It is the essence of good editing, and a guard against error or oversight where possibilities of libel exist. The publisher should read the *whole* of any MS. where these are suspected, concentrating with rigour on the wording of the dubious passages. It is his judgement on which the course of action to be taken depends, and, along with the author, he can take full responsibility for it.

It is not clear what distinction English libel law makes between an outright statement of a defamatory nature by 'our' author, on the one hand, and an authentic statement by another person, whether it has previously been published or not, which 'our' author quotes and attributes accurately to its author and previous place of publication. The latter is alleged to be libellous—repeating a libel apparently being as heinous as uttering one for the first time. Yet the fact of its not being an 'original' libel is advanced as a defence, and in my view—provided the repetition is not mischievous but a matter of historical record and/or public interest—it should be accepted as such. In my strictly personal view also, libel insurance is an encumbrance which a publisher of my type cannot bear.

Other matters arising from contracts

Delivery of the MS. Once at a publishing conference I heard the keynote speaker boast that he always rigorously enforced the contracted delivery date for MSS. While allowing for the difference between his world and mine—he worked in a big publishing combine—I thought then, and still think today some 20 years later, that it was the greatest nonsense. A reasonable and mutually agreeable delivery date must be stated in the contract as a marker; if it can be adhered to, well and good, but a wait can be to the benefit of the work, and of course can be due to one of many different reasons. It should not be allowed to go on indefinitely, and the publisher should be watchful and inquire regularly about progress before and especially after the contracted date has passed. Having been generous and flexible in allowing the author an extra year or more to complete the work, the publisher is in a better position to deal with that same author's impatience for it to appear in print once it has been delivered.

I can think of two instances where my firm had to wait for about 10 years for a MS. to be delivered, and in each the quality and the sales rewarded us. One is apt to think of such 'prodigal' offspring fondly.

But publishing is a kaleidoscopic business, and there are times when one will, within a narrow tolerance, enforce the delivery clause. It need hardly be said that no two cases are the same.

Control of publication. At different places in this book (above, pp. 29, 125ff.) allusions have been made to the tendency of authors to be strongly wedded to what, in the publisher's view, are misguided ideas about the most suitable format, title and cover design for their books. The contract gives the publisher the final say on these matters; authors know this, even if they have not at first fully absorbed it, and usually recognise in the end that over this if over nothing else the publisher's knowledge is superior to theirs. The publisher would be most ill-advised to compromise over this right, which is directly related to his professional skills.

Option on future works. 'The Author shall give the publishers first refusal of ... his/her next work of a broadly similar character and addressed to a similar readership, which is suitable for publication in volume form....' We often delete this clause for two reasons which may seem quixotic to our harder-nosed brethren in other houses:

1. Without apparent malice, some of our authors have proved to be absent-minded about this commitment, and we have found too late that a successor volume which we would have liked at least to consider has gone to a competitor. (This would be virtually unthinkable in trade publishing, where contracts are usually drawn up and enforced by agents.) Related to this is the next point.

2. I have long believed that a publisher of my type should resist any urging or temptation to publish a book by a friend; a pre-existing friendship might well not survive the changed relationship. On the other hand, lasting friendships can result from author-publisher relationships entered into in the normal course of business. In such a relationship it would be most unusual for the author not to give the publisher the option on his next work. But if the author wants to go elsewhere, will the publisher gain anything from more than the most delicate hint about mutual commitments, legal or moral? And what sort of publishing relationship would result from a contract entered into through *force majeure*?

However, we *will* let the option clause stand, and make clear our expectation that it will be observed, when we are taking a risk—either because the author is 'new' or because of the subject-matter. There can be other reasons, but in every case what is possible must be our criterion.

'Examination'. 'The Author or the Author's authorised representative shall have the right upon written request to examine the books of account of the Publishers in so far as they relate to sales of the Work, which examination shall be at the cost of the Author unless any errors in the sums paid to the Author are found to his/her disadvantage in which case the cost shall be paid by the Publisher.' This entire clause appeared in our author contracts for some 30 years after we started in business, and in this time no author ever invoked it against us. But in the late 1990s something possibly worse happened: one of our authors assigned his rights in a book to a newspaper publisher in the United States, fronted by a company in the Isle of Man. We only learned of this when the latter company wrote accusing us of not having paid royalties on the book for 10 years and demanding access to our books of account. The accusation was false, which we were able to prove with full documentation (the author was nearly 90 years old, and had become forgetful). I wrote that this surely removed any need for examination, and furthermore that no business relationship could flourish if it were started off with such a demand. After appearing to climb down, the company wrote again some months later repeating the demand and threatening legal enforcement through the county court if we did not comply. My accountant wrote a persuasive and emollient letter, whereupon the company's representative who had conducted all the correspondence phoned and offered me my only possible way out: to surrender my company's rights in the book (which, after a slow start, had for some years been earning a decent royalty income from the United States). I agreed instantly, because under no circumstances was I going to allow aggressive accountants to enter my office, especially on such a vexations pretext. For reasons of space I have left out all details concerning the book, and why the newspaper publisher was interested in it.

Perhaps not all publishers would agree with my extremely negative reaction to a request which is traditionally allowed for in publisher-author contracts, or my haste in surrendering our rights once I knew that I had no other practical means of avoiding compliance with it. Be that as it may, we no longer include an 'examination clause' in our contracts, and will never do so again. Any potential author who cannot accept this will have to go elsewhere. Without mutual trust we cannot do business.

An additional task for editors

This short treatise has concentrated on the processes of production and the mentality of those concerned with it. I have probably said enough to make clear my position that no one should think of him- or herself as a publisher, who is not capable single-handedly of producing a book from start to finish that is as near faultless in its editing, design and production as is possible for a mortal being. Is there any other *sine qua non*? In the concluding chapter of *The Truth about Publishing*, which starts with the passage quoted on page 105, Sir Stanley Unwin advanced two other desiderata: the experience of having sold books to the public in a retail bookshop, and to booksellers as a publisher's representative; and a good memory. But in an earlier chapter he asks: 'Is a formal agreement between publisher and author desirable?' To which he supplied a long answer, of which I shall only quote the following: 'A formal agreement is not only desirable, it is *essential*, ...'

I could write a chapter or two about publishing agreements—between publisher and author, and between one publisher and another concerning the trading of territorial, language or reprint rights, and garnish it with some memorable experiences. But the only proposition I can advance that may have some claim to originality is that analysing contracts is *par excellence* a task for an editor (in the sense of a publisher with a full range of editorial skills). In other (simple) words, working on a contract employs the same brain cells as working on a manuscript. In a small publishing house it is inherently probable that the head of the house will, in the normal course of events, have to read both scripts and contracts, so to that person my proposition will not appear strange. To an outsider it might seem that reading a script is something pleasurable, while reading a contract is arid and tedious. To the insider it will be clear that what drives him on in the latter case is at least partly the hunting instinct—the hope of tracking down lacunae, inconsistencies, plain errors and, of course, unacceptable conditions. With contracts offered by other publishers, that hope is usually rewarded. But it pays for at least two pairs of experienced eyes in the publishing house to examine the house's own standard author contract when it has been filled in with the details relating to a particular publication—to see not only whether those details are as they should be, but whether any of the standard terms and terminology can be improved. The publisher should be able, on a blank sheet, to write a contract of any kind afresh which holds water: it is the product of both knowledge of the business and the relentless logic whichthe task requires anyway, but which is all the more vital when the firm's interests are at stake.

In any discussion of whether publishing is a profession or merely a trade, I would argue that it is above all the legal and financial aspects of the business, as enshrined in our contracts, that do not just entitle us to *claim* that we are a profession, but force us to *acknowledge* that we are, and to act accordingly. To be accused—with justice—of lack of professionalism, because of a slip-up in a contract or a major oversight in the production of a book is the greatest slight we can suffer. (Failure to sell as many copies of a book as we should, or to acquire a good book because of dilatoriness or bad judgement, reflects more on our trading acumen than our professionalism—unless it becomes habitual, and overlaid with complacency.) Therefore it behoves us never to underestimate the importance of getting contracts right—and 'right' means absolutely right. It may be an unexpected discovery for some that ferreting away to get them right, and finally succeeding, can give enormous satisfaction.

APPENDIX

'THE MASTER-PRINTER'

I shall always count it a privilege to have had a book printed by Eastend Printers of Calcutta. In 1998 I met, for the first and only time, its founder and only proprietor, P.K. Ghosh, at his home in that city. The following account of that visit was published in *The Hindu* (Madras/Chennai) on 15 March 1998, and has since been reprinted in two British periodicals. P.K. Ghosh died in 2000.

In 1981 my firm published *A History of Sri Lanka* by K.M. de Silva, the distinguished professor of history at the University of Peradeniya. Calling it 'a' history was over-modest; there had been no complete history of the island by a competent scholar since Sir James Emerson Tennent's account in 1859, and scholarship had moved on since then. It was, without a doubt, 'the' history—all 600 pages of it.

How a small company, then very small and comparatively new, came to publish this magisterial and prestigious work is an interesting tale in itself, but not relevant here—enough to say that it fell into our hands. Of course we had to enlist the cooperation of a co-publisher in the subcontinent, and the obvious choice was the Indian branch of the Oxford University Press, of which Ravi Dayal was then manager. To make such cooperation economically feasible for OUP, the book would have to be printed in India. I then knew nothing of Indian printing facilities except that the results were generally unacceptable in Western eyes (we would not only have to market this Indian-produced book in our own European market but sell a complete edition to one of the leading American university presses, and their standards are notoriously demanding).

I had a good idea—I would go to OUP's London headquarters where an open library was kept of all the Press's recent publications. The librarian pointed out to me the 'Indian section' in a corner. Most of the books conformed more or less to our negative stereotype, but a sharp eye could not fail to be caught by just a few of them. I pulled these volumes out and beheld something wonderful: letterpress printing from metal type of exquisite quality. The paper and binding too were more than adequate, but the magic lay in the faultless typesetting and typographical proportion, unblemished inking (i.e. no pages or parts of pages darker than others), and correct imposition (i.e. margins in the right proportion to the type area, and facing pages matching each other).

I say 'magic' because it was then only a few years since the age-old process of setting in movable type of classic design and printing directly from it, thus giving an all but imperceptible third dimension to the page (you could feel the impress of the type), had been discarded in the main centres of publishing. Its replacement—electronic typesetting and litho printing—has practical advantages to which only a diehard could object, but few would deny the aesthetic loss. Are not books meant to be enjoyed for their form as well as their content? As state-of-the-art text composition has become more sophisticated and labour-saving, so aesthetic standards have withered away; but that is another story.

Who was this Indian printer who overturned all stereotypes? It was Prabhat Kumar Ghosh of Eastend Printers, Calcutta. I immediately informed OUP in Delhi that we wished de Silva's book to be printed by this firm, but OUP replied that this would not be possible because Eastend's capacity was limited not only by its small size but also by Calcutta's liability to power cuts; OUP wished to ensure for itself whatever Eastend could produce. But because of the importance of the book to OUP as well as to me, I was fortunately able to insist.

When the galley proofs arrived, my spirits lifted at the sight of the elegant Baskerville type, but I was also impressed by the thoroughness with which they had already been read by the printer. The printer's reader had once been an important personage in British print-shops—the compositor was not trained to do more than set precisely what was placed before him, right or wrong, but the reader was expected to correct or query errors which had escaped the publisher before the proofs made their first, relatively 'clean' appearance in the publisher's office: sending the publisher an unread set of proofs would have been unthinkable. Needless to say, this practice is long extinct, and the old readers—rumour had it that unfrocked clergymen and disgraced schoolmasters swelled their number—are one with the Tasmanian aborigine and the Mauritian dodo.

By now a profile of Ghosh of Calcutta was emerging in my mind, though at first my imagination conjured up a vision of his reader as a very poor man, despite his obvious learning, with fourteen children at home.

On the proofs were occasional cryptic remarks in green ink: this expression in Sanskrit seemed questionable; that construction in English might be better phrased; and an inconsistency had been found between two spellings of the same name—100 galleys apart. Here was a reader of no ordinary capability.

When it came to the actual printing, once the final proofs were passed, we were uncertain right up to the last moment over the exact quantity of preliminary pages—those numbered with roman figures. Until their quantity could be finalised, normally no printing of the text could begin, for the obvious reason that books are printed in sections of 16 or 32 pages, and while 'oddments' at the end of a book cannot be avoided, it is a first principle to avoid them at the beginning. Imagine my astonishment when Ghosh informed me that he had already begun printing the whole book from page one (i.e. straight after the last preliminary page) to make use of valuable machine time; the 'Prelims' would be taken care of later. I could only admire such improvisation.

As every publisher knows, the moment of seeing a finished copy of one of his firm's publications for the first time can be one heavy with foreboding. I felt none on the day in Colombo when I first beheld and opened a copy of de Silva's *History*. Every loophole through which an error might have crept into the finished book had been firmly closed; I knew this in advance. Since then, I have always held Eastend Printers in the highest esteem: an Indian printer, who by the 1980s could beat the best British printers for all-round quality.

I once asked Ghosh if he would accept another job from me, and he gracefully declined. Then, in the early 1990s, I heard that he had closed Eastend Printers down. His only son Ashok, a close collaborator in his (Ghosh's) enterprise, had recently died, and he himself was getting old. In February 1998 I was in Calcutta for the first time since 1966, and phoned Ghosh to ask if I might pay him a visit. He expressed friendly surprise at my request, but we duly met. Slowly, in the course of our talk, the essence of what had made Eastend Printers so special became clearer.

P.K. Ghosh was born in a village in 1917, the son of a general dealer. In the early '40s he was a lecturer in English literature at Calcutta College—for only six months. One day his subject was a poem by John Masefield and a student asked: 'What is democracy?'

'How is it you don't know that?' he asked and the youth replied he was a science student.

'I didn't think specialisation could go so far—how did you matriculate?' asked P.K.—a foretaste of the acid criticism for which he came to be feared by the less alert of his future customers. Casting pearls before swine was something against which, later especially, his whole being rebelled.

He owned and ran an advertising agency in 1944–51, but gave it up (because he was 'not talented enough') in favour of printing. Colour printing suitable for advertising required too much investment but he was able to set up shop as a book printer in 1952. In 1957 he went to Orient Longman and offered to print one manuscript for them, promising never to set foot in their office again if they were not satisfied.

For a time he was their favourite printer, but he started to receive inadequately edited work, and made the resounding comment: 'I was not born to print a MS. like this.' For he had studied every authoritative manual on style and editing on which he could lay his hands and knew how it should be done. Thus he was self-trained (never a bar to the highest excellence), and as well as practising perfectionism in his own business, he felt a mission to improve the quality of Indian printing. In this, he acknowledges, he failed—more than that, he was reviled by other printers; some in Delhi to whom Dipen Mitra, then production manager at OUP, showed his books retorted that he was mad.

His relations with OUP were long and close, but he constantly chided them over editorial standards, once writing a five-page letter of detailed criticism of which the theme was 'This is not work I would like to print'.

He asked Ravi Dayal if he was really so very fussy, and Ravi answered 'Not at all'. He demanded to see Charles Lewis, deputy manager, at his own press, not in the OUP office. After Charles had heard P.K. out in a three-hour session, he called a conference of editors and told them to improve.

Urvashi Butalia, who served at OUP before founding Kali for Women, told P.K. that he had succeeded in persuading her superiors to improve editing where she had failed. Latterly OUP editors came to dread—and wished to avoid—the lengthy feedback every time a MS. was sent to P.K., an exception being Rukun Advani who said he would only send him those he had edited personally.

It was a revelation to me that P.K. was his own reader—the green ink his virtual trademark. But for some 10 years he shared the work with a learned man who had fallen on hard times: Pratap Bonarjee, grandson of W.C. Bonarjee, founder of the Indian National Congress. This man actually lived in the press, his small personal space shielded by a curtain, and died there in his seventies. Between them they read every set of galleys twice and every set of page proofs twice. The machine minders were well trained. After the first impression of every job had been approved by P.K., the machine could not be interfered with till the whole job, however long, and despite the pressure of other work, had been printed. In the 1970s P.K. thought of replacing the machines, but was advised that because they were well maintained he should leave them alone. It was just as well, because in the end they were sold for scrap.

P.K. says that his business never made much money nor did he run it for money. He did it because he liked books and because of his son. Though never strictly in the business—he was a professor of English at Jadavpur—Ashok Ghosh was at the same time P.K.'s critic, pointing out defects, and, as P.K. freely acknowledges, his inspiration. It is no exaggeration to say that P.K. inspired me, back in 1980 and again in February 1998—just as in 1966 another famous Calcutta bookman, K.L. Mukhopadhyay, hardened my resolve to become an independent scholarly publisher.

P.K. and I parted after our meeting with many handshakes and a near-embrace of friendship. In our trade, to meet a colleague and recognise perfect identity of ideal and purpose is a moving experience, and it is rare.

(Reprinted by permission of *The Hindu*)

INDEX

By the same author

The View from King Street

An Essay in Autobiography

'Publishing needs more Christopher Hursts. There are plenty of accountants, sales people, editors, managers, designers and directors, but there are few uncompromising, determined, entirely candid, iconoclastic, single-minded, eccentric owner-publishers.

'Book I...contains both personal revelations of a somewhat intimate and often entertaining nature, and gems to fascinate the social historian of the upper middle classes in mid-20th-century England. Hurst has some wonderful tales to tell....

'Hurst tells two stories well, in eminently readable style, and with engaging self-deprecating humour. Not just nuggets, but whole seams of delight will be found by anyone connected with the book trade, anywhere.' (Colin Whurr, *Logos*)

'I have read every word with the greatest pleasure. It is so well written, for a start, but throughout you show a real gift for evoking both period and people...all the way through I felt caught up in the events you talk about.' (Letter from Alastair Niven, former Literature Director, the Arts Council)

'... I also greatly admired your forthright and intelligent prose style, with its firm logic, many apt...characterisations, and untrammelled expression of your own opinions and personality.' (Letter from R.B., classical scholar and man of letters)

'... your splendid writing made even the politics of the Publishers Association interesting.' (Letter from Dr W.N. Mann, MD, FRCP)

'Some distinguished authors there are ... who appear to have been endowed with the gift of total recall; so, unfortunately, has Hurst. ... Humour is conspicuously absent....' (J.H.C.L., *Times Literary Supplement*)

x, 464pp., illus. 1997. 1-85065-325-9

Dead Watch

By

Steve Liszka

First published in 2018 by Bloodhound Books

www.bloodhoundbooks.com

Print ISBN 978-1-912604-11-1

For my family

Part One

Chapter 1

The Bullshit Hour

'I still don't see what your fucking problem is,' the large, angry man said to the person seated next to him. He spoke without bothering to swallow the mouthful of egg sandwich he was chewing.

'My problem, Len,' Dylan said cheerfully, 'is that you have an appalling grasp of the English language.'

Lenny laughed, 'My English is just fine sunshine.'

'Really, then let's go through your previous statement, shall we? You said that you were working on the door, and some geezer started kicking off with the other bouncers.'

'Yeah.'

'And then, you said that when he saw you, he literally shit himself, and when you told him to fuck off, he literally ran a mile.'

Lenny nodded. 'Yeah, 'cos that's what happened.'

'No, it didn't,' Dylan said, 'that's my point. You made two factually incorrect statements in the course of one sentence.'

Lenny looked to the other men sitting around the table who were silently listening to the argument. 'Seriously, what the fuck is this prick talking about?'

Dylan sighed. 'It's not your fault, Len, you have an incredibly small brain. That's what happens when there's too much incest in one family. Chromosomes go missing and shit like that.'

'Really now,' Lenny said with an air of menace to his voice. 'I'm going to hurt you in a minute.'

Dylan held his hands up in defence and smiled. 'Kidding, silly. So, back to my point, did this guy actually poo himself? I mean, could you smell it?'

'Nah, but he did look pretty shook up.'

'Right, and did he really run a mile? I'm talking the full one thousand six hundred and whatever it is meters.'

'No, but he did leg it down the road a bit.'

Dylan clapped his hand together, 'So, there we go. That's not literal. Its figurative or maybe metaphorical, but definitely not literal.'

Lenny looked at him blankly.

'It's like when someone says "I literally couldn't get out of bed" or "It literally blew my mind." Unless their head exploded, or they were chained to their bed, they don't mean literally. That means it actually happened. Do you get what I'm saying?'

'I guess so. But do you get what I'm saying when I tell you that I really don't give a fuck?' As Lenny spoke, some of his sandwich shot out of his mouth onto the table.

Dylan looked hurt. 'Don't be like that. I'm just trying to teach you something, that's all.'

'Well I don't want to learn. I've learnt enough, thank you very much.'

Dylan shook his head in mock sadness. 'You know, there's nothing sadder than someone whose brain is closed to new things.'

'How about someone who has to eat his dinner through a straw because his jaw is broken in three places?' Lenny said. 'That's pretty sad.'

'True,' Dylan agreed. 'But I really think you're capable of working this one out.'

'Ok then, clever bollocks. You literally are a piece of shit. How's that?'

'It's wrong, is what it is. *Metaphorically,* I'm a piece of shit, but keep going.'

Lenny rolled his eyes. 'You're acting like a dick.'

'And that, my friend, is a simile. Try again.'

Lenny paused before speaking, like he was testing out his next answer in his mind. 'I've got it! Shut up or I literally am going to smack you in the face really, really fucking hard.'

'Yes!' Dylan punched the air. 'He's got it, by Jove.'

Lenny stared at him, unimpressed. 'I'm serious. Pipe down or I'm gonna knock your teeth down your throat.'

The unknowing spectator would probably have been concerned for Dylan at this point. Lenny had a voice of gravel and a face that looked unprepared to deal with such taunting. At six-feet-three and eighteen stone, he was also built like the proverbial brick shit house. If he'd wanted to, he could have easily carried out his threat, and there would have been little Dylan could have done about it. Although not much smaller in height, Dylan was gangly and awkward looking. He resembled a pubescent seventeen-year-old and, despite being ten years older, was often mistaken for one.

What the spectator wouldn't know was that this goading was part of the routine they would go through at the start of every shift. This was what the bullshit hour was all about; a chance to catch up with friends and colleagues through idle gossip and taunting. In four days' time, they'd be sick of the sight of each other, but it was Red Watch's first morning back on duty, and they had plenty to catch up on.

Wesley, the Watch manager, glanced at the clock on the wall with unease. It was nearly ten-thirty in the morning, the official time that tea break was meant to begin. The problem for Wes was that the other members of the Watch had very different ideas regarding timekeeping to him. At change of shift, they had checked their breathing apparatus (BA) sets and after carrying out an inventory of the lorry, made their way straight to the mess table and had stayed put ever since. Even though they'd been sitting there for almost an hour, he knew he couldn't get his crew to do any work until the official fifteen-minute break had finished.

Wesley was still uncomfortable with the merciless piss-taking that went on at Watch level. He was used to working in the offices of Fire Safety where such coarse language would not be tolerated. He'd been back on the lorries for nearly six months, but the vulgarities of the canteen table still shocked him.

'Okay, so now we've cleared up that,' he said, 'I was thinking we could discuss our plans for the rest of the morning.'

Lenny checked his watch. 'It's break time. We don't talk shop at break time.'

Wesley looked to Jimmy for support and was met with a shrug. Jimmy was the crew manager, which meant he was second in command, although everyone knew it was him who really ran the show. If he'd wanted to, Jimmy could have easily brought an end to the extended period of downtime the men had enjoyed. They'd moan about it, they always did, but they'd do as he asked. But Jimmy clearly didn't feel the need to intervene; this was Wesley's call.

'All I was going to say,' he went on, undeterred, 'is that after tea break, I'd like you guys to get your fire-kit on so we can do a bit of drilling in the yard.'

The five other men sitting at the table let out a groan; Wesley had mentioned the D-word.

'We've got a Home Safety Visit booked in at half eleven,' Bodhi said, not bothering to look up from his cup of coffee. 'If we drill, we're going to miss it.'

Bodhi looked exactly like what he was; a surf bum. Straggly, sun-bleached hair down to his ears, the broad shoulders/tiny waist combo, and the most laid-back demeanour you could find all helped create his image. Not that it was something he had to work on; Bodhi was a natural water-man. If you cut him, salt water would seep out. His real name wasn't Bodhi, of course, only people in films get cool names like that, and the person in question was Patrick Swayze's surfer guru and part-time bank thief in *Point Break*. Knowing no real-life surfers, the Watch had little choice when selecting his nickname. Even though he had moaned about it at the time, he secretly liked it, and it was far more interesting than Mark Godwin, his real moniker.

'Then can you do me a favour and cancel it please,' Wesley said. 'I'd like to show the Dep just how good you guys are when he comes in later.'

Lenny laughed. 'You mean you want us to dance for the fucker.'

Wesley's face reddened. 'What's that supposed to mean?'

'You know exactly what it means, and if you think we're playing that game, you've got another thing coming. We're not performing chimps.'

'He's coming to tell us he's closing our fire station,' Dylan said. 'Why do you want to roll the red carpet out for him?'

'It's not him that's closing the station,' Wesley tried to remind them. 'You can blame the government for that.'

Jimmy looked across to his boss. 'I didn't see him standing outside with us getting the public to sign our petition, did you, Wes?'

'Yeah, well, we've all got jobs to do.'

Lenny stuffed the remains of the sandwich into his mouth. 'And mine's not putting on a show for that fucker.'

Harrison Ford, the only person yet to speak, put down the document he was reading and took off his glasses. He rubbed at his eyes like the words had caused them discomfort. He was a slight man with grey, almost white hair. His real name was Pete Ford, but he had joined the fire service in the eighties when the original Star Wars films were at their peak. It had taken less than an hour on his first day of training school for the instructors to come up with his new name, and he had been called it ever since. Even his wife referred to him as Harrison.

'I, for one, am looking forward to seeing Mr Jacobs.' He held up the document he had been reading. 'So I can discuss this with him.'

Harrison was the most senior person on the Watch and one of the most respected in the station. He had been the FBU rep at East Brighton for almost two decades, and at some point, most people who worked there had gone to him for help in some form or another. He was a thoughtful, softly spoken man until he had to step up in his union capacity, at which point he could turn into a little pit bull if management was being difficult. Unfortunately,

with all the changes going on in the service, this side of him was becoming more and more visible.

'What's up?' Jimmy asked.

'It's the brigade's response to the hazard reports we've been putting in about the radios. According to them, the problems we've been having are our own fault. Human error is what they're quoting.'

Jimmy shook his head. 'I can't believe they're still trying to blame us for their dog-shit equipment.'

'Yeah, our stupidity is the real issue, apparently. They also say that whenever possible we should try and be in direct line of sight with each other when using the radios.'

'If we were in direct line of sight, we wouldn't need fucking radios,' Lenny said. 'We'd just wave or shout.'

Bodhi sipped the final remnants of his coffee. 'I was thinking of getting some plastic cups from the water cooler and attaching them with string. Maybe they'll work better.'

Harrison patted his colleague's arm. 'Don't worry, I'm not going to let it lie.' He paused and looked to Wesley before speaking again. 'I'll be letting the Dep know exactly what I think.'

'I appreciate your feelings on the matter,' Wesley said, swallowing hard, 'and I know how much effort you've put into highlighting the problems with the radios, but that's not what Mr Jacobs is here to talk about today.'

Harrison gave Wesley the look he usually reserved for senior managers. It made his boss wilt.

'No, you're right, the man is here to tell us he's closing our fire station and putting the lives of local families, including mine, by the way, at risk. And you can be damn sure I'll be letting him know how I feel about that too. If you think he's going to come here and get an easy ride, you're very wrong.'

Wesley nodded. 'I understand why you feel so strongly about it, Harrison, of course I do, and you're entitled to say whatever you like to the Dep. I don't want it to descend into a bunfight, that's all I'm saying.'

'And all I'm saying is, don't try to censor me. He's one of the architects of this station's closure, and he deserves everything he gets. Am I right, fellas, or is it just me?'

'Fuck yeah,' Lenny said to the nods of the others. 'He'll be getting both barrels from me.'

Dylan held his fist up in the Black Power pose. 'Up the workers.'

The conversation was interrupted by the sound of stiletto heels walking down the parquet flooring in the corridor. They looked to the doorway to see the station's secretary totter in. Linda was an attractive woman in her mid-fifties, who always dressed immaculately, and was universally loved by the rest of the staff. Despite the macho bravado, they all knew she was by far the most important person at the station, and without her to keep everything running efficiently, the whole place would quickly fall apart.

Lenny was all smiles. 'Linda, my darling, you look lovely as usual. Can I get you a cup of tea?'

Linda smiled back. 'Please. That would be lovely.'

He looked to Dylan with his angry face. 'Oi, new boy, make Linda a cup of tea, and while you're at it, you might as well get another pot of coffee on the go.'

As the most recent member of the Watch, it was Dylan's role to make the drinks. There was no point arguing; that was just the way things were, and until someone else came along, he would always be the new boy. Wesley looked at the clock again and did a quick calculation in his head, working out that if they got the coffee brewing it would take at least twenty minutes before he could even think about getting any work out of them. He went to say something to Lenny, but decided against it, and got himself another glass of water from the cooler.

As the others teased Linda about what she had got up to over the weekend, what with her being a young(ish), free and single woman, the phone rang and then continued to do so as nobody bothered to get it. After six or seven cycles, Wesley dragged himself to his feet.

'I'll get it then,' he mumbled.

He had a kind of waddle when he walked and was heavy around the middle and behind. Unlike Jimmy, who, despite his beer belly, was barrel-chested and powerfully built, Wesley had the soft, wobbly physique of a man who had spent his best years stuck behind a desk.

'East Brighton Fire Station, can I help you?'

'Is that Wesley?'

'It is.'

'Now there's a stroke of luck,' the voice said. It was a deep and raw, and reeked of South London.

'Who's this?'

'You're going to get a call in about five minutes to a boat fire at the marina.'

'I said, who is it?'

'You know exactly who this is, now shut the fuck up and listen. It's time you and your boys paid the piper. When you get to the marina, come and find me.'

'But–'

'And don't even think about speaking to the police. You know what happens to people when they cross me.'

'But–' was all Wesley could say before the line went dead.

When he turned back to the table, his usually ruddy complexion was ashen.

'What's going down, Wes?' Dylan asked.

It was a while before Wesley spoke again.

'We're fucked,' he finally said.

Chapter 2

West Street

Three Months Earlier

The little old lady who owned the flat was almost in tears as the water cascaded through her ceiling.

'This is the third time it's happened,' she cried to Wesley who was trying to manoeuvre her away from the drips. She dabbed at her eyes as she took in the damage.

'Try not to worry yourself,' Wesley said as sympathetically as he could manage. 'I've got my best firefighter up there dealing with it as we speak.'

He looked to Dylan who had just finished moving the large cooking pot full of water from beneath the light bulb and replaced it with a plastic bin. Water always took the path of least resistance, and in most cases, that was via the electrical fittings.

'Can you see if they've managed to get into the flat yet?' Wesley asked. He had left his own radio on the fire appliance.

Dylan nodded and spoke into his. 'How you getting on up there, Len?'

'Not bad, now that we've finally woken up Silly-Bollocks.'

After beating on the door for five minutes with his hammer fists, Lenny had managed to wake the drunken flat owner. They had heard his footsteps pounding down the hallway as he shouted and swore at whoever was on the other side of the door. It was only when he opened it and saw Lenny staring back at him that he quietened down and stepped aside. That was the thing about Lenny; he might have been an arsehole most of the time, but he was Red Watch's arsehole, and on occasions like this, he was exactly the sort of person you needed on the crew.

'I'm sorry,' the owner said, now that fight had gone out of him. 'I must have fallen asleep again.'

'No shit,' Lenny said, then added, 'Who the fuck has a bath when they come back from the pub anyway?'

As he interrogated the man, Wonder Woman took off her tunic and plunged her hand into the bathtub to remove the plug.

'If this happens again,' she said, 'we'll be charging you for wasting our time. Understand?'

Even though she was an incredibly good-looking woman, she could be just as scary as Lenny when she wanted to be, sometimes even more-so. Wonder Woman was the final piece in the jigsaw that made up Red Watch. Her real name was Joanne, or Jo as she preferred, and her nickname was well-earned.

When she wasn't being a firefighter, WW was a dedicated Triathlete. So dedicated, in fact, that she had recently qualified as a member of the Great British Squad for her age group. At thirty-nine, she was one of the fittest people in the brigade. There were few guys who could keep up with her in the sporting arena, and she was equally as focused at work as she was with her training. The phrase "doesn't suffer fools gladly" could have been invented for her.

'I promise it won't happen again,' the owner pleaded. 'To be honest, I never even thought the fire service came to things like this.'

That's how it was with most people; they had no real idea what the job entailed. Fighting fires was only a small slice of the pie; there were plenty of other things they had to deal with too. First, there were the car crashes, or "road traffic collisions" as the service now referred to them, and that tended to be where they saw the really nasty stuff, the things you didn't forget about in a hurry. Then, there were the lift rescues, floodings, lock-ins, lock-outs, chemical incidents and other hazardous substances, environmental protection and dangerous structures to name but a few.

On top of that, there were the animal rescues. Seagull impaled on a television aerial, dog down a hole, cow in a ditch or the good ol' cat up a tree; you got the fire service out. Then, there were the not-so-normal incidents. A stag gets handcuffed to railings

by his pissed-up mates who lose the keys; you call the fire service. A guy can't remove his cock ring, and it needs cutting off (this had happened to Red Watch); you get the fire brigade. Someone threatens to jump off the roof, falls down a cliff or gets their leg stuck down a drain, then, to quote the Ghostbusters, "Who ya gonna call?" The basic rule of thumb was, if you couldn't think who else to get hold of, then you got the firefighters.

After they had helped the flat owner clean up the water from his bathroom floor (it was for the old dear downstairs' benefit, not his), and Dylan and Wesley had done the same for her, they all headed back to the lorry.

So, this is probably a good time to talk about fire service terminology. A fire engine has almost as many names as the equipment it carries – appliance, pump, truck, lorry, rescue vehicle, water tender, shit cart, along with numerous others depending where in the country you worked. They all represent the same thing, though; the big red shiny thing that sits in the fire station bays, waiting to deal with whatever is thrown at it.

Just to confuse matters further, you may have noticed the words crew and Watch being thrown around. The Watch is comprised of all the people on a particular station who work together on the same shift pattern, and each of these is named after a colour – red, green, white and blue. The crew refers to the Watch members that were riding the fire engine on that specific day. If you have two appliances at your station, then you would have two crews. And one more thing, even though they work for Sussex Fire and Rescue Service, most firefighters still refer to it as the Brigade, just like it was known in the good old days.

When they got back on the truck, Harrison was sitting in the driver's seat waiting for them.

'Anything happening out there?' Wesley asked him.

He was referring to the main-scheme radio system. By listening to the messages being passed over the airwaves between various

fire engines and mobilising staff at headquarters, it was possible to get an insight into what was going on throughout the service.

'Central and Hove have just been sent to a make-pumps-four in Portslade,' Harrison answered. 'Looks like we're the only ones available in the city.'

'Shit,' Dylan said. 'How come we always miss the big ones?'

Like anyone with only a few years in the service, Dylan was desperate to get some good fires under his belt, and in this case, good meant bad. It wasn't like he was wishing ill on people, it was just that if there were going to be fires, he would prefer it if they happened when he was on duty. While the older guys were happy to have a quiet night and get a few hours' sleep, the young pups wanted nothing more than to be in the thick of it, putting out the flames.

Not that Red Watch had exactly had a quiet night. Things had kicked off a couple of hours earlier with a car fire near the racecourse. Some scrotes had nicked a Volkswagen Golf and, after having their fun, taken it onto the South Downs and torched it. By the time the crew got there, it was, to use a fire service expression, going like a bastard, with ignited petrol pissing out of the cracked tank. When this happened, unlike in the Hollywood films, cars didn't explode and shoot twenty feet into the air; it just meant the crews had to use a different approach to put it out as water didn't work so well when it came to fuel fires. As Dylan and Jo had hosed down the car, Lenny, who had hoped to escape doing any work, grumbled to himself as he dragged the foam reel off the appliance to tackle the burning petrol.

They were only back at the station for five minutes when they were called out to a lift rescue. An old boy in a high-rise was on the way to taking his dog for a late-night walk when the lift had stopped working. When they opened the doors, they were greeted by the smell of freshly laid Corgi shit that almost made Dylan puke. The appliance hadn't even made it back to the station when they got called to the flooding.

'Seeing as everyone else is out,' Wesley said, turning to look at the crew, 'we might as well head into town before mobilising send us there.'

East Brighton, as the name suggested, was located to the east of the city, with Hove situated to the west. Central, the largest of the three Brighton stations, was in the middle of town. It made sense that if there was only one pump available, then it should be located on Central's ground, where all parts of the city could be reached in roughly the same amount of time.

'You know what that means,' Lenny said. 'It's one o'clock in the morning on Saturday night, and we've got to go into town. Looks like we've got ourselves a West Street run.'

The fire engine came to a stop at the traffic lights, allowing the gaggle of cowgirls from the hen party they had just passed to catch up with them.

Harrison glanced back at them in his mirror. 'Brace yourselves. We've got company.'

Dylan leant forward so he could see past Lenny's bulk and talk to Wonder Woman. 'Watch the disappointment on their faces when they see what real firefighters looks like.'

'Speak for yourself, shit-pot,' Lenny said, then pointed both thumbs towards his chest. 'This is what they want. One hundred percent prime British beef.'

Jo looked at him in disgust. 'Pork, more like it.'

The hen party reached the lorry, and while the others stared into the back, the leader banged on Wesley's window until he felt obliged to lower it. She hid the look that Dylan had described as well as she possibly could.

'Come on then, Mr Fireman!' she shouted, tilting back her cowboy hat. 'Let's have a look at your hose.'

Wesley just about managed to smile through his grimace of embarrassment. 'Having a nice time, ladies?'

'Magic,' the woman responded. Wesley thought he detected a Bristol accent although it might have been Welsh. 'But it would be even better if the bride-to-be got a kiss from one of you lovely fellas.'

It was definitely Bristol.

Wesley faked a smile. 'We'd love to, but unfortunately, we're not allowed.'

The woman looked genuinely disappointed.

'Bollocks to that,' Lenny said as he pushed Dylan's face to the side and stuck his massive head out of the window. 'Where's the lucky girl?'

A shy-looking woman with red hair, sporting the biggest of all the hats, stepped up to the window.

'Good luck, darling,' Lenny said, leaning forward to plant a smacker on her cheek as he crushed the life out of Dylan.

The traffic lights changed as the rest of the party gave out a massive cheer. Lenny blew them a kiss before dragging himself back inside the appliance.

As they drove up the street, Wesley nodded at the two police officers standing in the central reservation. The man gave him a friendly enough smile, but the female officer was clearly not impressed.

Wesley turned to face the back. 'I wish you hadn't done that, Len. It really doesn't help our professional image.'

Lenny laughed. 'Come on, Wes, it was just a bit of fun. We just made their evening.'

'Maybe so, but I certainly don't think that police officer would agree with you.'

'Which one, the Doris?'

He turned to Jo. 'No offence.'

'None taken.'

'She can get fucked,' he said, 'I mean, what the fuck is she even doing standing on West Street on a Saturday night? She's about five foot one, if she's lucky, and weighs less than my right nut. What's she going to do if it all kicks off? No offence.'

'Actually, dumb-ass,' Jo said, 'I do take offence at that. Perhaps she's not here to be part of the muscle. Perhaps she's here to help avoid confrontation. As a bouncer, I thought you'd understand that. Or just maybe, if some young girl's been sexually assaulted by some scum-bag prick, she'd feel more comfortable talking about it to another woman than some meat-head like you.'

'Fair enough,' Lenny said, conceding the argument. 'You've made me feel like a proper nasty bastard now.'

And to be fair, despite his attempts to suggest otherwise, that was something he wasn't. If you asked him, Lenny would tell you his nickname came from his likeness to Lenny MacLaine, the hulking bareknuckle boxing champion, who, before his death, had found fame playing East-End tough guys in Guy Ritchie flicks. In reality, the name was given to him by his first watch in reference to Lennie, the mouse-squashing man-child in *Of Mice and Men*. You definitely wouldn't call him a gentle giant, he'd break your arm for suggesting it, but usually, his heart was more-or-less in the right place.

'Then, don't act like one,' Jo said, the tone of her voice easing.

As the engine neared the top of the street and slowed for the next set of lights, a group of lads ran alongside the vehicle, banging the lockers. As they came to a stop, the boys turned and held up their middle fingers before quickly taking off.

'This place is a shithole,' Dylan said. 'Don't these kids know there are plenty of better places to go out in Brighton?'

Lenny shook his head in disgust. 'Where would you rather be, knobhead? Drinking craft beer in the North Laine, telling the hipster cunts how great their beards are?'

'Why do you keep trying to associate me with the hipsters? I hate them as much as you do.'

'Yeah right. If we were allowed to, and you were capable of growing one, you'd definitely have a beard.'

'No, I wouldn't.'

'Yeah, you would, and one of those little twirly moustaches. Hipster lover.'

'If you say so,' Dylan said, slightly agitated.

Lenny looked out of the window and waved at the two massive bouncers standing outside The Heist. If he weren't working nights, he would have been there, accompanying them.

'You better get used to this place,' he said. 'Because if you get that transfer you want, you'll be here every weekend. The city boys love it.'

Dylan shrugged. 'If I'm ever going to rescue a baby from a burning building, then I'm more likely to do it at Central.'

He'd had a transfer request in for almost eighteen months, but no positions had become available. It was an understandable move for him. Central was a three-pump station, if you included the aerial appliance. It was also busier, what with it being in the heart of the city. East Brighton was quieter, and a place where many firefighters went to serve out the last few years of their careers. With the exception of him and Jo, the entire Watch had served their time at Central before ending up at East. That's not to say they didn't get their fair share of jobs, because they did, and being a one-pump station, when they did get an incident, the lack of manpower meant that things could get pretty hairy before backup arrived.

'Anyway, I don't know why you're being such a snob,' Lenny said. 'When Jo's not here, it's all "Check out the tits on that" and "Look at the arse on her."'

'No, I don't,' Dylan said as his face turned crimson.

Jo shook her head in mock disgust. 'And there I was thinking you were a nice boy.'

They were interrupted by the mobile phone going off in the front of the cab. Wesley picked it up and, after a few brief words, returned the phone to its housing and spoke to the crew. 'That was mobilising. Barcombe will be here any minute, so we can get back on our own ground ASAP.'

He actually said ASAP as a word and not separate letters. The others had heard it so many times, they didn't bother to make fun of him for it any longer.

'Thank god for our retained brothers,' Lenny said.

Jo gave him *the* look. 'You've changed your tune.'

'I like anyone who lets me get my head down for a bit of kip.'

The computer screen in the front of the appliance flashed as a miniature wailer went off notifying them they had a shout.

Wesley turned and smiled at them. 'Looks like your bed's going to have to wait.'

Chapter 3

RTC: Persons Trapped

'I'll tell you something for nothing,' Harrison said as he squinted at the road ahead. 'I'd rather be dead than in that place. When I can't wipe my own arse anymore, just give me a nice cocktail of painkillers and send me on my way.'

'What do you mean when?' Lenny said. 'I'll put you out of your misery now, if you want, you old bastard.'

Harrison laughed. 'Cheeky sod. I've still got a few years left in me yet.'

The fire call had taken them out to Rottingdean, a pretty little village to the east of Brighton. They had been sent to an automatic fire alarm activating in a care home for the elderly and dementia sufferers. As usual, it had turned out to be a false alarm. There was an ongoing system fault, meaning the alarm kept activating, despite there being no obvious reason. In such places, they had a stay-in-place policy, otherwise it would have been chaos as the scared and confused residents, many with mobility issues, tried their best to get outside into conditions that would probably give them hypothermia.

The drive back to the station along the seafront road was a beautiful one in the daytime. To the left, the land dropped away to chalky, white cliffs giving an unadulterated view of the horizon. On the other side were grassy fields that sloped up towards a row of large detached houses owned by Brighton's finest. Some were classy, some not so much. In the nineties, the Spanish villa look had become fashionable on the strip, with people trading their dull roof tiles for ones with garish blue or red glazes. But none of them could stand up to the one house that eclipsed them all.

'Look at that fucking eyesore,' Dylan said to no one listening.

Jo was still strapped into her BA set and had fallen asleep with her head hanging so far forward, it looked like it was about to fall off. Wesley was staring wide-eyed out of his window, and Harrison was focusing on getting them back to base before his eyes closed.

'It just goes to show,' he said, oblivious to the fact that it was a one-person conversation, 'money can't buy you class.'

'Stop being such a snob,' Lenny said, 'I think the place looks class. Now, shut the fuck up. It's too late for your bullshit.'

The house in question was huge. It was actually three houses that had been knocked down and been reborn as a neo-classical mansion complete with giant pillars, murals and fountains that were home to bow and arrow-toting cherubs. It was owned by the notorious businessman, property magnate and all round bad egg, Jonathan Bogarde. The man was one of Brighton's most powerful, not to mention infamous, residents. Not a week went by when he wasn't in the local rag for evicting dozens of families from one of his slum buildings, or making shady business deals with dictators in countries with dreadful human rights records. All in all, the man was an out-and-out bastard, and he didn't give a shit who knew it. The house had been more than five years in the making and had cost him a fortune. At least two construction companies had quit the job in rows over unpaid bills, and after years of legal battles, it was finally close to completion.

'Did you see that?' Wesley said.

Harrison looked out of his window. 'What?'

'Back there,' Wesley craned his neck to see whatever it was they had just passed. 'I saw some lights down the bank. I think a car may have gone over.'

'You sure?' Harrison said.

Wesley shrugged. 'I think so.'

'Then, we better go and check it out.'

While Harrison slowed the truck so he could find a spot to turn around, Wesley turned to the guys in the back.

'Look lively!' he shouted to them. 'We could have an RTC here.'

The others were up and ready for action in seconds. Such words were the sort of message that sent a flood of adrenaline into a firefighter's system and instantly switched them on, in preparation for the job facing them. In his head, Dylan ran through the procedures for an RTC. For him, it was still a conscious process, for the rest of the crew, it had become second nature.

No matter if it was a single car that had crashed into a wall or a twenty-vehicle pile-up, whether the car be on its wheels, side or roof, the rules always remained the same. As he put on his high visibility surcoat, Dylan went through each stage:

1. Scene Assessment and Safety. This one's a two-parter. Firstly, even before arriving at the incident, the OIC is already starting their DRA (Dynamic Risk Assessment) and weighing up the situation. In this early stage of the incident, they'll have an awful lot going through their heads. How many cars are involved? Do they have enough resources? Which vehicle do they work on first? Which casualty in that vehicle do they work on first? Nine times out of ten, the passenger who's shouting and screaming about their broken arm or leg is much less of a concern than the person sitting next to them who isn't saying anything at all. It's the quiet ones you need to worry about. Second, the crews have to consider their own safety before worrying about anyone else's. You wouldn't believe the number of firefighters that have been injured or killed at an RTC or car fire by some numbskull who couldn't be bothered to slow down. For this reason, crews need to be as visible to oncoming vehicles as possible. Fluorescent jackets, cones, signage, lighting and a fire engine parked in a good fend-off position all help to stop them getting flattened.
2. Stabilisation and initial access. Another two-hander. The vehicle needs to be stable before any work is done on it. Wedges, blocks and step chocks are used to achieve this goal. Making sure the handbrake is on is also a good one at this stage. Getting into the vehicle as quickly as possible is essential

in saving life. Just tilting back an unconscious person's head and opening their airway can be the difference between life and death. Opening a door, if it isn't jammed, or getting your hand through an open window will help to achieve this goal.

3. Glass management. Before you start cutting anything with the hydraulic rescue gear, you need to make sure all the glass in the vehicle is dealt with or, in other words, smashed, but in a controlled manner. The last thing you want is a window shattering on your casualty as you are cutting them out. Little oval shields called teardrops, and ground sheets are used to ensure the casualty remains safe.
4. Space Creation. Simple things like sliding seats back or reclining them can drastically improve someone's levels of comfort, thereby reducing stress and anxiety. Making space also creates opportunities for a dedicated casualty carer or paramedic to get into the vehicle and deal with any injuries.
5. Full Access. This is where the cutting gear finally comes into its own. Removing doors and structural posts allow crews to get into the vehicle with a view to getting the injured party out. More often than not, a roof removal is often the most effective way of getting hands on them and also provides the easiest route out. A good crew, working simultaneously, will have the roof off in minutes when they get to this stage of the rescue.
6. Immobilisation and Extrication. Another double-header to finish. If a casualty has suffered a neck injury, it only takes a few millimetres of movement to sever the spinal cord and cause permanent paralysis. The best way to avoid this, under the guidance of the ambulance crews, is to get them onto a long-board, or encased in the full body splint that paramedics seem to favour these days. Next, get them out. Usually, if a roof removal is involved, the long-board will be placed down the back of their chair. After lowering the seat, they can be slid out of the back of the vehicle on the board and taken into the ambulance. Most good OICs will have a plan B with

> regards to the extrication. If things go tits-up, and the casualty suddenly deteriorates, they'll have to come out in a different, less controlled manner. There's no point protecting someone's spinal column if they are bleeding to death or unable to breathe.

When they got closer, it quickly became clear that Wesley's assessment was right. In a ditch to the side of the road, about fifteen feet from the cliff edge, was a car on its roof. It had been difficult to see from the raised view of the fire engine, but at normal car height level, it would have been impossible to spot. The car may have been there for minutes, but it could have been stuck in that ditch for hours.

When the appliance stopped, Wesley got on the radio and called the incident in (this was known as a running-call), as the crew stumbled down the bank and took stock of the situation. Lenny had only glanced at it when he informed them the car in question was a BMW 7 Series that must have cost a small fortune.

Newer cars tended to fare better in crashes than older ones. The technology involved meant that they were filled with safety systems to reduce the effects of a collision on anyone inside. Airbags and air curtains were located at most potential impact points in the car, with passengers enveloped in virtual roll cages made of high tensile steel. If you considered that the cars also had seatbelt pre-tensioners to limit their impact, it was amazing that anyone was killed in car crashes anymore. Except they were, all too often. The vehicles may have been safer than ever before, but when you considered the forces involved in some high-speed crashes, those developments could never stop the massive amounts of damage that could be caused to a car and its fragile passengers.

Something else that firefighters learnt early on in their careers, was that the damage done to the vehicles involved was often not a true reflection of the damage done to its passengers. Every firefighter could tell you of an incident where a car had flipped three times or something equally spectacular and although

totalled, the driver had walked away with nothing more than a scratch on their arm. Similarly, the often innocuous-looking prang could lead to a fatality if the driver was unlucky enough to bump their head on the B-post.

Even though it had come down the bank and landed on its roof, the car was pretty much damage-free, other than a few minor scratches and bumps on the bodywork. The chassis looked to be intact, and the surrounding area didn't appear too torn up by the crash. Lenny tried the upside down front passenger's door and was surprised to see it open without any resistance. He got onto his knees, looked in through the door and half crawled in.

'How we looking in there, Len?' Wesley asked him. 'What do we need?'

After a few seconds of shuffling around, Lenny came out in reverse and looked over his shoulder to his boss.

'Nothing for us to do here,' he said with a shake of the head. 'This guy's brown bread.'

'Really?' Wesley said.

'Yep, looks like it's the curse of Dead Watch for this poor fucker.'

They had inherited their nickname more than a decade previously, following a number of particularly gruesome incidents in a relatively short time-frame. Just when it would start to lose its currency, another nasty fatality would come along and ensure the term remained in use for another few years.

Lenny got to his feet and aimed his hand at the open door. 'Be my guest.'

Wesley took him up on the offer and knelt down to inspect the casualty. When he looked inside, he could see why Lenny was so adamant. The driver was a lump of a man, bigger than Lenny and probably meaner-looking, too, before his accident. He was suspended upside down by his seatbelt and looked unharmed with the exception of the thick, sticky blood that caked around his temple. His mouth and eyes were both wide open, and when Wesley touched his face, it felt cold, with the effects of rigor

mortis already starting to kick in. The man had been dead for at least a couple of hours.

As Wesley regained his feet, Harrison looked down to him from the top of the bank. He had been busying himself making the scene as well-lit as possible and, after coning off the incident, had directed the vehicle's lighting stem at the car.

'You need the cutting gear down there?' he asked.

'We don't need anything, thanks. It's a Code One.'

Harrison nodded. 'I'll pass it on to control and wait up here for the police.'

'On a Saturday night? You may be waiting for some time.'

'Yeah, well, I've got nothing else to do.' Harrison turned and disappeared from view.

'Wes,' Jo said, 'you may want to take a look at this.'

When he looked down, he saw the rest of the crew on their knees, staring into the back of the vehicle. 'What is it?'

Lenny looked up to him with a smile that stunk of trouble. 'You gotta see this shit.'

Wesley joined them and shared the view. In front of them lay a sports holdall that had emptied most of its contents onto the roof of the upside-down car.

'Is that what I think it is?' he asked.

'Oh yeah,' Dylan nodded.

Dozens of two-inch-thick bundles of twenty-pound notes decorated the car's interior.

'Fuck me,' Wesley said in a whisper.

Lenny looked around at the others. 'Is anyone else thinking what I am?'

Jo turned her head towards him. 'Len! Don't even think about it.'

'Come on, guys, seriously. Look how much money's there. Are we really going to let the Old Bill shove it in some evidence room for the next ten years? That cash could go a long way.'

Dylan looked at the money and sighed.

'Not you too,' Jo said.

'What? I didn't say anything.'

'Have you pair of idiots gone mad? We'll lose our jobs. You know what, fuck that, we could go to jail. Please tell me you're joking.'

Lenny gave her his full attention. 'Like I said, I'm just pointing it out, that's all. This is a pretty fucking unique situation we're in right here. This is drug money, it's gotta be. That's the only way an ape like that is gonna drive a car like this with that much money stashed in it, and now, he's dead. It's the perfect fucking crime, I'm telling you. We take this money, no one's ever going to know a thing about it… I'm just saying, is all.'

Jo turned to Wesley. 'Boss, talk some sense into these boneheads, will you?'

Wesley looked at his crew. 'I say, we should take it.'

'You fucking what?'

'I say we should take it. It's like Lenny said, it's the perfect crime.'

'Perfect crime? Please tell me you're not serious.'

'I am, but only if we all agree to it. And if we are going to take it, we need to do it now. The police and paramedics will be here soon, not to mention one of our own officers.'

It was standard practice for an on-call officer to attend an incident that involved a fatality, otherwise known as a Code One in brigade speak.

'I'm in,' Lenny answered, before Wesley could finish.

'Me too, I guess,' Dylan said. 'I'd rather we stole it than the government did.'

Wesley nodded. 'Me too.'

Jo looked to each of their faces, waiting for one of them to smile and say it was a joke. The smile never came.

'Oh, fuck the lot of you,' she said. 'Don't put this on me.'

'It's the fairest way,' Wesley said.

'Fair? There's nothing fair about what you pricks are doing to me right now.'

'Then say no,' Lenny said. 'If you don't want to do it, just say no, and we'll walk away.'

'But think of all those carbon fibre bike frames you could buy,' Dylan added, attempting to liven the mood.

'Shut the fuck up, Dylan,' she snapped. 'This is serious.'

'Like I say,' Wesley said, 'it's up to you.'

Jo was quiet for a minute, then looked to the money, then back to the crew. 'Do what you fucking like.'

Wesley looked around like he was checking no one was watching them. 'Okay, let's get the money before someone turns up and spoils the party. Have you tried the back doors?'

Lenny nodded. 'Tried them. They ain't going anywhere. We need to go through the front to get them.'

'Dylan, you're the skinniest,' Wesley said. 'Get in there and get the money out quick sharpish.'

It was funny, but in all the time he'd been in charge of the watch, he had never come close to being as in control of an incident as he was at that moment. Dylan did as commanded and went in through the front passenger's side on his belly, then crawled between the seats and placed the money in the bag. From up on the road, the rest of the crew became aware of the faint sounds of sirens.

'Hurry it up!' Wesley shouted to him. 'I think we've got company.'

Dylan scooped up the last few bundles of cash and rammed them into the bag. There wasn't enough space for him to turn around, so he had to shuffle back out in reverse. As he got his legs through the gap between the seats, Lenny grabbed hold of them and yanked him out the rest of the way.

'Careful, big man,' he protested. 'You nearly bust my kneecap then.'

Lenny shrugged. 'Sorry, but we need to hustle, that siren is getting closer.'

He took the bag off Dylan and thrust it into Jo's hands. 'Quick, take this up the bank and chuck it in one of the lockers.'

'Make sure it can't be seen,' Wesley added unnecessarily.

'You better not show Harrison, either,' Lenny said. 'I don't think he's going to like this.'

Jo looked at the faces of her crew-mates. 'Anything else while you're at it?'

When no reply came back, she tucked the bag under her arm and leapt up the bank in half a dozen powerful strides. Luckily, Harrison had walked towards the red car with the flashing blue lights that was approaching them, and was oblivious to her presence. She opened the door to the back of the cab and, after flicking two quick-release catches, opened the locker underneath her seat. She quickly took out the casualty blankets that were inside and forced the bag into the empty space, before stuffing the blankets back in. As the car came to a halt, she closed the locker and went back out to see which officer had turned up.

'Shit,' she said when she saw who it was.

Chapter 4
Phil Collins

Phil Collins got out of the car and initiated a brief conversation with Harrison. This wasn't a fire brigade nickname that had been bestowed on him by his colleagues; he really had been christened Phil Collins, or Phillip, as he demanded to be called. Unfortunately for him, his demands were like a red rag to a bull. His wishes may have been respected by his more civilised fellow officers, but on the fire-ground, he was, and always would be, Phil. He had been the station manager of East Brighton for a couple of years, but since his job had been amalgamated with that of the station manager at Hove, he was spending far more time there. This development suited everyone at East just fine because Phil was not a well-liked man.

Along with certain other officers, he had had what was known in the trade as "the chip" well and truly inserted. The chip was a legendary (some say fictional) device that was implanted in these people in their transition from being a working, operational firefighter to a deskbound officer. It was the thing that allowed them to forget what life had been like at Watch level. This way, they could not only go along with, but energetically champion policies and ideas that only a non-operational manager could dream up and had no place on a fire station. The chip helped managers to engage in a level of doublethink that Orwell would have been proud of, and none was a better practitioner of the art than Phil Collins.

What was worse, and what people found even harder to swallow, was that during the strikes, Phil had been one of the managers who had quit the union and crossed the picket line to ride the resilience fire engines. Unlike most of the other officers

who tended to keep quiet about their actions (something that had caused a massive divide between them and the front-line staff), Phil took great pride in this, making sure everyone knew he had been only too happy to help undermine their cause. No, Phil was definitely not a well-liked man.

When he got to the bottom of the bank, he headed straight for Wesley, blinkering out the other Watch members. He tried to interact with firefighters as little as possible; his contempt for them was well known. Even talking to crew managers, like Jimmy, was distasteful to him.

Lenny gave him a friendly wave. 'Hi, Phil.'

'It's Phillip,' he answered without turning his head. As with most of the managers in the brigade, he had history with Lenny.

'What have we got?' he asked Wesley without so much as a hello.

Wesley swallowed hard before speaking. 'Code One. Not sure what happened. There's very little damage to the vehicle, so I doubt he was speeding. He's taken a bump to the head, looks to have been dead for some time.'

Phil nodded and looked away from Wesley to the car itself. He stared at it for some time before slowly bringing his gaze back. 'I'm assuming that you've done a thorough search of the area?'

When he saw the blank look on Wesley's face, he quickly went for the jugular. 'You did think of that, right?'

The fact was that Wesley hadn't thought of anything at all, other than the bag of money they'd discovered. Now that he *was* thinking, he knew exactly what was coming next. At an RTC, particularly one where a car had flipped and the forces of physics had had a field day, it was always a sensible idea to check the area for casualties. The canteen table was full of stories of how a passenger or driver had been thrown out of a vehicle and ended up in places they had no right to be. Sending a crew member for a scout around, especially as there were no casualties to deal with, should have been one of the first things done. It was unlikely, considering how little damage the car had

suffered, but one thing you learnt in the fire service was not to assume anything.

'I'm sorry, boss,' Wesley said. 'We had a quick look around, but we didn't see anything.'

Phil looked to the cliff edge. 'You checked over there yet?'

With the powerful hand lamp that Harrison had sent down to them, Wesley and Phil peered over the edge and swung the beam of light around the rocks below.

'You're lucky,' Phil said. 'Explaining that one could have been embarrassing for you.'

Wesley nodded as he stepped away from the cliff edge. 'It won't happen again, that's for sure.'

'No, I'm sure it won't.'

The sound of sirens made them turn and look up to the road. The police and ambulance had arrived simultaneously. As they negotiated their way back up the bank, Wesley spoke again. 'If the police want to preserve the scene and leave the body in situ, are you okay with us getting away? I don't see there being anything else for us to do now.'

'That's fine,' Phil said. 'I wouldn't want to spoil your crew's beauty sleep any more than is necessary.'

Wesley took on board what had been said and thought about it for a moment. 'You're an on-call officer, aren't you, boss?'

'That's right.'

'So, didn't you have to get out of bed to respond to this call?'

Phil turned to face him. 'I expect that sort of response from that idiot over there,' he nodded at Lenny who was air-drumming the solo of "In the Air Tonight," 'and not one of my officers… Don't make me regret the decision to make you operational.'

Wesley nodded. 'Sorry, Phil.'

The journey back to the station was almost silent, so much so that Harrison felt the need to intervene. 'What's up with you lot?' he said. 'You mourning that guy in the beamer? I'm sure he was very nice.'

It was true what people said; firefighters really did have a black sense of humour. They had to, especially when it came to RTCs. When you watched someone take their last breath in front of you, or you got to see up close the body of a small child that had taken the full impact of a crash, then you had to learn how to deal with it. For most firefighters, that involved making inappropriate jokes or comments that would have left the average member of the public in shock. Because that was what the firefighters were – in shock. The best way they knew how to deal with such traumatic events, without having to go off sick, was to laugh about it, discuss it with their colleagues who had also been there and then put it behind them and move on. If they didn't, they'd all end up going crazy.

It was Dylan who finally broke the silence. 'I can't do this. We've got to go back.'

'Do what?' Harrison asked.

Dylan looked to Lenny sitting next to him. 'If we go back now and explain what we did, I'm sure we'll be okay.'

'Shut up and calm down,' Lenny said.

Harrison looked over his shoulder towards his passengers. 'What's he talking about? Why do we need to go back?'

Wesley laughed. 'Don't worry about him. He's just playing silly buggers.'

'What's that supposed to mean?' Harrison said, not buying it. 'What's going on?'

'We fucked up,' Dylan spurted out. 'We just made a terrible mistake, and now, we need to sort it out, before it's too late.'

Harrison looked to Wesley as the vehicle slowed down. 'What the hell's going on here? Don't make me ask again.'

'Forget it,' Lenny said, leaning forward into the front of the cab. 'Just get us back to the station. I think he just needs a good kip.'

Harrison slammed on his brakes almost throwing Lenny into the front of the vehicle. Even though he had been told hundreds of times, he always refused to wear his seatbelt when he sat in the back.

'Now you listen to me,' Harrison said, 'I'm not going anywhere until you lot tell me what the hell is going on. Something ain't right here.'

Wesley turned to address his driver. 'There was a pile of money in the back of that car.'

'So?'

'So, we took it.'

'You did what?'

'We took it. I know we shouldn't have, but if you'd seen it lying there–'

'I would have left it and told the police, you fucking idiot,' Harrison looked over his shoulder again, but this time, he was staring at Jo. 'Please tell me he's joking?'

She shook her head.

'Right!' he shouted. 'That's it. We're going back.'

Lenny reached forward and placed his hand on Harrison's shoulder. 'Whoa, just hold on a minute, would you? What the fuck do you think you're going to achieve by going back?'

'He's right,' Wesley said. 'It's too late now. If you go back, we're all going to end up getting sacked.'

'No, we won't,' Dylan said. 'Not if we do it now, and explain it was just a moment of madness. If we don't, they'll find out, and we'll be fucked anyway.'

Lenny looked at him and shook his head. 'Do me a favour and shut the fuck up for five minutes. The adults are talking.'

'Adults?' Harrison said, 'I'd hardly say that what you morons have just done qualifies as adult behaviour. Now, all of you do me a favour and shut the fuck up. We're going back. I've got less than a year left in this job. If you think I'm going to risk my pension over this shit…' He put the vehicle into drive and turned the wheel to point them back the way they had come.

'That's right,' Lenny said. 'You just think of yourself and your nice big pension pot. If you were in the same situation as the rest of us, perhaps you wouldn't be so quick to judge.'

Lenny's comment was a low blow in anyone's book. Harrison was probably the most selfless person at the station. He had put other people's problems and worries before his own for as long as he could remember. So much so, that his own private life had come to resemble a train wreck as he struggled to help other people preserve theirs.

There was some truth to Lenny's outburst, though, no matter how unfair it was. As part of the government's decimation of the fire service, the contracts they had signed up to when they first joined the job had effectively been torn up. Firefighters would now have to work for at least five years extra, contribute a larger portion of their wages into their pension scheme (even though they already paid substantially more into their respective pot than almost anyone else) and get far less in return when they retired. Not surprisingly, they were furious, and this was one of the main reasons why they had reluctantly taken strike action.

The only people not being affected by these changes were the ones in their final ten years of service. This meant that Harrison would be leaving the job in just under a year with a lump sum and pension that was worth far more than his younger colleagues could ever imagine. None of the others on the watch fell into the category. Lenny had missed it by a year and Jimmy by a matter of weeks. For a man who had built his whole career on solidarity with his fellow workers, this anomaly did not sit at all well with Harrison. Lenny had succeeded in finding his weak point.

'How much money are we talking?' Harrison asked.

Lenny shrugged. 'Fuck knows, but it's a lot. Hundreds of thousands of pounds maybe.'

There was a pause before Harrison spoke again. 'You okay with this, Jo?'

She shrugged back at him, unwilling to meet his stare.

'And you, Dylan, you still want to take it back?'

Dylan shook his head, seeming to have calmed down. 'No, I'm okay now. We should keep it.'

He looked to Wesley with nothing but contempt. 'I don't suppose there's any point asking you.'

'I'm in, if that's what you mean.'

Harrison looked to each of their faces. 'There's one condition, actually make it two, for me to not go back right now.'

'We're listening,' Wesley said.

'First, I want nothing to do with this money. Like Lenny said, I get my lump sum next year. I don't need or want anything to do with it.'

'Fine,' Lenny said in a heartbeat. 'I can live with that.'

'Second, if you want to keep the money, Jimmy and Bodhi get equal shares.'

Chapter 5

An Inspector Calls

'Five hundred and fifty thousand pounds.' Wesley placed the final bundle of money in the bag then looked around the table.

'Five hundred and fifty mother-fucking thousand pounds,' Lenny corrected him. 'Not a bad night's work, I think we can all agree.

'Actually,' Harrison said, 'I think I made it pretty obvious that we don't all agree. I don't agree with what you've done one little bit, and if you'd told me then it was from drugs, there's no way I'd have gone along with it.'

The room fell silent, even though it was obvious that there were things people wanted to say. Lenny wanted to ask Harrison where else he thought the money might have come from. Who the fuck else, except for drug dealers, had just over half a million pounds stashed in a sports bag in the back of their BMW? Dylan wanted to argue the case for the drugs themselves. Why was it acceptable to drink beer and smoke cigarettes – both drugs that had screwed people up for decades, if not centuries – yet it still remained illegal to smoke a doobie?

They both wanted to ask the questions, but instead, they restrained themselves and said nothing. When it came to drugs, it was best to avoid the subject with Harrison, regardless of the context. That was one subject you never argued with him about. Ever.

'Maybe it's not drug money,' Dylan said hopefully. 'Maybe the guy just didn't trust banks.'

Harrison's stare told him not to bother.

'So, I take it you're still not interested in taking your share?' Lenny said finally. ''Cos you know, right, it is *your* share.'

Harrison shook his head. ‘No, it’s not. It never was, and it never will be.’

Lenny shrugged. ‘Fine, if that’s how you feel. The other thing I was thinking, and I know you’re just going to think I’m being a selfish bastard here, but are you sure it’s wise to get Jimmy and Bodhi involved in this?’

‘I meant what I said. They get equal shares.’

‘Fine, but what if they react like you did? I mean, they weren’t even there. They’re not going to understand what we did. What if they don’t want the money? What if they decide to go to management or the fucking police about it? We’d be fucked. Maybe it’s best we kept it between ourselves, is all I’m saying.’

Harrison shrugged. ‘That’s just the risk you’re going to have to take. If you’re not happy with those odds, then I’ll call the police now and tell them we’ve made a terrible mistake.’

Lenny sighed. ‘All right, Harrison, you win. We split it six ways.’

He looked across to Dylan. ‘You feeling a little bit calmer now, pissy pants? I think your career as a criminal may be over before it began.’

A faint chuckle went around the room, lightening the mood slightly.

‘I’m not going to lie to you,’ Dylan answered. ‘I shit myself there, big time. Right now, though, I’m not scared, I just feel pretty bummed out by the whole thing.’

‘Why? You’re nearly a hundred grand richer,’ Lenny paused and looked to Harrison, ‘or just over a hundred grand, depending on how we divvy out the money.’

Dylan nodded. ‘Exactly.’

‘What’s that supposed to mean?’ Jo asked.

‘I mean, I didn’t need the money. I was just being greedy. I’m happy as I am.’

‘Speak for yourself,’ Lenny said, ‘We haven’t all got a rich girlfriend to keep us. You may be happy, but I’m fucking not. I’ve got a heap of debts, a piece of shit car, and a rented basement flat

that stinks-to-fuck of mould. Money may not buy happiness, but I'm damn well willing to give it a try.'

'Fair play, and I'm not trying to piss on anyone's bonfire here, it's just… I guess this is what George Clooney must have felt like when he started selling cappuccinos, that's what I'm getting at.'

'Nah, mate,' Lenny said. 'I'll tell you how he would have felt. Financially better off, that's what. Now, quit your moaning and do what George did. Smile for the camera and think about the money.'

The beam of a car's headlights flooded the room with light as it turned onto the station's forecourt. The vehicle pulled up in front of the middle bay, blocking the fire engine's path, should they get a call.

'Go on see what that fucking asshole wants,' Lenny said to Dylan.

Without arguing, Dylan got to his feet and walked across to the window.

'Fuck!' he shouted when he got there and witnessed a policeman getting out of his vehicle and heading towards the door.

'It's the Old Bill!' he yelled at the others. 'We're fucked.'

'All right, just stay calm,' Wesley said. 'Perhaps they've come about something else.'

Jo approached the window and peered out. 'Like what? When do the police ever visit us?'

'Listen,' Dylan said, 'let's just take the money out to him now and explain what happened. It'll be better for us that way.'

Lenny got to his feet and grabbed the bag of cash. 'Fuck that,' he said, before charging off in the direction of the locker room.

Harrison calmly took a sip of tea from his mug. 'This is a surprise.'

'Thanks for that,' Wesley said, then turned to Dylan. 'Right, get over here, sit down and be quiet. I'll go and speak to him.'

The doorbell rang just as Dylan did as he was told. The officer that Wesley opened the door to was a youngish guy, probably not much older than Dylan. He recognised the man as soon as he saw him. He had been the first uniformed officer to turn up and meet them when they were back up the bank. Without trying to take over and throw his weight around, he had been involved in preserving the scene until traffic turned up and began their investigation.

'How you doing?' Wesley asked him. 'You want to come in for a cup of tea?'

The officer gave him a grateful smile. 'No thanks. I'm still on the clock.'

'So, how can I help you in that case?'

'I just thought I'd give you guys a heads-up about what we found back there. I know these things don't always end up getting back to you.'

'Tell me about it. The grapevine doesn't usually extend this far… So, what did you find out?'

'It's about the driver of the vehicle.'

'Oh yeah?'

'Yeah. If you were wondering why there wasn't much damage to the car, I think I can help.'

'Really?' Wesley said, swallowing hard.

'Really,' the police officer repeated. 'It wasn't the impact that killed the driver. Someone shot the guy in the head.'

Jo brought the coffee pot across to the table, sat down and pushed down on the plunger. 'What I don't get,' she said, 'is how in God's name didn't we realise he'd been shot.'

'That's easy,' Lenny answered. 'A bullet from most handguns is actually pretty small, probably no more than a centimetre in diameter.'

He pushed the tips of his fingers together, bringing them into a point, and pressed them into the palm of his other hand. 'It's not the entry wound that causes the real damage when someone is shot.'

He quickly opened his fingers as wide as they could go. 'The exit point is where the real damage is done. I'm guessing the gun didn't have much spunk to it, and the bullet got lodged somewhere in his skull.'

Jo looked at him with more than a hint of disbelief. 'And how would you know that?'

'Andy McNab. The man can tell you pretty much everything you need to know about modern warfare. His are the only books I bother to read.'

Dylan laughed. 'Explains a lot.'

'Actually, he's pretty much right,' Wesley said, 'or at least in that copper's opinion he is. He said you could hardly notice where the bullet went in, what with all the blood and snot hiding it.'

Dylan got up and paced around the table. 'This is bad, man, this is really fucking bad.'

'I thought you were going to stop being such a massive pussy about all this!' Lenny yelled at him. 'I mean, seriously, what the fuck are you going to do when Felicity wants her vagina back?'

Dylan stopped pacing and turned to Lenny. 'Tell me something, have you seen *No Country for Old Men*?'

'Yeah.'

'Well that's what we are in right now: a *No Country for Old Men* situation. And just in case you've forgotten, things didn't end well for anyone in that film.'

'Yeah, well,' Lenny said, 'that was just a film. This is real life, and shit like that don't happen in real life. Just because the guy was shot, doesn't change anything. Nobody knows we've got the money, and as long as no one knows, we're all safe. So, please, do me a favour and stop fucking panicking. Okay?

Dylan nodded reluctantly.

While they were talking, Harrison chuckled away to himself.

'What's so funny?' Jo asked him.

'No Country for Old Firemen,' he said.

The others looked at each other, then burst into laughter.

Lenny nudged Harrison with his elbow. 'No Cunt for Old Firemen, more like. Ain't that right, mate?'

Jo looked down her nose at him and shook her head. 'You really are a disgusting piece of shit. You know that, right?'

Their laughter was broken up by the sound of the bells going down, telling them they had another call.

Chapter 6

Jo

Jo dipped her arm into the water, cupped some into in her hand then splashed it onto her face. Even though it was May and she was in a river as opposed to the sea, the cold temporarily took her breath away. She inhaled deeply then submerged below the surface. When she came up again, she had to force herself not to gasp. The race would be starting in the next few minutes, and she had to be ready for the scrap that would inevitably take pace in the first fifty metres. The swimmers would be climbing over each other to try and get ahead at this critical stage, and fists, elbows and feet would be flying indiscriminately in the carnage. That was not the time to acclimatise to the water temperature. The other competitors would be ready for the chaos, so she needed to be firing on all cylinders too.

While the rest of the Watch were eating their breakfasts, Jo had driven to Arundel to take part in the triathlon. Ginger Balls off Green Watch had come in for her an hour early to make sure she was ready for the nine o'clock start. She had done him plenty of favours in the past, so hadn't felt guilty about asking him to give up his precious free time on a Sunday morning.

The events of the previous night were weighing heavily on her as she dipped her face again and waited for the onslaught. As Dylan had slept his way through the early hours of the morning in the dorm they shared, Jo had laid with her eyes wide open, staring at the ceiling, wondering what the hell they had done. It wasn't so much the thought of possible recriminations that was bothering her. She thought that, given the circumstances, it was highly unlikely anyone would ever find out what had happened.

What was really eating away at her was, for the first time in as long as she could remember, she had let other people influence her thinking, pushing her into making a decision that she usually would have resisted. Jo had spent her life doing the exact opposite of what had been expected of her. But less than twelve hours earlier, she had capitulated to peer pressure, and it bothered her greatly.

Some people would have let that worry affect their performance in the race, using it as an excuse when they finished in a far worse position than they should have done. But not Jo, not Wonder Woman. She would take that negative energy and channel it into something positive. She'd feed on it, using it to make sure she finished in a place she deserved to be. That was why, unlike so many people she met in her day-to-day life, she was a winner. She didn't let shit like that get in her way and slow her down. Jo was a hard-ass. A woman who had fought her way up in a man's world without ever giving an inch to the doubters who didn't believe she wasn't up to it. Long before she had joined the fire service, she had taught herself to not only ignore the men who hadn't believed in her, but to positively step all over them.

She hadn't listened to her parents when they told her she needed to go to university if she wanted to get a good job that paid well. Jo believed the best way to maximise your potential was to gain as much practical experience as possible. Armed with three C grade A-levels, she went out into the world with her newly typed up CV and posted it to as many companies as possible until she snagged her first job. The irony of her finding that role in a recruitment agency was lost on her at the time. All she cared about was that she was working and earning money.

Jo had flourished in the role, and after only a few months, she was earning as much commission as some of the seasoned veterans who had been doing the job for years. She was pushy, but not too much, staying just the right side of playful in her calls to clients. By the end of her second year, she was the top earner for the company. The jealous looks she received from the rest of the

staff meant nothing to her. Those people were her colleagues, not her friends, and if she was honest, she didn't give a shit about any of them. Success was what mattered.

Three years later, she didn't listen to her bosses when they virtually begged her to stay with the company and not move to London and take up the post she had been offered with a large corporate recruitment firm. Those guys were head-hunters, they told her, unscrupulous bastards who would do and say anything to make their commissions. They were the people who gave recruitment such a bad name. But she knew that already, and she didn't really care. That was where the real money was, not in some little company in Southampton where the money she got for finding a temporary PA who could type so many words a minute was hardly worth the effort.

When she got to London, she loved every element of her new job. She relished the lies and the underhand tactics she used on an everyday basis. Firms didn't want their staff speaking to head-hunters at any cost, and so the lengths she went to secure phone time with potential targets were downright shocking. In order to make first contact, she had told receptionists that their bosses' wives were in hospital and that she was a doctor. She had created CVs for potential recruits and applied for jobs on behalf of them without their knowledge. If they got to the interview stage, she would contact them and promise them the earth if they dumped their own companies and uprooted. If the candidate chose to do the honourable thing and stay put, then sometimes, because she was pissed at them for ruining her deal, she would phone up their bosses and tell them they'd been speaking to head-hunters; a sackable offence. No matter which way you looked at it, and she would admit it herself, she was a first-class bitch most of the time.

A few years later and she was again one of the highest earners in the office, and in a business like hers, that meant serious money, we're talking six figure basics before commission and bonuses were even taken into account. Her fiancé, Jake, was a junior partner in the company and made her pay scale look meagre. They had just

bought their first house; a three-bedroom Victorian terrace just off Clapham Junction that was worth far more than it had any right to. For Jo and Jake, the two Js, life was good. Business was booming, and in a couple of years, they'd be married, with her taking a six-month break to make little Js before they were carted off to boarding school. Yeah, she was happy, all right, at least she thought so, that was until the day that someone accidentally smashed the break-glass fire panel at work.

It was a shitty winter's day when the staff stood outside the building, shivering as they listened to the alarm sounding behind them. Some people were secretly pleased to have an extra ten minutes off work to drink coffee and smoke cigarettes, but not Jo; she had business to attend to and couldn't deal with this bullshit. She'd encourage Jake to find and sack the joker who'd smashed the glass, whether it was an accident or not.

But then, the fire engine had turned up, and she watched as a woman, no older than she, got out of the front seat and strode into the building. A man got out of the back of the vehicle and followed her inside, but it was clear she was the one in charge.

Five minutes later, the ringing of the alarm had ceased, and the young woman had left the building with her co-worker in tow. She had removed her helmet at this point and was carrying it proudly under her arm. As they got back in the fire engine and drove away, Jo had already made up her mind – she was going to be a firefighter.

Everyone told her that it was a crazy idea and she was mad for even considering it, especially Jake, who positively hated the thought. The pay cut alone was almost too ridiculous to talk about. Jo was having none of it; she may have loved her job, but she'd always had a sense that something was missing. It was only when that female firefighter had turned up, did Jo realise what that something was. The thing she most craved was action.

The name Wonder Woman was bestowed on her while she was doing her sixteen-week initial training course, and for the most part, it wasn't intended as a compliment. Jo had elbowed

her way onto the course, letting the other recruits know in no uncertain terms that even though it wasn't a competition, she was the one they needed to be worried about. When she found out that actually there was a competition of sorts running alongside the course and that the best recruit would win the prestigious Silver Axe, she swore that it would be hers.

It was too; she won it hands down. She worked harder than everyone else on the course, both on the fire-ground and in the classroom, and when it came down to it, she was pretty much unrivalled. She was also universally disliked by the other recruits, and the instructors weren't too fond of her, either. They quickly recognised what a momentous pain in the arse she would end up to be when she got posted to one of the stations. The Silver Axe was a warning to her soon-to-be Watch that they had a real handful heading their way.

Jo's ambition didn't stop at the training centre. There had been other female Watch managers in the brigade, but she decided that none of them would have reached the position in as quick a time as she intended. Her five-year plan was to complete her probation, become a crew manager, then after a couple of years gaining the necessary experience, take on her own Watch.

Things didn't happen that way. First, Jake left her. He said it was because he couldn't deal with her being away from him for four days at a time, but in truth, he was jealous, and the thought of her being surrounded by a bunch of men for long periods and in such close proximity was too much for him. She was phased for a while, but like anything in her life, Jo dealt with it and moved on. After the money from the sale of the house in Clapham had been shared, she had enough to put down a handsome deposit on her new flat in the heart of Brighton. She was still the main girl.

When she got sent to East, the Silver Axe warning proved to be true. Within days, Jo had managed to rub everyone up the wrong way. Her aptitude for the job was never in doubt; she just had a habit of pressing everyone's buttons. First, she refused to make the tea, letting the Watch know what a sexist bunch of

dinosaurs they were. They tried to explain to her it wasn't because she was a woman she had to make it, but because she was the probationer, and that's just what probies did, and all the guys had done it, too, but she was having none of it. Then, there was her constant nagging at the Watch manager to get out into the drill yard. No one minded helping out the new recruit with pump and ladder drills, it was part of the territory, but Jo wanted to be out there twice a day, on nights and even weekends. Red Watch weren't used to such demands, and their lazy afternoons being so rudely interrupted. In her quest for perfection, Jo even managed to make an enemy of Bodhi, possibly the most laid-back guy in the service.

Her biggest faux pas, though, was when she told Harrison that unlike ninety-nine percent of front-line firefighters, she would not be joining the union as she believed that a live-and-let-die mentality was what made people strong, not collective bargaining. Patiently, and with an abundance of facts at his disposal, Harrison spent two hours ripping apart her argument, highlighting just how much the FBU had done to improve the working conditions of firefighters, particularly women. It was the first time Jo conceded she might have been wrong and signed the joining papers. It wasn't the last time, either; the longer she did the job, the more she realised that the ambitions she had started with were not what was important to her anymore.

As time went on, she became less ambitious and, as a result, more accepted by the Watch. Rescuing someone from an RTC, or seeing the relief on a mum's face when they released her daughter from a locked bathroom, or the joy on a child's face when they sat in the back of a fire engine, had become more important to her than promotion. She learnt that being a part of the Watch and a team that functioned in unison, with everyone working towards a common goal, was far more rewarding to her than reaching the top. She stopped caring about being a high flyer (and subsequently being such a bitch), and rather than ruling them, she just wanted to be one of the team. Like many people before

her, once she understood the true nature of the job and what they were there to do, her ambitions took a back seat. That's not to say they still weren't there – she would still be a Watch manager one day – she was just in less of a rush to get there.

Jo's ambitious nature at work may have subsided, but that had only made her more of a competitor when it came to sport. Before she joined the job, she had always been fit but more of a lunch time warrior – circuit training, hot yoga, Zumba and anything else that got her sweating. Once in the brigade, she discovered and fell in love with triathlon, and like everything else she did, she was pretty awesome at it.

Jo was in sixteenth place when she got out of the water (swimming being her weakest discipline), ninth by the end of the bike ride, and by the time the run had finished, she had eaten up another six places and finished in third for the women, (first for her age group). Her time was good and kept her in the GB team. The race had been a good one for her, but she would have still liked to shave another few minutes off her time.

At the end of the race, Jo was awarded a ten-pound gift voucher for a website that sold equipment for triathletes. As she held it up to get her picture taken with the other podium finishers, she felt proud of her achievement. At that moment, the ten-pound voucher meant far more to her than the hundreds of thousands they had stolen from a dead drug dealer.

Chapter 7

Dylan

Dylan opened the bedroom door just enough to squeeze his head inside. Even though it was nine-thirty in the morning, the heavy curtains were drawn, and he could only just make out Felicity's form in the bed. He smiled to himself as he crept into the room. She hadn't stayed at Annie's house as she'd been considering the evening before, and that meant if he played things right, he could end up getting some early-morning action.

He tiptoed to the bed, peeled off his clothes, then lifted the sheet and slipped in behind her. Dylan spooned his fiancée, running his hand gently up her thigh before resting it on her toned stomach. He let it linger there for a minute or two, not wanting to rush things, then slid his hand up towards her naked breasts.

'Don't even think about it,' she said. 'I didn't get in until three, and my head's pounding.'

Dylan could do little else but smile; as usual, she had his number.

'I just wanted a cuddle,' he said, doing his best to sound innocent.

'That's fine,' she answered. 'Just so long as you remember that you cuddle with your arms, not your penis.'

Dylan laughed. 'So how was your night?'

'Fine,' she said. 'It's been a long time since we all went out together. I wasn't planning on getting quite so drunk, though.'

Dylan snuggled into her. 'So, was Nick out with you?'

Felicity rolled over to look at him. 'You know he wasn't. It was a girl's night. You've got to forget about what happened, Dyl.'

'I know I do... I'm sorry.'

'So, how was *your* night?' she asked. 'Busy?'

Normally, they told each other everything. That's how he knew the last time she had gone out with her work colleagues, she had got drunk and snogged her manager, Nick. What made it worse was he was only a few years older than her and a good-looking bastard to go with it. As Lennie often reminded him, when it came to Felicity, Dylan was punching well above his weight, and her kiss with pretty-boy Nick had done nothing for his confidence. She could have not told him, he would never have found out, but they'd always believed that honesty was the best policy, even if it didn't always make things easy for them.

When Dylan went on a stag-do to Amsterdam and paid the lap-dancer an extra twenty euros to let him kiss her tits, he went home and told Felicity about it, despite the protestations from his friends. He would have felt too guilty to keep it quiet. This time, though, he had no intention of telling her about what had taken place the night before.

At the canteen table, he had often said with the equipment they had at their disposal, they were the perfect people to commit a high-stakes crime, like break into a bank vault or a security van. He hadn't really meant it. Like most things Dylan said in the Bullshit Hour, that's all it was – bullshit. Yet, somehow, he and the rest of the crew had gone out and stolen over half a million pounds, and it looked like they had got away with it. It should have been awesome, but all he could feel about it was a massive sense of disappointment.

He already had a good life with Felicity; they didn't need the money. They were Dinkies – double income, no kiddies – and while Dylan's wage was decent, if nothing to get excited about, Felicity earned a very healthy sum, and in the future, that would only grow. They'd paid a deposit on the two-bedroom flat they owned with a (distant) sea view and had even had enough left in the bank to pay for the parking space outside. Not that Dylan ever got to drive their little Citroen. He cycled the mile and

a half to work every day. They went on three holidays a year: snowboarding in the winter, a beach break in the summer, and a European city break in a swanky boutique hotel, when they could squeeze it in. No matter how he looked at it, while they weren't rich by any means, the two of them had it good.

Dylan had always done his best to enjoy life. He loved his job, but he also loved the lifestyle it allowed him. He loved the excitement, the camaraderie and the fact he could say he was part of a crew. It made him feel badass, like he was in *Public Enemy* or the Wu Tang Clan. The shift system, however, was the thing he enjoyed most. The four-days-on, four-days-off rota meant that he got to spend an awful lot of time doing the things he enjoyed. Many of his colleagues did second jobs when they weren't at work. In most cases, they were the only employed person in the house, or at least the major earners, as their wives or partners often had to look after the children. As they had no kids, and Felicity earned plenty of her own cash, he didn't require extra work.

Dylan's days off revolved around him getting up late, looking at porn, then getting down to whatever he fancied doing for the day. If the weather was good, he'd take his mountain bike up onto the South Downs and spend a few hours taking in the Sussex countryside. If it wasn't so sharp outside, he'd go climbing at one of Brighton's indoor walls, stay home and read a book, watch a film or catch up on whatever series he was binge-watching on Netflix.

He kept telling himself he should be more like Harrison, a man he respected enormously, and devote his time to helping others. He'd been a member of Amnesty International and a number of other human rights groups since university, and the long-term plan was to get more involved with one or more of them and do some volunteer work. But that was where he and Harrison differed; unlike his colleague, who could walk the walk, Dylan was more of a talker. The problem was he was lazy. Bone idle, in fact. He knew it and so did the rest of the Watch. It wasn't something he was ashamed of, on the contrary, he had

used the Bullshit Hour on many occasions to praise the virtues of slothfulness.

Just like electricity and water, Dylan walked the path of least resistance. He would tell the others you didn't see animals busting their guts in the wild, busying themselves with unnecessary chores. They just ate, slept, shit and fucked; that was nature's way. It was people that had got things all wrong with their live-to-work mentalities. Dylan wasn't having any of it. He didn't want to look back when he was an old man and say how glad he was for busting his ass for someone else's gain. One day, though, he liked to tell himself, one day soon, he'd get his act together and help make the world a better place.

It was almost three years since he had become a firefighter. After they had finished their studies, Dylan and Felicity, who'd got together when they were freshers at Brighton Uni, decided they would make the place their home. First, they needed to get the travel bug out of their system. They had spent eighteen months travelling the world before eventually coming back and settling down in the city where they'd met. Felicity quickly found a job with a reputable accountancy firm as Dylan struggled to find a career of his own.

Their parents had given them some money to help settle them in, but it certainly wasn't an unlimited supply of wealth, so if they wanted to keep to paying the rent, he needed some work, fast. When he could find nothing else, Dylan returned to his boyhood dream of being a firefighter. Along with hundreds of others, he patiently queued up at the first recruitment day, waiting to see if he was up to it.

It was a strange experience, especially as it was based in the sports centre of his old university, but he made it through the basic Maths and English exams without trying too hard, and although not a fitness freak by any means, he cruised through the initial physical tests.

To his surprise, Dylan also got through round two of the selection process; the practical stage, and he breezed the interview

a few weeks later. For every vacancy that was available, up to thirty people applied. It amazed him that, given those odds, and as a man who had never achieved anything in his life, he had managed to bag himself a job.

Training school for him wasn't the massive success it was for Jo. He was competent enough when it came to both the theoretical and practical lessons, but it was the regimented nature of the whole affair that really got to Dylan. This chilled-out, easy-going young man was completely unprepared for the disciplined nature of training school. He was meant to be joining the fire service, not the goddamned army.

The recruits, as they were known, were expected to be immaculately turned when they were not wearing their fire-kit on the drill ground. This meant highly polished shoes, uniforms with creases so sharp, you could cut yourself and perhaps, worst for him, they were expected to be clean shaven at all times. This didn't seem to bother the girls on the course, but it drove Dylan crazy. He was used to walking around with a scruffy bum-fluff beard, and the shaving instantly set off a rash he couldn't get rid of for the entire sixteen-week duration.

Despite his initial concerns, he somehow made it through training school in one piece. It was a relief when he finally got sent out to his station and saw that life on the job was very different to the one that had been portrayed to him at the training centre. On his first day, as instructed by his course leaders, he arrived at the rear gates of the station in what is known as "full undress uniform." This involved him wearing his blazer with shiny buttons, a long sleeve white shirt, his clip-on tie, buffed up shoes and not forgetting, his brand new, just out the packet, peaked cap.

Ironically, considering the merciless piss-taking he would suffer from the man over the next few years, it was Lenny who saved him from complete humiliation that morning.

Just as Dylan was about to ring the bell to be let into the yard, Lenny pulled up on his motorbike and cast his eye down the

length of the skinny lad in front of him. He lifted his visor and shouted through the gap. 'You must be the new boy!'

Dylan nodded.

'If I were you, I'd take that gear off before you get inside. You look a proper cunt.'

Even though the lack of discipline on station was a pleasant surprise to him, Dylan struggled through the first couple of months. This was when he discovered that training school was only the start of his education as a firefighter. For the next few years, he would be a probationer, and in that time, he had much to learn. Within weeks, he was questioning if he had made the right decision in joining the service. The practical jokes and piss-taking he didn't mind at all, the big problem for him was he didn't feel he was up to the job. It quickly became apparent his colleagues were incredibly practical and able people who could turn their hands to pretty much anything. He, on the other hand, did not possess a practical bone in his body. He was the typical cliché of the student with plenty of brains but little common sense. When they were at incidents, he always felt out of his depth, and he had a strong feeling the rest of the crew felt the same way about him to. What worried him most was, when it really mattered, he would let down his colleagues.

And then, it happened. After weeks of waiting, at half past two in the morning, he finally got his first real call. A carload of female students was heading back to the university campus after a night out in the town when the driver had lost control of the car and smashed into a wall. The three girls in the back and the two in front all suffered injuries to some degree. The driver, whose side of the vehicle had taken the full force of the impact, had smashed her hip up pretty badly, and the girl sitting behind her had likely cracked a few ribs. The front passenger was suffering from whiplash, and the other two girls in the back had smashed their heads together and were plastered in blood and snot. When the appliance turned up, they were greeted by a wall of screams coming at them.

The best way of describing a working RTC is organised chaos. There was nearly always a lot of noise, not just from the casualties but also the roar of the hydraulic pack that powered the tools. The fire crews had to shout to each other to be heard, and often they were working simultaneously with paramedics to achieve the goal of safely extracting the casualties. At an RTC, there were always lots of people doing lots of things at the same time, and often the scene became extremely crowded. So much so, that if they didn't have a specific task to do, often the most helpful thing a firefighter could do was to take a step back to ease congestion.

It was while all this action was going on that Dylan discovered something important about himself. In high pressure, stressful situations, he worked incredibly well. As the incident became louder and more developed, his calm and focus grew. It was as if the opposite of what was going on around him was taking place internally. After using the hydraulic gear to make the final cut of the A-post that would allow the roof of the vehicle to be removed, he lifted his visor and wiped the sweat from his eyes. Bodhi, who had been keeping an eye on him throughout, patted him on the back before taking the tool out of his hand.

'Well done, bud,' he said with a wink. 'You'll do just fine.'

And he did. From that day on, Dylan realised, when it mattered, he was more than up to the tasks that would confront him in his day-to-day life as a firefighter. In all the things he had ever done, he had never been so proud as when he got back on the fire engine that morning. The rest of the crew wouldn't forget what had happened, either. Dylan's first big incident meant only one thing: cakes, and he was buying.

The one thing that never left him was the fear that one day he'd let the rest of the crew down at a job. He confided in Jimmy about it once who told him the feeling would never leave him, he still had it himself every time they attended an incident. It was the biggest thing that bonded firefighters; making sure everyone went home in one piece at the end of a shift.

As he reminisced about his time in the job, Dylan slowly became aware of Felicity's behind pushing into his groin, and it didn't take long before is groin responded accordingly.

'I thought you told me to keep my bits to myself?' he said.

Felicity continued to grind into him. 'And I thought you would have put up more of a fight. Don't you want me anymore?'

Dylan rolled her onto her back and, in one swift move, ended up on top of her with a smile plastered all over his face. 'You better believe I do,' he said. 'Now, brace yourself. What I lack in girth and size, I make up for with an incredibly fast ass.'

Chapter 8

Harrison

Harrison opened the oven and quickly pulled out the baking tray. He closed the door in the same movement, making sure none of its heat was lost. After placing the tray on the worktop, he smiled as he witnessed its contents. The pork was cooking beautifully. He had set it on a higher temperature for the first half an hour to allow the fat to crackle, and it had done so perfectly. The oil in the pan was spitting like crazy, and so, before it started to cool, he placed each individual potato around the meat, doing his best to not get burnt as the oil reacted to the moisture on their surface.

Different people had different opinions about the best way to make the perfect roast potato, but in Harrison's mind, by far, the best way was to par boil them to the point that you actually thought you'd ruined them. To get them to the stage that when you shook them up in the colander, the outside of the potato would fall away in a mush. It meant that you lost some of the mass of the thing, but if you wanted good roasties with a fluffy centre and crispy edges, that was the price you had to pay. It made him content to know that in forty-five minutes, both the meat and tatties would be spot on. He only hoped by then Janet would have surfaced. He didn't like the idea of getting her out of bed.

Despite his protestations at work when he was stuck in the canteen while the others were taking it easy, Harrison loved cooking. Unlike on most Watches where people took it in turns, when Harrison was working, he was always the mess man. Being part of the canteen wasn't mandatory, in fact, on many Watches, it had pretty much fallen by the wayside with people bringing their own food in rather than doing the whole communal thing.

That was unless you were on Red Watch, in which case, you didn't get the choice. It didn't matter if you were a vegetarian or didn't like the meal that was being cooked, Harrison was more than happy to make an alternative dish for the fussy ones, but on no condition could you exempt yourself from it. He was a big believer that the Watch sitting down and sharing a meal together was one of the most important things to improve the harmony on station. A Watch that ate together, he would say, is a Watch that stays together.

Not that anyone in their right mind would want to turn down the offer Harrison was bestowing on them. The meals he made for the Watch were fantastic and far too grand for the heathens that ate them. He could make just about anything – Italian, Thai, Moroccan, Indian curries that he prepared at home and would leave simmering overnight for maximum flavour – none of it was too much for him. His butternut squash and chorizo stew was so good, the Watch got a bit tearful when he said he was making it for them.

With the food cooking away nicely, he retired to the living room. He had ten minutes to sit down before he needed to go back in and start sautéing the red cabbage. Luckily, he'd remembered to go to the shop on the way home and get some balsamic vinegar that would give it the sweet little kick it needed.

When he collapsed on the sofa, Harrison let out a prolonged sigh. It was something he had been doing for years and was unaware of. It was kind of a signal of disbelief, usually combined with not a small amount of anger, and aimed either at the arseholes in government or the arseholes that ran the fire service, or the arsehole firefighter that had done something idiotic that he was going to have to defend in some way. But this time, the action was being directed towards his own Watch.

In his twenty-nine years as a firefighter, he thought he'd seen pretty much everything there was to see, but no. Somehow, his own Watch and managed to surpass all his expectations of firefighter stupidity. He wasn't a violent man by any means, but

when they told him what they had done, he'd wanted to grab the lot of them and bang their bloody heads together. What with all the shit he was already dealing with due to the station closure, it was the last thing he needed.

Other than his anger, there was another feeling growing inside Harrison that he had become increasingly aware of lately. Although he had been trying to ignore it, it was something that wouldn't go away. After twenty years of being the Fire Brigades Union rep at the station and doing his best to fight the good fight and not give in to intimidation, bullying, or Catch-22 style bureaucracy, Harrison was tired. He hadn't had the courage to say it out loud to any of his friends and colleagues yet, but he'd had a gut full of it all.

He'd had a gut full of the government continually attacking not only his profession, but the rest of the public services too. It wasn't about money, and he would never let anyone tell him any different. What was happening was an idealistic attack on the public sector, the welfare state and anything else noble in this country that his grandfather had fought to protect. As far as Harrison could remember, they weren't the people who had caused the gigantic financial fuck up that the country had found itself in. His father, a career firefighter and union rep, had warned him that everything went in circles, and he was right. When he first joined the service, he'd had to fight off Thatcher and her cronies as they tried to destroy his profession, and now, at the twilight of his career, he was in a similar scrap with the pretenders to her throne. In the last few years, as the cuts had taken hold, engines had been taken off the run, jobs had been lost and stations closed. If they continued acting the way they were and continually slashing the budget, the only people who would claim they could run a fire service successfully were the private vultures who were already circling the wounded beast. The thought of working for such a venture made him feel physically sick.

Harrison was also sick of the chief of the brigade itself and the management set-up. None of them had stood up to the

government against the cuts. They had kept quiet and said they could deal with the far smaller budgets they had been dealt, and public safety wouldn't suffer as a result. It was a lie, and Harrison hated them for it. If the chief had just said they were trying to make the best of a bad situation, he could have lived with it. But when he was being told the cuts were actually good for the people of Sussex and would make the service even safer, it made him want to go to HQ and call them all the liars he thought they were.

He'd even had a gut full of the selfishness of some of the firefighters themselves and their attitudes towards their profession. Throughout the strike action and the campaign to fight the closure of their fire station that followed, it was the same old faces Harrison would see again and again when they were out leafleting the public or collecting signatures for their petitions. Many of them were older guys like him who were protected from the cuts and had no need to be there. It pained him to say it, but some of his colleagues just weren't interested. Many of these were the same people who were only interested in the union when they needed representing in an investigation when they had fucked up in one way or another.

And now, there were the events of the previous night to deal with. No matter how he looked at it, he couldn't grasp the levels of stupidity they had displayed. The blame, in Harrison's mind, rested solely at the feet of Wesley. He was the officer-in-charge; it was his job to keep the troops in line and stop them doing anything so incredibly stupid. The man was weak. Harrison could just imagine Lenny hassling him to take the money, and he'd lacked the backbone to stand up to him. If Jimmy had been in charge, he wouldn't have let it happen, Harrison was certain of that. Perhaps it might have been easier to swallow if they hadn't told him about the drugs. If there was one thing Harrison hated, it was goddamn drugs.

Matthew had always been such a lovely little boy, and the two of them had a fantastic relationship. They were more than just father and son, Harrison was also the boy's best friend and

had been the coach of his football team from the time he and his mates were eight, right up until their late teens.

That was when the troubles started. Matthew started hanging around with a group of lads Harrison didn't know, and before long, he was more interested in being with them than going to football training. It didn't bother him at first. Some of the other boys in the team had developed attitude and stopped coming training unless he press-ganged them into it; Harrison put it down to them being teenagers. But Matthew seemed to take things further than the rest of them. After a couple more months, he stopped playing football altogether. Harrison kept coaching the other lads as he'd grown to love and care for them and wanted the team to win the league, but for the first time in nearly ten years, he was doing it without his boy being there.

Things only got worse from there on. Matthew stopped talking to him and his mum altogether, spending nights away from home and only coming back for the shower he desperately needed as he stunk of booze and God knows what else. Harrison would like to say he had done everything in his power to steer the boy from the path he was on, but the fact was, he was so busy with work and union activities, not to mention coaching the boys to league success, he didn't do nearly enough to protect his son.

Matthew disappeared a year later, and it was only through some of the boys on the football team that Harrison found out he was living in a squat in Manchester. How they found out, he had no idea. He should have gone up there and dragged him home kicking and screaming, if necessary, anything to prevent what was inevitably going to happen, but he didn't. Despite Janet's pleas, he didn't get involved. Matthew was a grown man now, Harrison would tell her, it was up to him to realise his mistakes and rectify them. But that was the problem with drugs, as Harrison soon found out. They didn't allow you to take a step back from the mess of a situation you were in and decide the best remedy. They dragged you in and ate you up until there was nothing left of you.

The police had found Matthew's body in another squat nearly a year after he'd left home. They said he had probably been there for at least a fortnight before anyone discovered him. Neither Harrison nor Janet could bring themselves to identify his body; his poor aunty Bev was given that task. Losing a child was the worst thing that could happen to any parent, and even though a part of Harrison died along with his son, he knew he had to keep going for the sake of his wife. He also threw himself into his union work with more vigour than ever. His guilt wouldn't allow him to stop fighting.

Janet hadn't managed to move on quite so well. She was devastated by what had happened and had never got over it. The depression that took over the once happy-go-lucky woman was paralysing. Some days, she could still resemble her old self, but more often than not, it was an achievement just to drag herself out of bed. She was lucky if she made it out of the house once a week. Harrison blamed himself for everything that had happened, and Janet had made it clear she blamed him too. If he were a real man, she had told him many times, he would have done everything in his power to stop his boy from dying. There was nothing he could say to that; he agreed with every word she said.

As he thought about his son, Harrison became aware of the sound of footsteps coming down the stairs. It was almost one o'clock when she peered into the living room, which was not bad going for her. Some days, she wouldn't surface until four.

'Hi, love,' he said. 'You hungry?'

The woman was attractive but looked like she'd had all the colour and life sucked out of her. Her skin was pale, and her eyes had sunken into her darkened sockets. Janet's grey hair was bedraggled like she'd just got out of bed, which she had, and the dressing gown she was wearing looked like it hadn't been washed for a very long time. Despite his protests, she'd been off her meds for weeks, and when that happened, it was almost impossible to get her out of the downward spiral.

'If you don't mind, I'll leave it 'til later,' she said. 'I don't feel like eating anything.'

She looked as if she was trying to match the smile her husband was wearing but quickly gave up on it.

'No problem,' Harrison said. 'How about a cup of tea?'

She shook her head. 'I think I'll just go back upstairs.'

Janet's second attempt at a smile was even more pitiful, and as quickly as she appeared, she had vanished.

He went back into the kitchen and stared at the vegetables sitting in their various saucepans. In his head, he did a basic calculation of how many meals it would make and how many he should consider freezing.

Chapter 9

Lenny

'I've got to say, Mother,' Lenny said as he pushed his empty plate into the centre of the table, 'that was bloody lovely.' He looked to his daughter sitting next to him. 'Wasn't it, Lexi?'

'Yeah, lovely,' she said. She had barely touched her food. 'Can I leave the table now?'

Lenny looked at her like she was crazy, 'But we haven't had desserts yet. Your nan has made your favourite. Treacle pudding and custard.

The girl wrinkled her nose. 'No, thanks. I'm not hungry.'

Lenny shook his head. 'Your mum's been feeding you up again, hasn't she?' He turned his attention from his offspring to his mother. 'She does this all the time. She knows we eat with you every Sunday. That woman's such a–'

'Go on, darling,' his mother cut in, looking at her granddaughter. 'You go and sit on the sofa. There's probably a film you like on.'

'Thanks, Nan,' the girl said.

By the time she was seated, she already had her phone out and was busy social networking or whatever it was eight-year-old girls did these days.

'Come on, Lee,' his mother said quietly, but with an edge to her tone. 'What have I told you about slagging that woman off in front of Lexi? All that's going to do is make you the bad guy, and that's just what she wants. The woman may be a…' She looked to her granddaughter, who was focusing on nothing but her phone, then spelt the word out in a whisper, 't-w-a-t, but Lexi doesn't need to know that.'

'I know, Mum, you're right, but the girl has been a pain in the arse all day, and it's that idiot's fault.'

After he had picked her up that morning, Lexi had promptly announced that she didn't want to go to Nanny's house anymore. Her house was too scruffy, and she didn't like the area she lived in. It was too common. Moulsecombe might not have been the most prestigious part of Brighton, by any means, and it might have had its share of scumbags, but most of the people who lived there were good, decent folk. And as for calling the house scruffy, that was plain out of order. Old fashion, yes, but not scruffy. His mother kept the place immaculate.

What a cheek that bitch had, he thought, to poison her daughter's mind with such bullshit. The woman had no right to judge anyone. She may have forgotten when they met, she was pole-dancing at the club he was bouncing in, but he hadn't. After she dumped him, she hooked up with the manager of the club and moved into his swanky pad overlooking Hove Park. Since then, she had turned into a first class snob, but living in a posh apartment didn't change who she was on the inside.

'Lexi's only eight,' his mother reminded him. 'You and your brother were far worse than she'll ever be when you were that age.'

'Fair point.'

'And speaking of your brother,' she went on, 'when are the two of you finally going to sit down together for lunch? I'm fed up with this two-sitting nonsense.'

For the past ten years, Sunday afternoons had followed the same routine in the Johnson home. Lenny's brother Paul would turn up at noon with his wife and son. They'd eat lunch, make small talk, do the dishes, then leave at quarter-to-two. Lenny would turn up fifteen minutes later and carry out the exact procedure. His mother would take it in turns to eat with each of her boys. It was Paul's turn to dine with her on this occasion, and so, she had sat at the table with her cup of tea and watched Lenny devour his dinner and Lexi stare at hers. The sons hadn't spoken to each other

for nearly twice that time due to Paul's extended stay in prison, and even though they lived in the same town and often saw each other around, they never acknowledged the other's existence.

'Come on, Mum,' Lenny said. 'Let's not get into all that again. You know it's never going to happen.'

'Don't "come on, Mum" me,' she snapped back at him. 'Stop thinking about yourselves and think of me for once. You're both my boys, and I love you so much it hurts. What the two of you are doing is breaking my heart… One day, I won't be around anymore, and then, you can hate each other as much as you like. But while I'm still alive, I want to see the two of you sitting around this table like you used to when you were kids. Is that really too much to ask?'

Lenny pulled his chair towards hers and placed his hand on his mother's shoulder. 'What's wrong, Mum? You're not ill, are you?'

She placed her hand on his and squeezed it. 'No, Lee, I'm not ill. I'm just getting old.'

'Bollocks,' Lenny said. 'You're not old…not even seventy yet, are you?'

'I will be next year, and when you get to my age, you realise you've got far more years behind you than you have in front. Honestly, son, life is too short for what's going on between you and Paul, and I tell you something, if anything does drive me to an early grave, it'll be all the worrying I do about the pair of you.'

The thought of losing his mother, the only person in his life who didn't consider him to be a full-time fuck-up, had a profound effect on Lenny. He didn't like what she was asking him to do, but if meant a stress-free existence for her, then maybe it was worth considering.

'Have you spoken to Paul about it?'

She nodded.

'And what did he say?'

The breath she exhaled seemed to deflate her. 'He said he wasn't interested.'

Lenny shrugged. 'So, there's your answer.'

For a second, there was anger in the woman's eyes, but it soon gave way to a smile. 'You know something, son, you're impossible.'

He did know it too. Over the years, Lenny had lost count of the people who had come to the same conclusion before giving up on him. He had spent much of his twenty-two years as a firefighter being bounced from one Watch or station to another. The problem wasn't his ability at doing the job, as despite what any of his previous managers would have said, the man was bloody good at it. Lenny's problem, as he had been told on more occasions than he cared to remember, was that he was unmanageable. Only Bob, his previous Watch manager, whose authority he had happily worked under right up until the man retired, had been able to harness him. But now Bob was gone, and he had been dumped with Wesley, who didn't even know where to begin when it came to Lenny.

It wasn't that he refused to follow orders, on the contrary, if he agreed with the instruction he was given, he was more than happy to carry them out. If, however, he felt his orders were preventing him from doing his job to his best ability and achieving the desired outcome, he would think nothing of disregarding them and doing what he felt needed to be done. And that was just the operational side of things. When it came to the mundane day-to-day tasks that needed to be completed around the fire station, he was even less accommodating.

In Lenny's mind, he didn't go to work to suck up to his boss' boss by making sure they did their quota of Home Safety Visits or keep the station squeaky clean. His job was to fight fires and save lives; all the rest of it was bollocks, and he was happy to point that out when his manager's viewpoint differed from his own.

Even though the fire service was regarded as a disciplined service, it was a very different animal from the army or navy, or even the police. While there was a clear rank structure and code of discipline that was expected to be adhered to, unlike the armed forces, it was far more difficult to enforce. It was the only one of the services you could refuse an order if you felt it put your safety

in danger. If an over-zealous officer-in-charge tried to send a BA crew into a fire they believed to be a lost cause and there was a risk of a ceiling collapse, the crew could refuse the order, and nothing could be done about it by management.

This ability to challenge authority was rarely enforced as, generally, crews trusted their managers. Lenny however, took things to a whole new level. For example, if Lenny's boss decided they were going to do a school visit during the Bullshit Hour, he had no right to refuse the request. He could, however, make things as awkward for the manager as possible by saying that he needed a shit before they went out, and would then spend the next twenty minutes reading the paper on the toilet as the rest of the crew waited on the appliance. If he was told he had to wear a shirt to an inspection they were carrying out, he would say, in that case, he would have to iron one, and spend the next half an hour fannying around before appearing in a shirt that looked like it had been ironed with a cold pebble.

When he displayed these levels of dissent, Lenny's managers had two options. Firstly, they could report him to the station manager, at which point, disciplinary procedures could be started against him. The problem with this was it made the manager look weak in front of the rest of the Watch and that they couldn't keep their own house in order. So, more often than not, they took the second option and chose to deal with the situation themselves. Knowing they were dealing with an eighteen-stone powerlifting bouncer, they usually chose to let the offence slide.

That's not to say he always got his own way. In his time, Lenny had accrued more disciplinary investigations against him than anyone else in the brigade. His shoddy time-keeping, awful sick record and poor attitude towards his superiors had made him public enemy number one at headquarters. The big stumbling block that prevented them from firing him, and it was something that really drove them crazy, was that the only thing to rival the number of investigations Lenny had been involved in, was the number of commendations he had received.

When he wasn't being a royal pain in the arse, and when he felt like it, Lenny could be well and truly awesome – a one-man force of nature. He got his first commendation for kicking in the front door of a flat, and instead of waiting for the BA team to appear, he ran into the smoke-filled building and dragged out the elderly resident who had collapsed in the hallway. What he had done was against policy, and if it had gone wrong, he would have been hung out to dry. As it was a success, he was considered a hero and duly recognised by management.

His second commendation came at a fire alarm activation when he saw a woman get her bag snatched. Rather than get on with his job, he chased the mugger down the street, rugby tackled him, then frog-marched him a mile and a half to the nearest police station while his bemused OIC looked on and wondered how he was going to explain losing one of his crew.

The most infamous and widely recanted of his commendations also involved him earning himself a written warning at the same time. Red Watch had been called to a persons reported flat fire in Whitehawk, and he and Bodhi were the BA crew. When they got there, the screaming neighbours told them there were two kids inside, and so the pair of them had fought their way through the intense fire on the stairs and found the two of them hiding under the bed holding hands and barely conscious.

When they got outside, the pissed-up father, who had left the kids at home alone, turned up and gave Bob a load of grief for not rescuing his kids quicker. In seconds, the man was up against the wall with his feet six inches off the ground as Lenny throttled the life out of him. It was only the rest of the crew dragging him off that prevented the man from being a statistic. That incident kind of summed up Lenny's career in the fire service; acts of heroism sandwiched between moments of stupidity and ill-discipline, but when you considered the start the man had in life, it was a miracle he wasn't in prison or dead.

Every town had a rough neighbourhood, and every rough neighbourhood was in possession of a family whose name was

enough to send panic into the residents' hearts. In Brighton's case, that family was the Johnsons. Lenny's father, uncles and older cousins were responsible for eighty percent of petty crime in the area when he and his brother were growing up. They were involved in theft, the fencing of stolen goods, small time drug dealing and anything else illegal that made them a few quid. Their dad, Mick, was without doubt the worst of all of them. When the man wasn't under arrest for one misdemeanour or another, he was either in the pub getting pissed, or at home beating the shit out of his wife. When Lenny and Paul were fourteen and eleven respectively, they foolishly stepped in and tried to stop the man from busting open their mother's head. The beating they suffered was so severe, neither boy could get out of bed for a week.

Luckily for them, the old man's reign of terror came to an end a year later. Amazingly, it was not through his incarceration for the many crimes against society he had committed, but because the randy old fucker found some dumb barmaid at the King's Head who bought into the bollocks he talked and ran off to Blackpool with him. They found out later that he owed a man even scarier than him an awful lot of money, and this was his solution to the problem.

With the old man out of the way, life was good at the Johnson house. Lenny's mother was free to be the mother she wanted to be to her darling boys without worrying about the jealousy of a violent drunk. Paul became Lenny's surrogate father over the next few years, fiercely guarding his brother from bullies like their old man. Not that he needed to worry; no one in their right mind would go near a Johnson if they valued their health. The old man may have been out of the picture, but there were plenty of other family members around to uphold their reputation.

Eventually, you could say inevitably, Paul got sucked into the family business when he was reaching the end of his teen years. The boy had no qualifications and no friends in high places to find him a decent job, so knowing that the old "crime does not pay" adage was as phony as a soap opera, he plunged headfirst

into the world of illegality. It started with thieving-to-order for his uncles, but before long, the boy was organising his own burglaries and quickly discovered he had a real knack for it.

When things went up a level and he started breaking into shops and warehouses, he realised he needed a crew if the jobs were going to be profitable. His mate Deggsy was a shoe-in as his driver. The boy was something else when he got behind the wheel, and they'd stolen enough cars together to know he wouldn't panic if things got heavy. What he really needed was some muscle to do the fetching and carrying of merchandise, once they were inside. The answer to Paul was a no-brainer. His younger brother may have only been sixteen, but the boy was already six-foot-three and as strong as they came, plus there was no one he trusted more. So, Lenny became the third man in the team, and for a while, they cleaned up. The boys were so good that, sometimes, they were pulling two or even three jobs in one night, and they stole anything and everything. Clothes, electrical goods, foodstuff; any-fucking-thing.

As with all good things, it had to come to an end, and when the police turned up at their ram-raid of a popular clothing retailer, the bubble was well and truly burst. Deggsy hadn't been available to do this particular job as he was fucked-up on the dodgy E he had taken the night before, so Paul and Lenny had done it on their own. When the police turned up, Lenny, who had been dumping a load of jeans into the back of the van, managed to get away but Paul, still inside, got caught and was dragged to the local cells. The police were able to connect him to at least a dozen other jobs, and due to the fact he was unprepared to reveal his accomplices, Paul went down for four years; the first of his three spells in prison over the next decade. Ever since that night, the two brothers had never spoken to each other.

When he had finished his dessert, Lenny kissed his mother and gave her a giant bear-hug, almost crushing the woman.

'Come on, then, princess,' he said to his daughter, who could barely prise herself away from her phone. 'We better get you back home.'

'Just remember,' his mum said to him after they had said their goodbyes, 'life is too short not to make things right.'

'I know, Mum,' he said and kissed her again. 'I promise I'll think about it.'

But when they headed back to the car, the last thing he was thinking about was a reunion with his brother. What *was* going through Lenny's brain was the best way he could spend his treasure without attracting the attention of the law or the taxman.

Chapter 10

Mac

'I've said it before, and I'll say it again,' a bemused Lenny said to the rest of the Watch. 'The boy is a fucking idiot.'

As usual, his disbelief was aimed at Dylan.

'I mean, what the fuck can be wrong with a TV programme giving money to charity? How can you possibly have a problem with that?'

'I haven't,' Dylan answered super calm. 'It's when they don't give them the money, that's what I have a problem with.'

He looked around at the others, saw that he was holding court and began his tirade.

'Okay, so let's say you've got this show packed with Z-listers… I dunno, let's call it Celebrity Snakes and Ladders or some shit like that. Then, let's say *that* girl from *that* thing gets to the final, and if she answers the question correctly, she wins fifty grand for her chosen charity, which, in this case, is this little locally run thing that looks after kiddies with cancer, let's call it, Kiddies with Cancer. So, let's go further and say she gets the answer wrong, and because she doesn't know how many inches Brad Pitt's dick is, the charity gets nothing. I mean, think of the morality of that for a minute. Just because she can't answer some ridiculous question that means nothing to anyone, the makers of this show are prepared to withhold the money that would have benefited dozens of kids, maybe even saved a few of their lives. I mean, they might as well roll little Johnny, the leukaemia-suffering kid, out on stage and tell him they've just given him a death sentence in the name of Saturday night entertainment.'

Lenny shook his head. 'See, the boy's sick in the head.'

'It's not me who's sick, it's the world we live in. And I haven't finished yet, 'cos those knobhead celebs who starred in this piece-of-shit show are all paid a fee for appearing on it. So, the public end up happy, 'cos they got their hour of bubble gum for their eyes, the so-called celebrities are made up, as they've just made five grand for an afternoon's jolly, but poor old Kiddies With Cancer, they get nothing, and little Johnny's mummy has to plan the boy's impending funeral, 'cos she can't afford to pay for the op in America the charity would have funded if some bimbo knew the answer was seven and a half inches. That's what's sick, Len.'

Jo gave the boy a look that was a mixture of pity and confusion. 'Seriously, Dylan, you need to get out more.'

'Lucky bastard,' Lenny said. 'Not only is Brad a good-looking son-of-a-bitch, but he's packing some heat too.'

Since they'd started work at six o'clock, everyone had acted like it was business as usual. There had been no mention of the money, even though it was the only thing on all of their minds. After the change of shift routines, instead of heading to the canteen as normal for a brew and a catch-up, the Watch members shuffled off to various nooks in the station where they could avoid talking to the others about what had taken place the previous evening. Jo disappeared into the gym for a particularly long session on the running machine, Wesley lost himself in the office as Dylan read his book in the dorm and Lenny sat in the yard chain-smoking.

It was only when Harrison summoned them to the canteen over the loud speaker for their evening meal, did they finally gather together for more than five minutes. Unlike the rest of them, the chef hadn't changed his routine one bit. They were used to paying him compliments, but on this occasion, they lavished more praise and discussed the meal in far greater detail than normal. It wasn't even a particularly impressive meal by Harrison's standards; just a cold meat salad due to it being Sunday night and he'd already cooked one meal at home, even if he was the only one who ate it. When Lenny had asked if any of them had seen the repeat of Celebrity Catchphrase that afternoon, the others were, for once,

pleased to hear Dylan take up his attack on the subject. There were only so many ways you could praise a cold Scotch Egg.

'I'm glad you lot enjoyed the food,' Harrison said when they had all finished their meals, with none of them finding the energy to take their plates into the kitchen and start the washing up, 'but I think we need to stop avoiding the issue and talk about what happened last night.'

Somehow, the silence in the room intensified. The others looked at Harrison like he'd just done a particularly loud fart.

'What?' he said to them. 'Have you all forgotten that you stole half a million pounds from a casualty's car last night, because I haven't. So, unless any of you have anything better to do, which considering the seriousness of the situation I very much doubt, I think it's time we cut the bullshit and talk about the money.'

Wesley was the first to reply to the request. 'Harrison, I know you're far from happy about what happened last night, but maybe it's best that we wait a few days for the dust to settle before we drag it all out in the open. How about the first day of next tour? I'm sure things will make far more sense then.'

Even though the others said nothing, their approval of Wesley's suggestion was clear; they had as little desire to discuss the situation as he did. Unfortunately for them, Harrison was not in agreement.

'I'm sorry, Wes, but I don't see what difference four days is going to make. We'll be in exactly the same situation then as we are now, which just in case you're not clear is this: you clowns were stupid enough to steal an awful lot of money last night and drag me into something that I wanted no part of. And now, just because you haven't been caught, yet, you think you've got away with it. Maybe you bunch of arseholes need to consider perhaps there could be some comeback from what happened, and if there is, we need to get our stories straight so we don't all end up in prison. So, if you don't mind, and with all due respect, fuck waiting until next week. I want to talk about the money right now.'

'Good idea,' a voice from the doorway behind them said. 'Let's talk about the money.'

The man who had just entered the room was in his mid-to-late fifties and had white hair kept short with shaving clippers. None of the people sitting around the table had ever set eyes on him before. With his black trousers, shiny shoes and light blue shirt with no tie, he looked like a used car salesman who had just finished a day of hard selling. A senior salesman that is, for the man looked like he would hold a position of authority, regardless of his profession. On his forehead, he wore a long plaster that ran parallel to, and was almost as long as, his left eyebrow, and when he walked towards the table, he dragged his right leg behind him.

'Can we help you?' Wesley asked, startled by the man's presence.

The man ignored him and continued his slow path to the dining table. The discomfort on his face suggested that the injury he had sustained to his leg was a new one.

'Who the fuck are you, and how did you get in here?' Lenny said, less politely.

'Easy, big fella,' the man said when he finally reached his destination. 'Let's keep things friendly, shall we?' He nodded at the empty chair that was situated between Wesley and Jo. 'Mind if I take a seat? My leg's throbbing.'

Without waiting for an answer, he pulled the chair out, and with slow and deliberate concentration, lowered himself into it. The look of relief on his face was instant.

'Don't make me ask again,' Lenny said when no answer was forthcoming. The man however, seemed content to study the faces of the people around the table.

'You can call me Mac,' he finally said, 'but that's the least of your problems. All you people need to know is I am the man you foolishly tried to steal from last night. That fact alone is all you need to concern your good selves about.'

'Shit,' Dylan said, unintentionally verbalising his thoughts.

'Holy fucking shit would be more appropriate, son,' Mac said, 'because you silly sausages fucked up in the worst of ways when you decided to take what belongs to me.'

Summoning all the strength he had, Wesley stood up on his jelly legs, feeling like he was going to be sick and doing his best to stop his knees from knocking together. 'Listen, sir, let me please take this opportunity to apologise for what happened. This is my Watch, and I should take responsibility for what we did.'

Mac smiled. 'That's very honourable of you, but sit the fuck down and shut up. I haven't finished yet.'

Wesley returned to his seat so quickly, it wasn't clear if he had sat down or his legs had given way.

'See the thing is, gentlemen, and lady, of course,' he said, turning to Jo, 'even though you took what was mine, I can't really find it in this big old heart of mine to blame you. You must have thought, at the time, that the money belonged to Tony, my unfortunate and now deceased driver. So, taken from that point of view, it's hard to be angry with you for coming to the conclusion that as its owner was no longer with us, the money in turn became yours. Perhaps if you'd known I was hiding in the bushes nursing my injuries,' he pulled a sad face and pointed at the plaster on his head, 'your decision would have been very different.'

He looked around the table at his audience, as if gauging their reactions.

'Also, I have to take into account that you are firefighters, a profession I have always had the utmost respect for. I'm guessing none of you have ever seen such an amount of money before, and so naturally, you were tempted. So, like I say, I understand your predicament, and if I were in your situation, I may have felt the urge to do the same thing...'

When he spoke again, his voice lowered in tone. 'But here's the rub. As I'm sure you are aware from the copious amounts of money you found, I happen to be a drug dealer, and drug dealers are not known for their humanitarian services. My business is all

about keeping face. Without that, you have nothing. So, if I were to simply let you off the hook, it would make me look weak to others in my trade, my competitors, if you will. That weakness would mean my rivals would try and take from me what is mine, which, if you haven't guessed, is what happened last night, and why poor Tony is with us no more. The message I would be better off sending to those people, especially in the light of what happened to Tony, is to be fucking ruthless and kill the lot of you. Your big friend over there understands, I'm sure. He looks like a man of the world.'

Despite the threat on his life, Lenny nodded.

'But, then again,' Mac said, his voice now upbeat, 'like I've already said, I like you guys. So, there's my dilemma…What to do?'

'Look, mister,' Dylan said, trying his best not to show the fear that leaked out of him, 'there's no need to do anything silly. No one knows we took your money. What if we just go and get it for you right now? None of us will ever mention it to anyone, I swear.'

'Tell you what, son, why don't you do that, and I'll sit here, have a chat with the big boys and see if we can't thrash something out.'

Dylan looked to Wesley who dug his hand into his pocket and produced a key that he pushed across the table. Dylan picked it up and almost ran to the locker room to retrieve the stolen loot.

The man pointed at Dylan's back as he left the room. 'Is he really a fireman? Doesn't strike me as the type.'

Without waiting for an answer, he turned his attention to Jo. 'And what about you, honey? What brings a good-looking girl like you into a messy job like this?'

'It's got to be all the interesting members of the public we meet,' she answered without missing a beat.

The man acknowledged the quality of her answer with a quick smile, then switched things to Lenny. 'You're quiet, big man.'

Lenny shrugged. 'Not a lot to say really, is there?'

Mac studied him before speaking again. 'You'd just love to get hold of me, wouldn't you?'

Lenny's face gave away nothing.

'But the fact you haven't tells me you're not as stupid as you look. You're the one I'm going to have to keep my eye on, I reckon.'

'Thanks.'

'And you,' he said, addressing Wesley, 'you say you're the head honcho around here?'

Wesley nodded.

'That's not the vibe you give off to me. You sure you've got your dogs on a tight enough leash?'

Before Wesley could answer, the sound of Dylan's heavy feet echoed around the room. The boy charged in moments later, almost falling over as he changed direction and headed for the table. When he reached the man, he placed the bag on the table, then sat back down again, taking gasping breaths. He had run all the way to the locker room and back.

Mac unzipped the bag and smiled when he observed its contents. Then, careful to put as little weight on his bad leg as possible, he got to his feet, dug his hand into the bag and pulled out a wad of cash which he threw on the table in front of Dylan. He then repeated the procedure with each of the other crew members like he was dealing out cards.

'So, the conclusion I've come to,' he said, 'is rather than make the tedious decision of the best place to dump your corpses, I'm going to make a deal with you. Those little stacks are worth five grand each, and before you get all uppity with me, I'd just like to state I'm not blackmailing you, that would be insulting to such honourable professionals as yourselves. No, the money is a simple token of gratitude for your retrieval and safe care of my goods, and I would deeply appreciate it if you were all to accept my humble gift… It would mean, though, should you decide to accept my offering, that you would stay quiet about what happened last night and tell neither your loved ones, nor any of our other uniformed friends.'

He let them absorb his words before he spoke again. 'So, are we in agreement?'

The reply was one of the presents he had just given out landing in front of him on the table.

'Keep it,' Harrison said, the first thing he had uttered since the man had entered the room. 'I'm not interested in your money.'

'Ah,' the man sighed. 'Now, I don't believe I saw you there last night, did I?'

'That's right, because if you had seen me, we wouldn't be having this conversation.'

'I see. So, you're the guy who really runs the show. That makes sense.'

'I don't run anything, I just wouldn't have let what happened happen, that's all.'

'That's a shame,' the man said, 'because that makes me feel uncomfortable. And unfortunately for the others, this is only going to work if you're all in on it. But if you're not happy, I guess I'll have to draw up some other plans.'

'I didn't say I'm refusing the deal. I won't talk to anyone about what happened. It's the money I'm refusing.'

'Sadly, it doesn't work like that. This thing is all about acceptance. For you to accept my deal, you have to accept my money. Call it symbolic or a token gesture, I don't give a fuck either way. But you *will* take the money or else you and your colleagues' lives are about to get a whole lot more exciting. Understand?' The playfulness in the man's voice had evaporated.

'Leave it on the table,' Harrison said. 'This lot can share it between them.'

Mac smiled. 'See, that makes me feel far more comfortable with this situation already… Now, there is one other thing I should mention. Apart from silence, this money also means should I ever have need of them in the future, I can call on your services.'

'What's that supposed to mean?' Harrison asked.

'You're firefighters. If anyone can understand the concept of a retainer, then I'm sure it's you.'

'And like *you* said, we're firefighters, not the law. There's nothing we could do to help you.'

'See, that's why I like you guys; you're humble. You underestimate your talents. Now, don't sweat about this, fellas, it's very unlikely, but a day may come in the distant future where I may need the talents of my local fire service.'

'Then call 999,' Harrison said, 'like everyone else.'

The man smiled at him again. 'I'd love to get it into this deeper, I really would, but I've got business to attend to, what with some upstarts murdering my driver and all. You guys take care now, and remember: loose lips sink ships.'

Mac picked up the bag and limped towards the exit leaving the room in silence. As he reached the door, he looked over his shoulder at his still captivated audience. 'Keep safe,' he said. 'It's dangerous out there.'

When the man's footsteps could be heard no longer, the silence in the room didn't seem to want to leave. It was Harrison who eventually kicked it out.

'Is now a good time to say I told you so or shall I wait 'til later?'

Chapter 11

Persons Reported

Where the fuck am I?

This was the first thought that went through Jo's mind when she sat up in her bed. The lights were on in the room, but she could not recognise any of its features. It definitely wasn't her own bed, and she was pretty sure she hadn't ended up in some guy's flat. She felt awful, but knew she hadn't been drinking.

Where *the fuck* am I?

It was only when she became aware of the ringing noise in her ears that was steadily getting louder, she finally realised she was at the station and they had a call. She jumped out of bed and quickly put on her trousers and T-shirt. She wasn't worried about her roommate perving at her almost-naked form; Dylan was even worse at waking up, and she almost had to step out of the way as he caught his foot in his trouser leg and stumbled towards her.

When her shoes were on, Jo blinked her eyes to try and clear the fog, then jogged towards the appliance bays. Being a small station and based on only one floor, there was no pole for them to slide down, a fact that bothered Dylan greatly. Sliding down the pole was one of the reasons he joined the fire brigade, and the others teased him that was the real reason for his transfer request.

As they got on the lorry, Wesley greeted them with a look of concern on his face. 'Fire. Persons Reported. Whitehawk.'

That was all he said, but it was enough to fully wake up Jo with a dose of adrenaline that charged through her body.

If he had told her they were going to a fire alarm at one of their regular haunts, she would have strapped herself into her BA set and most likely fallen asleep on the way. But the words

"Persons Reported" were enough to prepare her for action. The term referred to a member or members of the public who were believed to be trapped inside a building that was on fire. It didn't always prove to be a correct call, in fact, more often than not, a Persons Reported would turn out to be nothing. Quite rightly, mobilising would always err on the side of caution, so if someone called 999, and there was even the slightest doubt in their mind that someone might be inside, it was always sent out as a Persons Reported.

As Lenny turned the key and waited for the roller shutter doors to rise, the main-scheme radio on the appliance fired up,

'Multiple calls to this incident, smoke issuing. Still believed to be Persons Reported.'

Wesley turned and looked to his BA crew. 'You got that right, guys? I want you under air before we get there.'

The image that television and the movies portrayed of internal firefighting was about as far from the truth as possible, and with good reason, too, because if you wanted to make an exciting film about brave firefighters tackling an inferno, you definitely wouldn't want to base it on fact. In the movies, some brave young fireman would usually tell his boss he didn't care about rules, there was a life to save, goddamn it. Then, he would take a deep breath, kick the front door in and charge headfirst into the building armed only with an axe or crowbar. Once inside, he would look around and take stock of the situation; everything in the room would be on fire, and visibility would be excellent. He would grit his teeth and run up the burning staircase, fight his way into the bedroom, throw the pretty casualty over his shoulder in the good old fireman's lift, then bring her out to high fives from his concerned colleagues.

That's how it usually goes down in the films, right? This, however, is what really happens:

If the OIC decides to tackle the fire offensively, they will send in a BA crew or crews, which 99% of the time will consist of two firefighters. No one ever goes into a fire on their own.

Before committing to the incident, the pair will first report to the Entry Control Officer (ECO) who will take their tally (a little piece of plastic with their name and cylinder pressure on it) and place it into the BA board. They will then do a little calculation on the board based on their cylinder pressure and estimate how long they have until their air runs out. This isn't always an exact figure; if a crew is busting their asses dragging charged lengths of hose in the building, they will fly through their air; if they're standing around dampening down at an incident, it might last twice as long as predicted.

The crews will then do a buddy check to make sure no bare skin is showing around their flash-hoods or gloves. Unlike in the old days, they had to be protected from the extreme heat they were about to face. It wasn't unheard of to encounter temperatures of over a thousand degrees, and so the modern kit they wore had to reflect that.

When the ECO had checked them over again, he would brief the crews on what was expected of them, then make them repeat the brief back to him before allowing them into the building. A BA crew always took some form of firefighting medium into the building with them. If it was a small electrical or oil fire, that may be an extinguisher or fire blanket, but in most cases, they relied on the high-pressure hose reel on the appliance, or if they needed greater volumes of water, then the larger, lay-flat hose would be used. Contrary to movie folklore, axes had proved to be rather ineffective at putting fires out. While this was going on, one of the crew members (usually the driver) would be trying to locate a hydrant to provide them with a sufficient water source. The two thousand litres of water the fire engine contained would be gone in no time at a serious incident.

Before entering the building, the BA team would test their hose by opening it up to make sure they had sufficient pressure from the pump operator, then, when they were finally ready, they would carry out their door procedures. Kicking in a front door looked awesome in the movies, but it was a moronic and potentially

lethal thing for a firefighter to do. They could be walking into a room where an oxygen-starved fire was smouldering away, waiting for a sudden influx of air that would create the perfect explosive mixture for the flammable gases that filled the room, creating a backdraft. If you've seen the film, (even though it's exaggerated Hollywood bullshit), you'll know that's something you don't want to happen.

If it is hot in the room, then those gases need to be cooled down to take them out of their explosive limits. This is where a firefighter really earns their dough, because if they get their gas cooling techniques wrong, they could be in big trouble. Despite what people think, if they use it incorrectly, the water the crews are taking in with them can be deadly. The stuff expands thousands of times when it turns into steam, and if a crew uses too much, they can end up boiling themselves alive. A good BA team will use only the necessary water on an internal, unventilated fire, delivering short, controlled bursts with their branch, making the conditions in the room as beneficial to themselves as possible.

When they've done their door procedures and pushed into the room, the crew then need to start searching, whether that be to find casualties or the source of the fire itself. Unlike in the films, visibility in these situations is usually zero, or pretty close to it anyway. We're talking "can't see your hand in front of your face" shit, here. If you ask any firefighter, they'll tell you it's the smoke that's the real bastard at most incidents, not the fire itself. Not only is it fucking hot, but it makes their eyes virtually useless. That's why when the crews enter a building, they are meant to keep in constant physical contact with each other.

Crews then have to carry out a systemic search of each and every room in the building while not being able to see a thing and dealing with the furniture and general clutter that fills people's houses and gets in their way at every turn. The system most usually employed is a left or right-hand search, room-by-room, floor-by-floor. For this to work, the team leader, the number one, makes contact with a wall, their point of reference, and follows

that wall as their partner moves parallel with them, within an arm's reach. They turn when they get to each corner of the room until they finally get back to the door they first entered, checking on and under beds, in cupboards and anywhere a casualty could possibly be located as they go.

As the team push forward, they sweep the floor with one foot, feeling for holes or what could be a casualty and not just a cushion or cuddly toy. At the same time, they wave one of their arms up and down in front of them in order to identify any objects they could bump into or get snagged in. Getting caught up in low hanging cables that have fallen from melted trunking is every firefighter's nightmare, and something that has been responsible for more than one fatality. This search method is called the BA shuffle, and although it looks ridiculous to anyone who may be watching with a thermal imaging camera, this tried and tested method provides a vital means of moving around in the dark.

If they do find a casualty, the fireman's lift is a no-no. It looks great on TV, but all the heat and smoke is located at the top of the room, and that is not the place you want your casualty's head to be located. The way to bring them out is for one of the team, usually the one with most air left, to grab the casualty under the armpits and drag them out backwards as their partner guides them out.

The crew's lives are made even more difficult by the impairment of their other senses. Wearing a flash-hood, helmet and BA mask, it is extremely difficult for them to hear each other, and they often have to shout to make themselves understood. The gloves they wear do an excellent job of preventing their hands from being burned, but it also means that jobs that require a level of dexterity are extremely difficult. Sometimes, it feels like wearing boxing gloves when they are trying to open a door or pick something up off the floor.

So, that's what a real fire looks like; two firefighters stumbling around in the dark, bumping into each other and doing their best not to get disorientated and lost. And, just for the record, the only time everything in a room is on fire is usually just before it

flashes over, and if that happens, then the crews are really fucked, but we'll come back to that later. So, all-in-all, you couldn't really blame the films for their portrayal of firefighting in action. It was a hell of a lot more exciting than the real thing.

When they arrived at the incident, they could see that mobilising were correct. Thick black smoke was issuing from the second floor of the three-storey, purpose-built block of flats that had long seen better days and was known for housing some pretty unsavoury characters. Many of them were now standing outside, watching the drama unfold. Its name, Seaview Court, was slightly misleading, as only the flats on the top floor had a clear view of the ocean, and that was only because Whitehawk was nestled on one of the highest points in the city, and was a good mile from the beach.

After Harrison checked them over, tucking Dylan's flash-hood under his mask to hide his exposed skin, he checked their gauges for their pressure readings, then passed the hose reel to Jo. She opened it up and turned the ring on the front of the branch, adjusting the cone of water until she was happy with it. They did their final gauge check and were about to enter the building when Wesley grabbed Jo's arm.

'One of the neighbours has just told me on the quiet that the guy who lives there is a drug dealer. Be careful the place hasn't been booby trapped. If in doubt, get out, quick sharp. I don't want you doing anything silly.'

'No problems,' she said, then looked to Dylan. 'We'll be all right, won't we.'

It was a statement not a question.

Wesley was right to be concerned. In recent years, there had been a spate of fires at drug production labs. It sounded high-tech, but these were normally scrubby little meth labs running out of houses or flats like the one they were about to enter. The guys who ran these places made sure they were safe from any rivals who fancied getting hold of their products, and often rigged the places up to be death traps. Bars were put across the windows

and then wired up to a live electrical feed so that anyone touching them would be instantly vaporised. Inside, they often removed floorboards and placed a bed of six-inch nails in the gap, then covered it over with a rug. Or sometimes, a door would be rigged, so if it was opened, some horrible spiky thing would swing into the poor person, just like that scene in *First Blood*. Basically, they were not the type of places you wanted to be fumbling around in the dark. Luckily, they hadn't encountered any in Brighton yet. It was hydroponic dope in people's lofts they normally dealt with, but there was always a first time.

When they got to the second floor, Dylan was already breathing hard due to him dragging the hose reel up the stairs. It was the number two's job to do the donkey-work, while number one led the way and acted as path-finder. There were three doorways on the floor, and it was clear from the smoke-blackened edges the fire was located in the west-facing one. When they got to the door, Dylan took hold of the handle and dropped to his knees. Jo did the same as she positioned the branch in front of her like she was about to fire a rifle; they were ready to carry out their door procedures.

'Crack!' Jo shouted, and a second later, Dylan opened the door six inches, keeping a tight hold of the handle. If there was potential for a backdraft, it could be ripped right out of his hand as the rush of air into the building sucked the door inwards. Jo opened and closed the branch quickly as the black smoke poured out of the flat and consumed them. She waited a few seconds to see how it reacted then put another couple of pulses of water up into the smoke.

'And open.'

As Dylan pulled the door, Jo went in low, staying on her knees with him following behind. The neutral plain – the dividing line between the smoke layer and the clean air – was about a foot off the ground. After checking behind the door for casualties, Jo got down on her belly, as this was the only place there was any visibility, and had a good look around. Satisfied, she got

back to her knees (it was too hot to stand) and placed her hand on the wall to her right, then with Dylan on her outside, they pushed forward no more than six feet until they came to an open doorway. Peering inside, Jo's sight partially returned as the fire illuminated the room.

Through the black smoke, on the other side of the room, she could see a sofa that was engulfed in flames. The fire plume that rose up from it had already reached the ceiling, and the flames were now rolling towards them as the super-heated gases at the top of the room caught alight. If it wasn't dealt with quickly, the situation would become extremely dangerous.

A number of things were happening here. Everything in the room was fuel for the fire, and the heat radiating from the plume was causing objects nearby to give off hot, flammable gases in a process known as pyrolysis. Those gases would rise to the top of the room and grow in depth, giving off tremendous amounts of heat themselves, and along with the fire plume, warm its contents up even further, as well as the walls, floor and ceiling. The heat they radiate helps create even more gases, and the vicious circle goes on. This thermal radiation was the real concern because if not cooled down, those gases, along with everything else in the room, would suddenly ignite, resulting in a fully developed fire. It would be like the inside of an incinerator with temperatures reaching well over a thousand degrees. Not surprisingly, anyone or thing in the room would be toast. That was what was known in the trade as a flashover.

Luckily, Jo was trained in how to deal with such situations and so without any panic or fuss, she shot a couple of pulses of water into the gases. She watched how they reacted before applying more; she didn't want to create too much steam and make her life more difficult.

After a few seconds, she repeated the action, then did the same again soon after. The effects of her actions were immediate; the water had soaked up massive amounts of energy not just from the fire, but the walls and ceiling, too, and with just a few simple actions, cooled it down by a couple of hundred degrees.

As she was getting the better of the fire, she crept forward, still on her knees, with Dylan following behind, helpfully pointing out the areas where the flames were still licking at her. When she had successfully subdued them, plunging the room into darkness, Jo concentrated on the sofa itself. The next time she opened the branch up, it was only cracked slightly, reducing the volume and pressure of the water. She trickled it onto the fire; too much would steam the room up, and she didn't want that at this stage of the game. It looked kind of like a large man pissing on the offending item and was known as painting the fire. As she continued to apply water to the sofa, she turned to Dylan.

'Get the windows open and search the room.'

Technically what she was asking of him was wrong, as it involved the crew not being within an arm's reach of one another, but as the fire was pretty much out, and the room desperately needed ventilating, Jo was happy with her decision.

Dylan quickly did as instructed, and as soon as the smoke was allowed to escape, the conditions in the room improved. Within seconds, they could make out that they were in the living room, and things like the TV and coffee table became visible. As she continued to damp down the sofa, Dylan edged his way around the room, using his leg to feel at the objects on the floor. Now that the fire was out, and there was suitable ventilation, he was able to stand up comfortably without the heat getting the better of him.

Just as she closed off the branch, Dylan called out to her. 'You better get over here. We've got a body.'

Jo's head turned to face her partner, 'Then grab hold of them, for fuck's sake. Let's get them out of here!'

Dylan's answer was slow in coming. 'There's no point; they're already dead.'

'That's not for you to say. Now, grab hold of the bastard.'

'That's the thing!' he shouted back at her. 'I've got a body, but there's no head attached to it.'

Chapter 12

Tears Before Bedtime

They didn't get away from the job for hours. Within no time, every man and his dog were at the incident. There were police, forensic units and paramedics everywhere, even though it would take a miracle to get this one walking again. A host of officers in their white helmets huddled together in a tight knit group and were deep in conversation. They had instructed Jo and Dylan to find a quiet corner and make notes of the exact sequence of events they had gone through. The police wouldn't take their official statements until the next morning, but Phil Collins, who had taken charge of the incident on his arrival, had encouraged them to get the events down on paper while it was still fresh in their minds. It was probably the most sensible thing the asshole had said in a long time.

There was little for the others to do. As soon as the body was discovered, the incident was taken over by the police, and their priority was the preservation of the scene until SOCO arrived. It was just a case of standing around and drinking tea, for the firefighters. It was meant to be confidential, but one of the coppers had told Wesley the headless guy was an Albanian who lived there with two of his countrymen. They'd found a stash of pills and dope in one of the bedrooms but as yet, no head.

'The Daily Hate Mail will love this one,' Dylan said when Wesley passed the information onto the rest of the crew. 'I can see the headline now. *Immigrant Drug Scum Beheaded.* They'll probably give out a reward to the guy who did it.'

Wesley inspected his crew member as the young man spoke. It was the worst incident Dylan had been to in his short time in the job. 'How are you feeling? That wasn't a very nice thing to see.'

Dylan lifted his palms to sky. 'I'm alright, I guess.'

'You do realise,' Lenny said, 'they'll be calling us Dead Watch for the next twenty years after that.'

There was no real need for them to stay as the fire was long since out, but Phil wanted to keep some presence there until the fire investigation team arrived. Wesley had argued he wanted to take his crew back to the station, considering what his BA team had had to witness, but the two of them insisted they were fine. If they had seen such a spectacle in their day-to-day life, it probably would have traumatised them, but one of the effects of wearing a uniform was it acted like a kind of filter that allowed the wearer to look at things from a far more objective viewpoint.

Some of the gorier things that firefighters encountered, and this definitely counted as one of them, often took on a slightly surreal view. It was like watching a cheap sci-fi or horror film where the blood and guts they encountered didn't actually seem real. It was only when they got home later and had a chance to reflect on what they had seen that it normally hit them. That was why, after such events, the crews would have to take part in a critical incident debrief and talk or even just listen to the rest of the crew about what they had seen and done. It had been proven to be the best way of dealing with traumatic incidents, and although a relatively new idea, it was something fire crews had been doing for years. That was where the infamous black humour came from. It wasn't to make fun of the dead but to help the crews find a way of dealing with it.

The sun was already rising when they finally got back to station. It was nearly five o'clock, but no one bothered trying to squeeze in an hour's sleep. After such an incident, most people just wanted to sit down, have a cup of tea and put it behind them.

When he'd finished his brew, Lenny got off his seat and headed for the toilets. As he passed the ladies', he heard a strange heaving noise coming from within.

'Jo, is that you?'

He knew it was a pointless question; she was the only woman on the Watch. When she'd disappeared five minutes earlier, he'd assumed she was off for a shit. Women didn't usually like to inform you of such things, he'd learnt that much about them. The sounds from the room stopped for a few seconds, then an even louder one that sounded more like a snort, erupted from the toilet. She had been unsuccessful in keeping in her cries.

'Jo, I'm coming in. Make sure your knickers are up.'

Without waiting for a response, he opened the door and stepped in. Jo was standing in front of the mirror, the little mascara she was wearing had run, leaving thin tracks down her cheeks. She smiled at Lenny then from nowhere, she let out another cry that sounded like she was gasping for air.

'You all right, girl?'

She nodded.

'Don't feel bad about being upset. That was a pretty horrible thing you had to see back there.'

'Thanks, Len, but that's not why I'm crying.'

'You don't have to be embarrassed about it. Shit like that's not normal.'

Jo shook her head. 'I said that's not why I'm crying, didn't I? Seeing the body didn't bother me. It's what happened that I can't get my head around. Why the hell would anyone want to do that to another human being? Tell me, Len, 'cos I can't work it out.'

Lenny shrugged. 'It's a fucked-up world out there, that's all I know. But I don't expect that helps much, does it?'

'Not really, but you know something, when I see shit like that, it just makes me feel glad I never had kids.' She used her hand to wipe away the snot from her nose. 'Why would anyone want to bring them into this crazy fucking place?'

'I can't answer that.' Lenny shrugged again. 'My little girl was an accident. But what I *can* tell you is I don't regret her being born for one minute. There's a lot of bad out there, but there's a lot of good too. I guess we've just got to make the most of the good stuff.'

In a move that was extremely delicate for Lenny, he placed his hand on her shoulder and gave Jo the warmest of smiles. Then, just to make sure he'd done nothing to damage his reputation, he rubbed her hair roughly and patted her on the shoulder with force. 'Come on, you daft cow. I'll make you another cuppa.'

As they headed back to the canteen, the phone went, almost knocking Dylan off his chair as it woke him from his slumber.

'I'll get it,' Wes said, not that anyone else was showing any intention of doing so. 'It's probably Phil telling us we've left some kit up there. Green Watch can get it later. There's no way I'm going back now.'

His time on the Watch had ignited a little fire in his soft belly.

'Hello?'

'That guy you found tonight,' a voice said, 'old headless Harry, it was a shame what happened to him.'

Wesley didn't bother asking who it was; he recognised the voice straight away as the one that had intruded on them at the station the night before.

'Thing is, it wasn't even him who shot Tony. But I'm fairly certain he knew who did. Never said a word, though. Not a fucking dickie bird. Can you believe that? Not giving up his mates, even though he had a pretty good idea what was going to happen to him if he didn't spill the beans. I didn't warn him about the whole beheading thing. Mind you, I didn't even think about it until after I done him in. It just seemed kind of appropriate, if you know what I mean.'

Wesley didn't, but it felt, at that moment, like he'd lost the power of speech. All he could do was listen to the voice on the other end of the phone.

'If ever there was a case of misguided loyalties, I'd say that was it. Anyway, my point being I was willing to kill that poor fuck because he didn't tell me what I wanted to know. Now, with that in mind, can you imagine what I'd be prepared to do to you and your boys if you decide to do anything silly, like, I don't know, maybe speak to the police about the things that have gone on between us… You still there, boss?'

'Yes,' Wes just about managed to answer.

'Good man. So, that's all I wanted to say, other than good job back there. Your team dealt with the fire very professionally. You should be proud of them.'

'I am,' Wes answered, surprising himself when he found his voice.

'Get some sleep, then, chappy, you deserve it.'

He hung up before Wesley could say anything, not that there was anything to say. The man had made his point.

Part Two

Chapter 13

A Debt Repaid

Three Months Later

'Come on, Jimmy,' Wesley said. 'I'll explain later, I promise. But we need to get going, or mobilising will start asking questions.'

Jimmy sat in the driver's seat of the fire appliance, unaffected by Wesley's pleas. 'I don't give a fuck what mobilising have got to say. You tell me what's going on, or I ain't going anywhere.'

Harrison leant over from the back of the engine and placed his hand on Jimmy's shoulder. 'Please, Jim, I think you need to listen to Wesley. It's for all our sakes.'

Jimmy looked to his old friend then back to Wesley. 'Okay, I'll do it. But it's for their benefit.' He directed his thumb towards the crew. 'Not yours.'

He drove out of the bays and begun the short journey to their destination. The marina was less than half a mile from the station.

Jimmy had known something was wrong from the off. When Wesley put the phone down, his face was rinsed of colour, and when the bells went down two minutes later, he almost jumped out of his skin. The others were no better. Dylan and Lenny, who normally wouldn't shut up, had suddenly lost the ability to speak and even Harrison wasn't his normal self. The only person not acting strange was Bodhi, who, in his usual laid-back way, just sat there and said nothing. When they got the call and the others were flapping around, he strolled to the pump like he was heading to the shops to pick up the morning paper.

Jimmy said nothing else on the short journey. He just wanted to get the call out of the way as quickly as possible so he could

find out why the hell everyone was acting so weird. If he had to kick a few arses to find out, well, that was just fine.

The Marina was situated directly south of the fire station, and unlike many other areas of Brighton that carried their own unique charms, the Marina was pretty much devoid of any such personality. The place had been built at the tail end of the seventies and, like many other construction of the time, was a testament to the ugly functionality of breeze block and concrete. It was based at the bottom of the chalk cliffs that lined the area and much of the South East coast. Other than sheltering hundreds of boats and yachts, the place was also home to a supermarket, cinema, ten-pin bowling centre and a host of shops that sold cheap clothes, books and stationery. The half-dozen restaurants and pubs there all played up their nautical settings with names that involved sailors, ships and marine life.

After descending the ramp, they drove straight past the shoppers until they reached the area where the boats were anchored. Only the boat owners could enter this area, with a swipe of a security card that raised the barrier arm. Usually, if they had an incident there (and there had been a number of boat fires over the years), a security guard would be present to open it up for them. On this occasion, they were met by an army of police officers, riot vans and cop cars. It looked like they meant business.

Behind them, and in plain view, one of the yachts, a forty-two-footer, was ablaze with the flames ten feet in the air. The heat was so intense the main sail on the boat to its left (or maybe that should be its port) had blackened and was catching alight around its edges.

They pulled up at the barrier, and Wesley got out, heading toward the most senior looking of the police officers. Just like with the fire service, it happened to be the man with the most stripes on his shoulder and markings on his cap.

'What's going on?' Wesley asked. 'And are we okay to get in there?'

The officer nodded. He was pushing sixty but had that stern look that would have made a man half his age and twice his

size wither. 'Drug raid. We've had intel that one of the yachts has smuggled a shitload of cocaine in from Europe, and it's still here. When we shut the place down and started our search, that boat went up in flames. We think the owner panicked and is trying to destroy the evidence.'

Wesley nodded, wondering when he would encounter their newfound friend.

'We've evacuated the area, and I'm happy for you to put the fire out,' the officer went on. 'But do you think you can save the boat? We need to try and get any evidence off it that we can.'

Wesley pursed his cheeks and blew, like a mechanic just before quoting a job. 'I don't know. It's going to take a lot of water to knock that thing down, and boats prefer to be on water than carrying it. They've got a tendency to sink when we start filling them up.'

The officer bit his lower lip, unimpressed. 'Do your best. We want to save as much of it as we can.'

When Wesley got back to the lorry, the lever arm went up, and they drove through, parking a few feet from the water's edge. When you were fighting a serious fire, it was important to secure a water source as early as possible. If the crews were using the high-pressure hose reel, the two thousand litres they stored on the appliance would last twenty or so minutes before it ran out. If they used a jet from the lay flat hose, it would last for less than five.

As they had an endless supply of water right next to them in the form of the sea, they could have set in to that, but it would have taken a few minutes to get the large-diameter hard-suction hose to work and involved a small degree of fannying around. Luckily for the crews, from the drills they did at the marina, they knew there was a hydrant situated less than one length of hose away from the appliance. It would take them a minute or two to access Sussex's finest drinking water.

As Harrison and Lenny put on their BA masks and went under air, Wesley turned to his driver. 'Jimmy, you and Bodhi stay here, set in to the hydrant and get a jet run out. Me and Dylan will go up the jetty and see what needs doing.'

Usually only one crew member, normally the driver, would stay at the lorry and do the tasks Wesley had requested, as well as act as the pump operator, but on this rare occasion, there were six of them riding the appliance. Normally, it was only five, or more likely four, if people were sick or on leave. With the luxury of an extra crew member, Wesley was able to keep Bodhi and Jimmy away from the boat.

He had only taken a couple of steps and had not even passed under the police cordon tape, when he heard someone call him. He looked to his left and saw their agitator staring back at him. It was only three months since he had seen him last, but Mac looked different. Maybe it was the suntan or lack of the plaster across his eyebrow, but he oozed healthiness and vitality. He smiled at Wesley like they were old acquaintances finally catching up.

'What's going on?' Wesley asked.

Mac looked to the burning boat. 'Unfortunately, I lack your firefighting knowledge, but I think I'm going to risk it and say that boat is on fire.'

'What I'm asking,' Wesley said, 'is other than put it out, what do you want us to do? The police said they think there are drugs on the boat. Is that right?'

The man laughed. 'Now why would I burn my own drugs?'

He nodded at the boat downwind of it, the one whose sail had caught alight and whose bow was also beginning to blacken as it absorbed the heat.

'No, that's the one you need to worry about. What I need you boys to do is get my product off it and out of this marina before the police get their mitts on it. Do that, and your dealings with me will be over.'

Wesley wanted to tell him to go fuck himself, that he must have been mad if he thought that he was going to help him shift his drugs right under the noses of the police. He wanted to say that, but then he remembered the headless Albanian they had found, and the words deserted him.

‘It’s under the seats in the galley, the ones facing the TV. Lift the cushions and the wooden board underneath, and you’ll find what you’re looking for.’

‘How much are we talking about?’ Wesley asked. ‘Can two people carry it on their own?’

The man smiled. ‘You’re big strong boys. I’m sure you’ll manage just fine.’

With Dylan in tow, Wesley went through the charade of walking up to the jetty and taking a look at the situation. He knew exactly what his crew were going to do, he’d already decided on that, but he needed to appear like he was considering his options.

When he got back to the appliance, he beckoned Harrison and Lenny towards him. They had donned their BA masks and handed their tallies to Bodhi, who was wearing the black and yellow-checked tabard of the Entry Control Officer. The jet they would be using was charged and ready. Jimmy had already set into the hydrant and, along with Bodhi, had moved towards Wesley to hear the brief. When he saw the look of panic on his boss’ face, he grabbed Bodhi by the shoulder and held him back. It was clear whatever was being said wasn’t meant for their ears.

‘And you agreed to do it? You’re a bigger idiot than I thought,’ Harrison said after Wesley had instructed them of his plan. Wearing his breathing apparatus, he sounded like an asthmatic Darth Vader.

‘I didn’t really have much choice,’ Wesley said. ‘You were there that night, you know what this man is capable of.’

Harrison shook his head. ‘Once this is done, I swear, I’m over with this shit.’

With Dylan’s help, they manoeuvred the hose down the jetty. Moving a charged jet around was always tricky, but the line bags that both men had draped over their shoulders made things even more difficult than usual. The bags were about the same size as a sports holdall and were used to hold the two lines (or rope, in layman’s terms) that were kept on each appliance; one fifteen

metres long, the other thirty. It made good sense to take them. Lines had a multitude of uses on the fire-ground, and no oncoming crews would think it strange to see both men carrying the bags, especially as there was a chance some of the boats might come loose from their moorings and need tying down. If the plan went right, by the time they got off the boat, it would no longer be lines that filled the bags.

As they got closer to the fire, Harrison opened up the branch and hit the flames that engulfed the boat. As the water made contact, something went bang, making both of them jump and bring their hands up to protect their faces. The smoke was now pouring over the yacht they were about to board, which meant they'd have to be extremely careful not to fall off into the water. Visibility was going to be pretty awful. On the plus side, the smoke would act as cover for them to get the drugs and not arouse the suspicions of the police.

With Harrison fighting the fire from the jetty, Lenny clambered onto Mac's yacht and, doing his best to keep his footing, made his way to the hatch, before disappearing below deck. Technically, he had left his BA partner, but given the circumstances, he was willing to overlook their faux pas. The galley of the yacht was a sight to behold; all teak and mahogany and impossibly clean. It was more spacious than the one bedroom flat he called home. He headed straight for a built-in sofa and as instructed, removed the cushions and wooden panels below.

'Fuck me,' he said when he saw his prize. There were at least twenty packages stacked under there that he could only guess must weigh a kilo each. He had never touched the stuff himself, but he knew from his work on the doors that a kilo of coke had a street value of at least thirty to forty grand in Brighton. He was no mathematician, but he was pretty sure the gear he was looking at was worth hundreds of thousands at least. He tipped both lines out of the bags, and as quickly as possible, replaced them with the packages. When they were packed to the point of bursting and he could only just do up the drawstrings to prevent anyone seeing its contents, Lenny swore again. 'Fuck me.'

There were two packages still left, and as he was pretty sure their new friend would only be happy if he had them all in his possession, Lenny tried to figure out the best way to store them. Looking around the cabin, he became aware of the two large pockets located on the thighs of his leggings. They were designed to hold any equipment a firefighter might need on the job, but cocaine was unlikely to have been on the designer's mind.

'Fuck me,' he said again, then stood up and stuffed the remaining two bags into each of his pockets. It made his leggings bulge, but if anyone queried it, he would tell them, in true Lenny style, it was his massive balls that were creating the lumps. Before leaving, he put the lines in the storage area the drugs had once been in, then replaced the cushion and returned the boat to its pristine condition.

When he dumped the line bags on the jetty, he could see that even though it wasn't quite out, Harrison had kicked the bollocks out of the fire. The yacht had also sunk an extra couple of feet below sea level due to all the water it had taken on. Looking across to where their appliance was situated, he could also see that Central's pump had arrived, and a couple of the crew were heading toward them with a charged jet in tow.

'I know I don't need to say this to you,' Lenny said to Harrison, 'but don't let those fuckers anywhere near those bags.'

The approaching firefighters were not wearing BA and so were easy to identify. It was Barney, one of the old boys who had been in the job almost as long as Harrison, and PB, Poster Boy, the newest member of the Watch. Lenny rolled his eyes when he saw him. The two stations had a good working relationship, and the guys all got on well with each other, but PB was the exception. He had done less time than Dylan, but already thought he was a twenty-year man, despite his lack of experience. Such an attitude does not lend itself to getting on with your fellow workers, and as such, few of the East guys were keen on him.

PB could have just as easily stood for Personal Best due to him spending every spare moment in the gym, desperately trying

to lift heavier and heavier weights. He was also one of the most groomed men to have ever put on a fire-kit, with immaculate hair, eyebrows and complexion. His nickname came about when he confessed to his watch that his main career aim was to get his picture into the firefighter's calendar. He'd already tried on two occasions, but had been rejected both times. His Watch attributed it to him being such a short-arse. Lenny put it down to him being a first-class A-hole.

The Central boys positioned themselves about twenty metres along the jetty and safely out of the smoke. They'd worked out that if they stayed upwind of the boat, they could forsake wearing BA and save themselves the hassle of changing their cylinders and cleaning their sets when they got back.

With the two jets working, it didn't take long to knock down the rest of the flames. When they looked to have it beaten, the yacht seemed to creak and cough before the stern suddenly dropped into the water. In seconds, it went from horizontal to vertical before quickly disappearing below the surface. For a minute or two, a steady trail of bubbles marked its resting place. When the last of the smoke was carried away in the wind, it was like the burning wreck had never even been there.

'That's the end of that,' Harrison said as he pushed the lever forward on the branch to turn off the water.

Lenny grabbed both of the line bags and hurled one over each shoulder, 'Good, now let's get this lot back to the lorry before the old bill join us.'

Harrison dragged the hose back down the jetty, and Lenny followed, scooping up a length himself to lessen Harrison's burden. As they edged past the Brighton crew who had remained in situ on the jetty, Lenny had to turn to his side in order to get past without falling into the water. As he dropped his shoulder, one of the bags fell onto the wooden planks. Before he could get hold of it, Poster Boy had bent over and picked it up.

'Don't worry, Len, I've got it,' he said. 'You're getting a bit old for all this heavy lifting, aren't you?'

Lenny snatched the bag out of his hand, almost ripping the younger man's shoulder out if it's socket. 'It'll be a long time before you can out-lift me, you little gobshite!'

PB almost fell in the water as he sank away from Lenny's bulk. 'All right, Len. I'm only kidding.'

'Well, don't fucking kid. Now, do me a favour and fuck off.'

He threw the bag back over his shoulder, and grabbing hold of the hose, followed Harrison back towards the lorry. After a few steps, he stopped and turned back to PB. 'And by the way, you've got shit hair.'

Wesley looked at the police officer in disbelief. 'What do you mean, you need to search the vehicle? Haven't you noticed, it's a fire engine.'

The man responded with a shrug.

'I know, mate, I do, but that's what I've been told. No vehicle is allowed to go past here,' he patted the barrier arm behind him, 'without being fully searched first.'

As he spoke, the other officers approached him.

'What's the best way to do this?' the policeman asked. 'Would you rather your guys took the gear off as they know where to put it back, or shall we just get on with it.'

Before Wesley could answer, the commanding officer, the guy who had briefed Wesley earlier, suddenly appeared.

'Can I have a word?' he said to the guard, then looked up to Wesley to give him the evil eye.

The guy had been super pissed off since the yacht sank. Wesley had done his best to explain a vessel could only float when it displaced more water than it weighed, but the man didn't seem to be interested in having a physics lesson. All he wanted to do was swear at them for making a boat full of drugs sink. Except the drugs weren't on the boat, and never had been. They were on the fire engine and were about to be discovered.

With the police distracted, Wesley turned to Jimmy. 'Quick, Jim, we've got to get out of here or we're screwed.'

Jimmy looked to the police officers, then back to Wesley, then without saying a word turned the sirens on, making the four police officers jump. Before any of them could say anything, Jimmy leaned across Wesley and yelled, 'Sorry, fellas, but we've got a shout! We need to get going.'

He turned on the blue flashing lights for added effect.

The grumpy old bastard running the job shook his head. 'You're going nowhere until I've searched your vehicle.' The guy was even more pissed off now they'd almost made him pee himself.

'Listen, pal,' Jimmy said, all business like, 'we've got a woman hanging out of her flat window in Kemptown. If you're going to stop us from going then I suggest you go and tell her family why she burned to a fucking crisp instead of us saving her. How does that grab you?'

'Tell your control to send the nearest available fire engine instead.'

Jimmy nodded at the Brighton pump who were still making up their gear. 'They *are* the nearest, and all the other pumps in the city are busy too. So, unless you want that woman to wait for Lewes to turn up and rescue her, I suggest you let us out.'

The man thought about it for a second then nodded at the officer next to him. Seconds later, the barrier arm lifted.

'If you're that bothered,' Jimmy said, 'we can come back when we're done.'

The officer shook his head. 'Just go.'

As they drove up the ramp out of the marina, Wesley mimicked the officer, shaking his head back and forth like a child who had just mastered the art.

'What the hell did you do that for? If they check with mobilising and find out there was no call, we're fucked.'

'We were fucked anyway, that's what you said. So what difference does it make? At least there's a chance they *won't* check. Listen, Wes, you asked me to come up with something, so I came up with something. If you don't like it, then next time, don't do

whatever it was you still haven't told me about. In fact, this has got fuck all to do with me, maybe I should just turn back around and let them search us. Would that be better?'

'No, I'm sorry,' Wesley said. 'You're right. We've asked way too much of you today. But, believe me, we are grateful.'

'Then fucking act like it,' Jimmy said as he stepped on the accelerator and headed back to the station.

Chapter 14
Confession

'And that was the point you decided to steal the money,' Jimmy said, shaking his head. 'Jesus Christ, you fuckers are even more stupid than I thought.'

After hiding the drugs in the spare locker that had once housed the stolen loot, the crew replaced the lines with spares they had in the store room. When that was done, they sat down with a cup of tea and explained what had taken place *that* night to Jimmy and Bodhi. Like with anything else, Bodhi took everything in his stride, nodding occasionally and casting looks to Jimmy who looked just about ready to explode.

'And you were in on this?' he said to Wesley, even though he already knew the answer.

Wesley offered nothing but a sheepish nod back.

'There's no point having a go at him,' Lenny butted in. 'We were all in on it. We've already explained that to you.'

'I bloody well wasn't,' Harrison said.

Jimmy nodded at him, acknowledging the statement.

'The thing is, Len, I expect this sort of bullshit from you. Wesley was in charge. He should have known better.'

'Fuck you,' Lenny said. 'What, like you're so much better than me? You can say what you like now, Jim, but if you'd been there, you would have done exactly the same thing. You ain't no fucking saint. Now, do me a favour and pipe down. You're starting to bore me.'

'That's right, dickhead, I'm not a saint. But I'm no idiot either. Did you really think you'd get away with this, you fucking moron?'

Lenny tapped his thick fingers on the table. 'If I were you, I'd watch your mouth.'

Jimmy pushed out his chair and stood up. For once, he towered over Lenny. The seated man was normally a good six inches taller than him. 'Or what? What the fuck are you going to do about it, big boy?'

For the first time since the confession, Bodhi spoke. 'Come on, bud, cool it. There's no point getting into this.'

'Isn't there? Because this fucking asshole has had it coming for a long time.' He turned his attention back to Lenny. 'So, come on, then, shit-for-brains. Let's go in the yard and have it out.'

Lenny shrugged. 'Whatever. It's your funeral.'

Except that wasn't necessarily true. Lenny may have been twice the size of him and spent most of his adult life dealing with hostile drunken men, but Jimmy was an ex-marine and a tough fucking one at that. He'd done a bit of boxing when he was in the service, meaning his fists could back up his legendary temper. No, if the two of them had it out, there was no saying who would come out on top. The only thing that *was* certain was it would be messy.

It was Dylan's turn to act as peacekeeper, 'Please, fellas, let's not go down this path. We're in enough shit as it is without turning on each other.'

'Dylan's right,' Wesley said, finally finding his voice. 'I think it may be best if you and me discuss this further in the Watch room.'

Jimmy turned away from Lenny's I-don't-give-a-fuck gaze. 'I think that's the smartest thing you've said all day.'

'Look, Jim,' Wesley said, 'I don't disagree with a single thing you've said. We fucked up big time. We shouldn't have taken the money, and I should have taken charge and stopped it. All I can say is I'm sorry.'

Jimmy rubbed his hand through his hair. Away from Lenny's goading, he had calmed down considerably, but was still a few degrees above his normal cooking temperature.

'I know why you did it,' he eventually said. 'It's obvious now.'

Wesley looked shocked. 'Really?'

'Yeah, it is. You're not the popular guy on the Watch, and I know you haven't had the easiest time since you went operational again. You thought if you went along with taking the money, the guys would look at you differently. Maybe accept you as part of the team.'

'I'd like to say that was the case, but unfortunately, that's not it.'

'Oh, come on. You were just trying to get in their good books. It makes sense.'

Wesley shook his head. 'No, you're wrong, Jim. That's not it.'

'Yeah? Because I was willing to swallow that as some sort of excuse for what you did. But if you're saying that wasn't your motive, do you mind telling me what the fuck you *were* thinking?'

Wesley paused before answering. 'I'm skint. I haven't got a pot to piss in. I didn't take the money to try and fit in. I took it to stop me from going under.'

'Bollocks,' Jimmy answered. 'How the fuck can you be skint? You're on a better wage than the rest of us, and your missus has got a decent job too.'

'That's just it. She's not my wife anymore. She left me nearly a year ago.'

Jimmy thought about this for a second. 'And you never told anyone?'

'What's the point. No one's interested, and there's nothing anyone can do anyway. She's gone, and that's all there is to it.'

Jimmy suddenly felt guilty at his and the rest of the Watch's attitude towards Wesley. One of the best things about their job was that even though they argued from time to time, they were as close as a group of people could ever be. The nature of their work, the trust they had to put in each other, and the sights they had to witness meant they were more than colleagues, they were family, even if they would have laughed for suggesting such a thing to them. But that was it, not only did they laugh together, they also shared their problems and worries without thinking about it. For Wesley to be outside of that circle must have been pretty difficult for him.

'So, what happened?' Jimmy asked.

Wesley shrugged. 'I don't know. One day, she just came home and told me she didn't love me, that I wasn't the man she married and she didn't think she could live with me any longer. I moved out a week later, and other than to pick the girls up, I haven't been back since.'

'Shit… And what about the girls, how are they taking it?'

He shrugged again, and Jimmy noticed his eyes were beginning to well up. *Please don't cry*, he thought. He was ex-forces; he didn't think he could deal with tears and cuddles, what with everything else he had experienced that day.

'The girls are okay,' he answered. 'I mean, when I spend the day with them, they keep asking when I'm coming home, but I think they understand it's not going to happen.'

'So, where *are* you living?'

'I'm renting a flat in town. It's only a little one-bedroom place, not as bad as some of the ones I've seen, but you know what Brighton prices are like.'

'You kept that quiet. I thought you were still commuting to work every day.'

Wesley's family lived in Milton Keynes, the place he had been born and raised, and as far as the rest of the Watch was concerned, was still living.

'I'm serious, Jim, this whole thing is nearly bankrupting me. I'm still paying the mortgage on the house. I mean, I can't see the girls getting kicked out of their home. Then, on top of that, there's my rent, and as for the solicitor's fees, I won't even tell you how much that's costing me. When we found that money, I wasn't thinking about impressing the guys. I just needed enough dough to keep my head above water for a few months.'

'Fuck me,' Jimmy said. 'I wasn't expecting that. So, do I take it you've spent the hush money this guy gave you?'

Wesley nodded. 'It went in a couple of weeks.'

'There's no point worrying about it anymore,' Jimmy's voice had softened. 'What's done is done, and once we give this fucker

his drugs back, we can put it all behind us. Pretend the whole fucking thing never happened.'

'Let's hope so,' Wesley said. 'For all our sakes.'

Before they could say anything else, the office phone went.

'Want me to get it?' Jimmy asked. 'Could be him.'

'No, I'll do it. He'll probably want to speak to me.' Wesley walked over to the phone, breathing a sigh of relief when he recognised the number. 'It's all right, it's just Central.'

He picked the phone up and held it to his ear, 'Smudge, how can I help you, my friend... That's right, we did leave on blue lights... No, you're right, it wasn't an actual call, but if we hadn't got out of there sharpish, I think Jimmy would have smacked that copper and spent the night in a cell.... I know, I know, and I do realise that, but I didn't know what else to do... Yeah, he was... okay, mate. Take care, I'll speak to you soon.'

He looked back to Jimmy who had heard enough of the conversation to know exactly what they were talking about. 'Did he sound convinced?'

'I think so. He enjoyed bollocking me for abusing the blues and twos, mind you.'

'Considering the circumstances,' Jimmy said, 'I'd say that was the least of our problems.'

'Yeah, well, let's just hope he keeps his mouth shut, or we could still be in the shit.' He stared back at the phone. 'Perhaps our man won't get in touch with us today. Maybe he'll wait until things cool down a bit.'

As he spoke, the phone rang.

'Or then again,' Jimmy said, 'maybe not.'

Chapter 15
Rendezvous

Wesley looked out of the window across the empty car park. 'I still think this was a mistake. He said for me to come on my own. He's not gonna like you being here.'

Jimmy sat on the seat next to him, looking uncomfortable in such a confined space. His transit van felt positively massive compared to the interior of Wes' poky little Fiat. The boot of the vehicle was only just big enough for the four black bin bags they had stuffed the drugs into.

'The man won't say shit,' Jimmy said. 'All he gives a fuck about is his stash.'

'I could have done it myself, you know. You didn't need to babysit me.'

'Didn't I? I don't want to keep going on about it, but we both know what happened last time you were left to your own devices.'

'Like I said, we all make mistakes.'

Wesley looked around again. The car park at Brighton Race Course was quiet, but the lights on the main road provided the place with far too much light for his liking.

'I mean, what if they've got CCTV?'

Jimmy shrugged. 'No one cares about us. If there are cameras, they'll just think we're doggers looking for a bit of action.'

Wesley gave him a look. 'Is that meant to make me feel better?'

Jimmy smiled and shrugged again. 'You know, if this all works out, there's something I'd like you to do for me.'

'Anything. It's the least I can do.'

'When the dust settles, I want you off the Watch.'

Wesley turned to look at him, but Jimmy kept looking straight ahead.

'You're a liability, and I'm not just talking about all this shit. You're dangerous, and you shouldn't be on the lorries. You're going to get yourself killed,' Jimmy turned to face him, 'or even worse, one of us. Now, do yourself and everyone else a favour and go back to your desk job.'

'Don't worry,' Wesley said. 'I intend to.'

After five minutes of silence, the Bentley pulled into the car park and headed slowly toward them. It parked just close enough so its doors wouldn't touch the other car if they opened, then the blacked-out passenger window lowered, revealing the smiling face of Mac.

Wesley wound his own window down to hear the man.

'I have to say; you boys were pretty fucking awesome today. I knew I was right to put my faith in the fire service.'

His smile dropped a little when he looked past Wesley to see Jimmy sitting there.

'I told you to come alone, but seeing as you did such a good job back there, I'm willing to let this one go.'

Jimmy got out of the car without saying a word then opened the boot of both vehicles. He took the bags out of the Fiat and threw them into the Bentley then slammed them shut again. When he was done, he walked around to the other side of the car and leant into Mac's window.

'There's your drugs. Now, do us all a favour and get fucked. I don't want to see you at our fire station ever again. Got it?'

Mac held his gaze for a few seconds, then moved his head so he could see Wesley. 'This one's got some balls on him, hasn't he? And there I was thinking it was the old boy who ran the show.'

Jimmy lowered his own head so they were level again. 'Now you know how things really work. My guys fucked up when they took your money, and if I'd been there, it wouldn't have happened. But the fact is, it did, and what we did today more than made up for it. We're all square now, and we don't owe you shit. Got it?'

Mac laughed and looked across to his driver. 'This here is Don,' he said. 'My new driver.'

For the first time, Jimmy looked across and took the man in. Even though he was sitting, it was clear he was a unit. He must have been at least six-four and a good sixteen stone. He wasn't as big as Lenny, but he was younger and more athletic looking, with a face just as intimidating. Jimmy weighed the guy up and reckoned that he'd fought worse in his time.

'See, the thing with Don,' Mac said, 'is he may look like a real piece of work, but I can't say just how good he is. He tells me he's the sort of person who can do the things I need doing, but so far, it's just talk. Now, Tony, my sadly deceased ex-driver, that guy was a real nut-job when he needed to be. I mean, the man would shoot someone in the face, then drive me home without once going over the speed limit. He was ice cold, but then, those fucking Albanians went and put a bullet in him. But, anyway, back to Don here. If you want to keep this attitude going, my friend, then I may just have to see if he really is as good as he thinks he is.'

He turned and looked to the stone-faced man next to him. 'What do you think, that sound good to you?'

Don nodded, then opened his jacket and showed Jimmy the pistol he had stuffed down the front of his trousers.

'Now, we could go that way,' Mac said, 'or I could just say thank you once again for what you did today and pass on this token of appreciation to you.'

He nodded at the driver who leant into the back of the vehicle and passed him a package. Mac leant out of the window and offered it to Jimmy.

'There's fifty grand there,' he said. 'That's just to show you how good I'm feeling about what went down today. Take it and give it to your boys. They deserve it.'

Jimmy's face remained stony. 'I'm not interested in your money.'

'Is that right?'

'Yeah, that's right.'

Moving far quicker than a man of his age had any right to, Mac reached out with his spare hand and grabbed hold of Jimmy's wrist. He was a strong little fucker too.

'Right, sunshine, I'm rapidly getting tired of your bullshit. Take the money or else tomorrow morning, some poor dog walker is going to find the two of your bodies in a fucking ditch not far from here. Now, I'm sure you wouldn't want to spoil some old dear's day in that way, would you?'

'No, I wouldn't,' Jimmy said, shocked at the fear he could feel in his chest.

At the same instant, Mac loosened his grip and stuffed the package into his hand. 'Good man. That's what I like to hear.'

He leant forward and looked across to Wesley again. 'He's feisty, this one. I can see I'm going to have to keep my eye on him. Thanks again, fellas. I'll be seeing you around.'

He closed his window as Don fired up the engine and drove them away.

'Fuck,' Jimmy said as he slammed the car door and threw the package into the backseat.

'What's wrong?' Wesley asked, 'You should be happy. It's all over now.'

Jimmy shook his head. 'You really don't get it, do you, Wes. At first, I thought you were just a bit dim, but you really haven't got a fucking clue, have you, pal?'

'What are you talking about? It's over with. He's finished with us now.'

'That package,' Jimmy said, 'means it's never going to be finished.'

Chapter 16

Wesley

'Get out of the sodding way!' Wesley yelled at the car in front of him.

The grey Skoda Fabia was barely doing sixty miles an hour and had no place in the fast lane of the M23. Wesley beeped his horn and told himself he'd be doing the same thing, even if it was a car full of lads rather than the little old lady, oblivious to his ill feeling toward her. Even as he thought it, he knew he was lying to himself. If there *was* a car full of boys in front of him, he would have sworn under his breath but done nothing about it.

To be fair, he wouldn't normally have beeped at the woman at all, but the man just wanted to get back home to see his kids. The last couple of days had scared the shit out of him. Now, all he wanted to do was hug his girls and tell them how much he loved them.

He'd just about made it through the previous day without losing it, and as there was enough of them on duty, he'd taken the opportunity to book his night shifts off and go back to Milton Keynes. His soon-to-be ex-wife had been shocked when she'd heard from him; he wasn't meant to be having the girls until the weekend, and it had taken more than a little persuading to convince her to let him have them for a few days. It was the school holidays, for Christ's sake, he had wanted to say, but had managed to refrain himself.

Every time he saw the girls, he felt like he had to jump through hoops before he got them to himself. As soon as he got there, he would have to turn around again and drive them straight back to Brighton. He was no longer welcome in the house that he still paid for and rightfully owned. Nina had made it painfully clear

after nearly ten years of comfortable if unspectacular marriage that she thoroughly despised him and struggled to look at his face without wanting to throw up. It hurt him that she felt that way, who wouldn't it hurt?

He knew he was no Daniel Craig and might not have been the most exciting man in the world, but he had loved her, even if he hadn't always shown it. But it was the girls that mattered most to him. He could just about deal with what she had done; it was the thought of their rejection that really terrified him. The five-hour round trip was a pain in the ass, but it would be worth it when he got the girls back to Brighton for a long weekend together.

The old woman finally moved out of the fast lane, and Wesley stepped on the accelerator, cursing as the Fiat slowly passed her on the outside. The pissy little engine was not made for long distances, and Wesley yearned for his much-loved Audi that he'd been forced to sell to help pay for his lodgings.

His conversation with Jimmy two days earlier still sat heavy on his mind. He hadn't been completely honest when he told him it was his financial situation that had prompted him to take the money. Obviously, that was a major factor, but it certainly wasn't the only one. Wesley was aware he wasn't well regarded on the Watch or even in the brigade as a whole. Just because he acknowledged the fact, though, it didn't make it any easier to accept. No one liked being the boy the captains didn't want on their team.

He knew why they didn't like him too. When the strikes had kicked off, he had left the union, rather than take industrial action. It wasn't that he was opposed to it ideologically, but at the time, he had been working in fire safety, and nothing he did could have had a meaningful effect on the strikes. It was the firefighters downing tools and taking the engines off the run that really made an impact. When he had been on the lorries in the previous strikes ten years earlier, he had done the same as the rest of his colleagues and joined them on the picket line. Whether that was because he was new to the job and his Watch would have eaten him alive if

he had gone against them, or because he felt it was the right thing to do, he couldn't say with any degree of honesty.

What he hadn't done, though, in the recent strikes and what seemed to be overlooked by people like Harrison, was that unlike many of the other officers, he hadn't ridden the resilience fire engines, or scab lorries as they came to be known by the men. During the strikes, a few of them had decided to post pics of themselves on social media; smiling and laughing as they put on fire-kit for the first time in years. When the firefighters were trying to protect their pensions and hard-earned conditions of service, such jovialities went down with them about as well as being offered a shit sandwich for lunch.

But Wesley hadn't done it, despite the pressure that had been placed on him from above. He may not have joined the crews in solidarity, but he was not prepared to undermine the strikes either by making it easier for the brigade to continue like it was business as usual. That was the real reason why he had ended up back on the appliances. It certainly wasn't, as was stated, to give him more experience on the frontline before he could advance in the job. No, the man had bitten the hand that fed him, and it was unlikely he'd ever be promoted again. Making him operational was management's way of punishing him for his dissent. There were other officers who had taken the same stance as him and whose reputations had remained intact. But not Wesley's; his act of resistance had done little to improve people's opinions of him. His reputation hung around his neck like an albatross and was formed long before the strikes had ever taken place. No matter what he did, he doubted it was something he'd ever shake off.

Wesley had never had a desperate urge to join the fire service, but as his father had been the Deputy Chief of Buckinghamshire, he knew what was expected of him from the family, and followed the old man into the business. The incident that had really put the dampeners on his career had happened before it had really got started. He was on Blue Watch at Central at the time, and only just out of training school. Although he had never displayed

any signs of excellence, he had been coasting along nicely with no real doubts about him, other than the usual things probies encountered. On the night in question, both of the Brighton engines had been called to a house-fire with smoke issuing. When they arrived on the scene, there was indeed smoke pumping out of one of the windows upstairs. Thankfully, everyone was safely out of the premises.

The BA crew was made up of Wesley and Fat Terry, one of the older members of the crew. As his name suggested, Terry may have been more than a few stones overweight, but the man was one of the best BA wearers in the business. Even though he smoked like a chimney, he was legendary for using less air in an incident than anyone else. Years of doing the job meant his breathing remained steady throughout, and he didn't waste energy doing unnecessary tasks. In BA, Terry was the true measure of efficiency.

They had taken a hose reel into the building and, after quickly pushing upstairs, searched the rooms. The neutral plain was almost to the floor, making it impossible to see anything, and by the time they had searched two of the rooms, they were getting hot and still hadn't found the fire. As they pushed into the third bedroom, the hose reel snagged, and Terry, who was the number one and had hold of the branch, could progress no further. He tugged at it a few times, but it had got well and truly stuck. The only option for them was to go back and release the hose from wherever it had got caught up.

Going by the book, a BA crew should never split up, but as he would be going over ground they'd already covered and would not encounter the fire, Terry sent Wesley back into the hallway to deal with the situation. It was the number two's job to drag the hose into the job, and if Wesley had done a better job of managing it, then perhaps it wouldn't have got snagged. While Terry continued his search of the bedroom, Wesley followed the hose back into the hall, tugging it as he went, to try and locate the problem. Once outside, that was when his problems began. The hallway had suddenly got much

hotter, and even though he still couldn't see any flames, he was aware the situation was getting worse. Unless they found the fire soon, conditions would only escalate. He followed the hose into the previous room they had been in and, after a lot of messing around, managed to untangle it from the bed post that it had somehow got stuck around.

When he got back into the hallway, the temperature had increased further, forcing Wesley down to his knees. It was the first time he had felt this hot outside of training school, where the instructors were close at hand and could step in at any time. With zero visibility and the skin on his ears and neck starting to burn, Wesley began to panic. He tried to find the entrance to the room he knew Terry must have been in, but even though it was only a few feet away from him, Wesley was unable to locate the door. The only thing he could think of with any clarity at this point was to get out of the building as quickly as possible to a place that was safe and cool. Instead of yelling out for Terry and calling him back to the hallway, he turned and headed to where he thought the stairs were located.

When he got outside, he ripped his helmet and BA mask off, and as he stood there ventilating, the rest of his crew stared at him in disbelief. He had broken the cardinal rule of BA wearing. You never leave your partner in the building. Terry had fucked up, too, by letting an inexperienced firefighter leave his side and would get his arse kicked for doing so, but his real mistake was to overestimate the level of Wesley's skills.

Trying to protect the new boy, Terry tried to laugh off what had happened, telling the others when he emerged five minutes later that it was just a mattress alight, nothing serious, but it was too late for Wesley, he had committed the ultimate firefighting sin: YOU NEVER LEAVE YOUR PARTNER IN A FUCKING JOB. It was a mistake that he had never been allowed to forget. So, when he had agreed with the crew and instructed them to take the money, there was just a part of Wesley that hoped this decision would be enough to wipe the slate clean and erase the

view of him that he knew his Watch held. It had become clear all too soon that, unfortunately, this wasn't the case.

He pulled up in front of his old house at noon. It was a bit later than he had expected, but considering he'd battled through the Friday morning rush hour traffic on the M25, and he was driving a 1.2 litre shopping trolley, it hadn't been too shabby.

Standing at the front door, he braced himself for Nina's icy reception. Her attitude was pretty rich, if you asked him. It was she who had told him to leave, and he had made sure that none of them had wanted for anything since his departure, yet somehow, he was always made to feel the bad guy. When the door opened, he was immediately hit by the wall of vitriol that surrounded her. Nina was an attractive, if slightly horsy looking woman who always dressed like she was about to take part in a business meeting, which was ironic considering she hadn't gone back to her job as a human resources manager for the local council since Olivia was born.

'Are they ready?' he said, trying his best to sound pleasant. He could do without the bullshit.

'Olivia's just finishing doing her hair,' Nina said in the manner he had been expecting, 'and Emily is sitting in the living room with her bag on her lap. You said you'd be here nearly an hour ago.'

Wesley bit his tongue and shrugged. 'Blame the M25.' He wanted to say that it was more like half an hour ago, but that would just be asking for trouble.

'The M25 didn't phone me up last night and ask to have the girls without prior notice. That was you, Wesley.'

'What can I say, I miss them. You should try living without your family. It's not easy.'

He suddenly felt an overwhelming urge to tell Nina that he missed her too and to ask her to take him back. He didn't know why. He hadn't expected to say it, and he wasn't even sure that was what he wanted. Did he love her? At least part of him felt like it did. Some days, all he could think about was being back there with the three of them, and other times, he kind of enjoyed the solitary nature of his newfound predicament.

Fighting the urge to say anything, he followed Nina into the house. The place was immaculate as usual. Even when she was working, Nina had always been slightly OCD about the housework, but now that the girls were both in full-time education, her day-time hours seemed to revolve around making the place look like a show home. Perhaps that was why she kicked him out, maybe he was the one thing that was preventing her having her dream house.

She led him into the living room where Emily was sitting quietly with her Peppa Pig rucksack on her lap, watching an episode of the same animal on TV. When she saw him, she did that shy sideways look that kids did when they were really happy to see someone but didn't want to show it. Wesley sat next to his little girl, and lifted her and the bag onto his own lap. She was getting heavy; she was nearly six now and was already in year one at school. He hadn't noticed himself getting older until he had children. Now, the girls acted as a visual indicator of his own mortality.

'I know this one,' he said, looking at the TV screen. 'This is where Pedro Pony breaks his leg.'

He did know it, too. Emily had it on DVD, and he must have seen every episode on it at least fifty times.

Emily laughed and snuggled into her father. 'Yeah, and then, Peppa and the others write on his cast.'

Wesley tickled the girl under the arms, almost making her fall off his lap. 'Yeah,' he said, imitating her voice, 'and then, Peppa tries to fall over and break her leg so she can get a cast too. Silly piggy.'

He tickled her again, and they both laughed.

The door of the room flew open, and Olivia waltzed in like she was a model on a catwalk. Now, he felt really old. She was nine going on nineteen and already up to her mother's shoulder. He hoped that both the girls would follow Nina in the height department. She was tall, at nearly five ten, and a good inch or two bigger than him. When she wore her heels, as she often liked to do, he felt like Tom Cruise, or maybe that should be Dudley Moore, with some gangly supermodel at his side.

'Hi, Dad. How are you?' Olivia asked.

'I'm fine, thanks, darling,' he said, feeling strange that it was him answering the questions. She reminded him so much of her mother, it scared him. 'You look beautiful.'

'Shut up, Dad,' she said, bringing Nina to Wesley's mind more than ever.

'That's told me, hasn't it, you cheeky monkey.'

He wondered how long he could keep calling her lame-o things like that without her rolling her eyes and saying "whatever," or whatever it was that kids said now to uncool old farts like him.

'Right, then, girls,' he said, getting to his feet. 'Let's skedaddle. We want to get back before the traffic starts building up again.'

Nina followed them to the front door and just as they were saying their goodbyes, Wesley looked past her into the kitchen and, for a moment, thought that he was seeing things.

'Is that Gregg I just saw in the kitchen?' he asked. 'What's he doing here?'

Gregg was married to Paula, Nina's best friend since they'd been in little school. They'd been out together on plenty of occasions, and while he could be a bit of a bore, waxing lyrical about his job as a supermarket manager or his adventures on the golf course, Gregg was okay, if slightly dull.

Nina looked over her shoulder briefly then back to Wesley. For a split second, he thought he detected a slight chink in her armour.

'Oh, yeah,' she said, like it was obvious. 'It's Gregg. He lives here now.'

Her nonchalance made Wesley think he had misheard her. 'He what?'

'I thought I told you, he moved in a few weeks ago. Surely the girls must have said something.'

'No,' he said, 'I'm pretty fucking sure the girls didn't.'

'Wesley!' she shouted. 'Watch your language in front of our daughters.'

He looked again and saw Gregg's head pop out from behind the free-standing fridge. The man smiled and offered Wesley the

smallest of waves. Wesley shook his head and started towards him until Nina stepped into his path.

'And where do you think you're going?'

'Where do you think I'm going? I'm going to speak to Gregg over there and find out what the hell is going on here.'

'No, you're not. This is my house. Now leave please.'

'I'll think you'll find it's my house, actually. I'm the one who pays the mortgage.'

'And I'm the one with my name on the deeds right next to yours.'

Emily tugged at her father's hand. 'Come on, Daddy, let's go.'

'See,' Nina said, 'you're upsetting her.'

Gregg came out of the kitchen and positioned himself about five yards behind Nina. 'Come on, Wes, don't be like this.'

Wesley gave the car keys to Olivia. 'Do me a favour, honey, take Emily into the back of the car and wait for me. I've got the DVD players set up, and I think *Frozen* is still in there from last time.'

'Yay,' Emily said, instantly brightening up as her sister led her towards the vehicle.

'So, tell me, Gregg, what does Paula think about all this?'

Gregg shrugged. 'She's not happy.'

Wesley laughed. 'I bet she isn't. You've run off with her best friend, you piece of shit.'

'Don't talk to him like that,' Nina said. 'How dare you.'

'How dare I? How fucking dare you look down your nose at me when you're living with your best mate's husband. Jesus, you've got a nerve.'

For once, Nina was temporarily silenced. Wesley seized on it, turning his attention to Gregg.

'And as for you, you're happy to live here in my house while I'm paying the bills. I thought you had more pride than that.'

'Come on, Wes, don't be like that. I still have to pay for things my end with Paula and the kids.'

'And so do I, Gregg. But the difference is, I've also got to pay for my shitty little flat, and now, it seems I'm paying for you too.'

'So that's what this is all about, is it?' Nina had found her voice again. It hadn't taken long. 'Money. I should have thought as much. That's just typical of you, Wesley, it really is.'

'You know what, Nina?' Wesley said. 'Why don't the two of you just fuck off.'

'Hey!' Gregg shouted. 'Don't talk to her like that.'

'Or what? What are you going to do about it, tough guy?'

Nina laughed. 'And what are you going to do, Wes? All this riding around on fire engines again suddenly make you think you're a real man, does it?'

Before he could answer, she spoke again. 'I'll tell you exactly what's going to happen. Things are going to continue just like they are now. Gregg is going to keep living here, and you're going to keep paying the bills. If you don't like it, then forget seeing the girls anymore. Understand?'

'You can't do that. I've got my rights.'

'Can't I? Do you know how long it will take you to get those rights? Months, years, most likely. I'm their mother, and I get to say if you can see them or not. You start making our lives difficult, and I'll make yours a whole lot worse, understand? Act like an idiot, and the only time you'll see the girls is at Christmas and birthdays. Is that what you want?'

'You wouldn't do that. I know you've proved yourself to be a pretty disgusting piece of work, but not even you would stoop that low.'

'Wouldn't I? How about you try me and find out.'

Wesley stood there looking at the two of them for a long time; Gregg hiding behind her like Wes was a heavyweight boxer. He laughed, then turned and left the house. 'You're fucking welcome to each other.'

When he was almost at the car, Nina shouted to him, 'You know you never used to swear like that when you worked in fire safety!'

'Go fuck yourselves,' Wesley said without looking back.

Chapter 17

Jimmy

'Calm down, son. You're gonna give yourself a hernia.'

Bob watched with amusement as Jimmy demolished what was left of the two-foot-high brick wall. The couple who owned the house had come into some money and decided to replace their aging conservatory with a flat roof extension, complete with skylights and bi-folding doors. The existing footings were too shallow and not wide enough for building regulations, so Jimmy and Bob were knocking down and starting again. It was a pretty standard job for them.

Many firefighters had a second job, or fiddle as it's usually referred to, and many of those jobs were often found in the trades. There were people out there who got sniffy about this, but as most insiders knew only too well, it was those skills they brought with them from the outside world that helped firefighters achieve their goals effectively. The Fire and Rescue service was all about problem solving and improvisation. One person on their own might not have the solution, but between them, a crew could usually muddle through and come up with a decent working plan.

Tradespeople were usual practical hands-on types, and their specialist knowledge was often the thing that saved the day. If a car had crashed into a building, causing a partial collapse, and you had a builder on your crew, they would have a much better idea than most about how the structural integrity had been affected. An electrician could give a far better assessment on the extent of the damage caused by a fire in fuse box than the average crew member. If you were sent to a serious flooding and you had a plumber on the crew… you can see where this is going.

Jimmy put down the sledgehammer and took a slurp of his tea. It was almost cold; he should have drunk it ten minutes earlier like Bob had done. The older man had never missed the opportunity to have a cuppa. When he was in charge of Red Watch, the boys knew that all they had to do to avoid him getting them out in the yard drilling was to keep him plied with tea. Since he had taken his retirement and become a full-time builder, he had made sure to keep up this most important of rituals.

'What's got into you today, boy?' Bob asked. He still called Jimmy a boy, even though he was in his mid-forties and a good ten years older than both of Bob's kids. 'You're like a dog chasing a bone.'

'There's no point fucking around, old man,' Jimmy said. 'The quicker we get this wall down, the quicker we can make a start on getting those footings done. You did bring the breaker, didn't you?'

Bob rolled his eyes. 'Did I bring the breaker? Of course I brought the sodding breaker. But the fact is, I have no intention of using that breaker until I've eaten my lunch. They ain't going to pay us any more money for doing it quicker.'

Jimmy threw the cold tea into the pot of lavender next to him, then dug into his holdall for a plastic Tupperware box.

'Don't tell me,' Bob said. 'Soppy Bollocks has got you boys running around the yard again.'

Indirectly, Bob was one of the many reasons that Wesley had found life so hard since arriving on Red Watch. Everyone loved Bob, and he was as good a Watch manager as you could find. He wasn't a drill pig like some other people who held his rank, and he couldn't give a shit about polished shoes and freshly ironed shirts. All that mattered to Bob was that when they got a call, his crew had the ability to deal with the situation effectively and with the minimal of fuss. And you could say what you liked about Red Watch, they might have been lazy sons-of-bitches, but when the shit went down, they knew exactly what they were doing. You could try, but you'd struggle to find a more professional group of firefighters in the service.

Whenever he got the chance, Bob liked to drop Wesley's name into the conversation. He enjoyed hearing Jimmy bitching about the man, and romanticising about how much more fun it was when he had been the Watch manager. Bob knew it was petty, but Jimmy's moans were his only link to the job nowadays.

'Something like that,' Jimmy said as he opened the foil that enveloped his ham sandwiches.

The two of them had been working together for nearly twenty years, pretty much the entire time Jimmy had been in the fire service. When he turned up for his first day at Brighton, the two of them had hit it off immediately. Bob quickly took Jimmy under his wing, not that the man needed looking after. He had just come out of the Marines and was as tough a fella as you were likely to meet. But for all his bluster, Jimmy reminded Bob of a little lost kid, and so he made the conscious decision to become his mentor, teaching him everything he knew about the fire service as well as giving him an unofficial apprenticeship in the building trade. More importantly, he also became a father figure to Jimmy.

In a way, Jimmy's life had taken a similar path to that of Lenny's. Perhaps that's why they found themselves bumping heads so often; they were too alike. Both of them had been brought up in less than ideal situations, and both of them had experienced life outside of the law. But while Lenny's old man had used him and his brother as punch bags when he got the booze inside of him, Jimmy's old man had never laid a hand on him. The fucker had never laid eyes on him, either; he had pissed off as soon as he found out that his girlfriend was pregnant. Jimmy was brought up by his mum in a one bedroom flat, halfway up a tower block in East London, and even though the woman had done everything in her power to keep her son in line, it was never going to happen.

It was easy to understand why Jimmy fell in with the wrong crowd at such a young age. With his old man out of the picture, he needed someone to look up to, and those people just happened to be the older kids who lived in the block. They hung out in the

basketball court at the bottom of the tower until late at night and rode around on their BMXs like they were the kings of the estate. Jimmy used to look over the top of his balcony and watch them in awe as they showed off the goods they had stolen from the shopping centre, getting drunk on the cheap booze the older boys were able to buy from the store. His mother did her best to steer him away from them, but there was no stopping Jimmy. He was going to be one of the bad boys too.

Considering the things he got up to in his teens, it was amazing that the boy escaped without a criminal record. Stealing, fighting, dope dealing and selling anything they could get their hands on, Jimmy and his mates did whatever took their fancy. He knew there was no future in what he was doing, but it was fun, and he felt like he belonged with a group of mates that would always have his back no matter how bad things got. Yeah, right.

When he was sixteen, they got involved in a little turf war with the boys from the block next to his. Both groups thought they were little Mafioso, trying to sell their dope to the older, better off kids who had to walk through the estate to get to the art school they attended.

One night, the two gangs had got a bit mouthy with each other on the courts, and the bravado and name calling quickly turned to pushing and shoving, which quickly turned to punching and kicking, which quickly turned to Baashi, the little Somali kid who lived a few doors down from Jimmy, being stabbed in the heart with a kitchen knife. As the two gangs ran away, Jimmy sat there cradling the boy's head in his lap, crying like a little baby as his friend bled out.

Two days later, he went down to the Navy recruitment office and signed up for the Marines. He was skinny then, and unfit too. The nearest thing he had done to exercise in the past couple of years was knock a football against the wire fence that surrounded the courts.

A few weeks later, he kissed his crying mother, who was relieved that he was getting away from his friends, but terrified he could end up going to war. Jimmy went straight to the train

station to begin his journey to Lympestone, Devon, the place that would be his home for the next eight months.

He wouldn't say he loved being a marine. He certainly enjoyed his time as a commando and he was good at it, too, a natural in the field. Jimmy was grateful to the marines for what they had given him; a new life, travel, decent money for the first time, of which he passed most on to his mum, but he never loved the lifestyle like some of the other lads did. Most of them defined themselves as being marines; it was the thing that made them who they were. He just felt like a bloke who had joined up to get away from far worse shit.

Two years after he joined, the first Iraq War kicked off. His mates were gagging to get out there and prove their worth, but instead of fighting in the desert like some of the marines in 40 Commando, Jimmy found himself on manoeuvres in the freezing cold tundra of Norway. He wasn't bothered about missing the war. He had no idea what the fuck it was all about anyway, none of the lads did really, they just wanted to get out there and finally put their training into practice. He had joined up to escape a war zone, not find one.

After eight years, two tours of Northern Ireland, and a spell in both Belize and the Falklands, Jimmy left the marines and not knowing what else to do, he applied for and was accepted into the fire service. The marines had been good to him, but when he finished training school and turned up at Brighton, Jimmy knew he had found his real home.

'So, what's the numpty got you doing now?' Bob said. 'Bridging drills over shark infested custard again?'

Jimmy laughed as he snapped off one of the sticks of his Kit Kat and shoved the whole thing into his mouth.

'It ain't just Wes, Bob. Did you ever get the feeling that sometimes you were the only sane person in the job?'

For the first time since he'd been on the Watch, Jimmy felt like he didn't trust them. It was a strange, alien feeling.

When they had returned to the station, he had hidden the fifty grand in the spare locker and made Wesley promise not to tell anyone about it.

'Did I?' Bob laughed. 'I spent most my working career thinking it. Management are mental, and the boys aren't much better, either. Sometimes, I felt like Jack Nicholson in that film with all those crazy bastards. It was a good thing I had you there, or I reckon I would have ended up like the rest of 'em.'

'Aw, thanks, darling, you say the nicest things.'

'Piss off, smartarse.'

Jimmy had been on the same Watch as Bob for most of his career. When Bob decided to take things a bit easier and move from Brighton to Roedean (the busy nights were getting too much for him), Jimmy took his exams and was promoted to leading fireman. He moved around the Watches for a few years, but when a LF's vacancy came up on Bob's watch, Jimmy jumped at the chance of working with him again.

'So, how's the family?' Bob asked after finishing off the last of the vegetable soup he kept in his thermos flask. He'd had the same thing for lunch for as long as Jimmy had been working with him. 'Jen, all right? The kids good?'

The best thing that came out of Jimmy's time in the marines was meeting Jenny. On pretty much his first day of basic training, his staff sergeant had warned the recruits about the local girls. All they wanted, he said, was to marry a marine and get the fuck out of Devon. They didn't care who they got, they just wanted out. On his first weekend off, when he and the other recruits hit the town, Jimmy had met Jen in one of the local pubs, and it was love at first sight. He didn't care what his instructors or anyone else said; he knew when he first clapped eyes on her that he would marry the girl. If it was true that she just wanted to get away from her hometown, then he didn't care. That was what he had done, after all.

When he finally settled in Brighton with just enough savings for a deposit on a house and a mortgage advisor who made sure

they got more than they could really afford, the young couple bought a bungalow in Saltdean, a quiet, coastal little village a few miles to the east of the city that escaped the exorbitant prices of London-by-Sea.

A couple of years later, Becky was born, and a few years after, George entered the world, and the family lived happily ever after. Or at least that was supposed to happen. When Jimmy joined the fire service, one of the things that most attracted him to the job was the family friendly shifts. He had never known his old man, but when his own children came along, the four-on, four-off system meant that he would be able to have a hands-on role in their upbringing.

That was the idea anyway, but in reality, it never really happened. It wasn't that he didn't earn a decent wage in the fire service, because he did; he had friends who would be happy to take home his pay packet. But by the same token, he knew labourers who took home more money than he did once he had paid his tax and pension contributions. Jen worked when she could, she had a part time job in a care home down the road, but her work hours had to revolve around taking the kids to and from school, and his shifts.

In order to pay the mortgage, the bills and all the other bollocks that went with it, Jimmy had found himself working more and more with Bob, and seeing less and less of Jen and the kids. Becky was going on eight, George was four, and he knew he should have been there more to watch them grow up. Before long, they'd be stroppy teenagers not wanting to know their old dad, so while they were willing, he should make the most of it. Yet, it seemed like it was only at the weekends that the family got to be together, and by then, he was too knackered to do much of anything.

Jen also felt it and would encourage him as often as possible to do less work and spend more time with them. It usually ended up in them fighting, especially when he had to remind her that unless they wanted to end up knee-deep in debt, like so many

other people they knew, he would have to keep working. Becky had been nagging them for riding lessons for months, and for some reason, Jen had agreed to it. Who did she think was going to pay for them? There was no riding lesson fairy who could wave her wand and give the girl what she wanted.

So, yes, things had been bit a sticky for the two of them lately, and money, or the lack of it, seemed to be at the core of their problems. But would Jimmy have done what the others had done that night and taken the cash? Would he bollocks. He knew with complete certainty that if he had been in charge, it wouldn't have happened, simple as that. Yet, as usual, it was him trying to solve the mess they had gotten themselves in. If that bastard came around again wanting to get his money's worth out of the Watch, then Jimmy was worried he would have to take matters into his own hands, and all he could see if that happened was things getting very nasty, very quickly. The guy had frightened him the day before, and it was a feeling Jimmy hadn't felt for a long, long time. Even so, if he needed to, he would protect his Watch. That's what he was there for.

'Come on, then, sunshine,' Bob said. 'These footings aren't going to dig themselves. Now, do me a favour and get the breaker from the van. My old legs aren't what they used to be.'

Jimmy rolled his eyes. 'Seriously, what would you do without me, you lazy old bastard?'

Chapter 18
Bodhi

Bodhi sipped the last of his coffee and stared at the Adur River. He had been watching it for the last hour. It was one of the things that he liked to do to every day; sit and watch the river from the comfort of his home. At high tide, the water would raise his boat completely out of the water, but it had receded to almost a trickle, and he could barely see it over the sand and grasses that would be underwater in a few hours. This was his favourite time, when low tide would soon be on them. He loved the low tide, because if the wind was right, and that day it was, then it was time for him to get out and do his thing.

He got up from his hammock and took another glance at the windsock that hung from the twelve-foot pole next to him. As was normally the case, the wind was blowing from a south-westerly direction and looked to be gusting at around twenty miles per hour. It was perfect. He stretched his arms into the air until he was standing on tiptoes and could reach no higher, then he bent over like a jack-knife, grabbing his ankles so that his curly hair brushed against the floor. He held the pose for nearly a minute then performed half a dozen sun salutations. When he was done, he left the deck of his houseboat and headed below to grab his gear.

Shoreham-by-Sea was a rapidly growing ex-fishing village situated six miles to the West of Brighton. For years, the town had been a pretty but rather quiet place, with not an awful lot going on. The crazy price hikes that had taken place in Brighton, as more and more commuters moved down from London to live out their seaside dream, now meant Shoreham had become a highly desirable place for young families to live. As a result, the

town had changed a great deal in a relatively short time. A large development of swanky flats and townhouses had sprung along the river, and was soon followed by gastro pubs, restaurants and a newly pedestrianised high street where every other building was now a coffee shop with outdoor seating in the summer months. It was a nice town, all right, but certainly not spectacular.

The one talking point that did mark Shoreham out as different, and even brought tourists in to view the attraction, was the thirty or so houseboats that lined the southern bank of the Adur. The river travelled down from the north alongside the western edge of the town, then just before it hit the coast, it meandered sharply to the east for the best part of a mile then turned south again and met up with the sea. The spit of land that the river's course had created was known simply as Shoreham Beach, and for many years, the place had been home to all manner of interesting people.

At the end of the beach was a fort that was created in the 1850s when the government was still paranoid about being attacked by the French. The whole venture turned out to be a waste of time as they stayed away, and no action was ever seen there. Instead, in the early twentieth century, the place was transformed into a film studio due to the good light that was meant to bestow the place. The studio brought with it a number of actors who no one could probably name anymore, but at the time were superstars of the silent movies. Many of them ended up staying in the area and buying houses on the beach.

If you took a stroll along the pebbles and checked out those houses, it would be hard not to be impressed by the sheer variety of architectural styles. There were art deco towers, concrete monoliths, New-England-style wooden houses and a couple of mansions with more bedrooms than you could count on first passing. It was an impressive gathering of styles and ideas, but nothing on the beach could match the originality and eccentricity of the houseboats and their owners.

The first of the houseboats had rocked up in Shoreham in the seventies on a tide of flower power and hippy positivity. These boats

were owned by artists, artisans, musicians and anyone else who had tuned in, turned on and copped out of a society they felt isolated from. When you looked at the boats, it was easy to see which came first. The one with a bus welded to the sides and a giant butterfly on the front immediately grabbed the visitor's attention, but there was also the giant minesweeper that had to wait for the largest tide in years before it could make its way up the river without getting stuck on a sandbank, or the tugboat that on a low tide leaned so much to one side, it was a wonder that the residents could walk in a straight line without holding on to something.

Many of the newer boats that made Shoreham their home were not there for the alternative lifestyle, but to find an affordable home in an increasingly unaffordable area. Some of these boats looked more like floating penthouses displaying swish lines and curves, and made of cutting-edge materials. Bodhi's boat fell somewhere in between. Five years earlier, a friend of a friend had moved their crumbling boat out of its moorings and sold it to him for what was a ridiculously cheap price. He had bought the hull of an old disused coal barge for pennies, then spent the next few years building a timber framed construction on top of it that was worthy of any house builder's praise.

He had decked out the interior of the boat in a mash-mash of things he had salvaged when he was still working as a trio with Jimmy and Bob. The open plan living area was a sight to behold. The kitchen cabinets were constructed of old wooden pallets, and the worktops were made from sanded and varnished plywood that had cost next to nothing. The furniture was constructed of scaffold planks and driftwood he had collected from the beach, and parquet tiles taken up from a school hall they had renovated, lined the floor. In theory, it shouldn't have worked, but anyone who had visited would have told you it did. It had taken three years to get the boat as he liked it, and Bodhi had done every single scrap of work with his own bare hands.

When he first joined East Sussex Fire Service, he swore he would never move there. Despite what most people said, he didn't

think that Brighton was that great a place. It was all right, yeah, but if you wanted to go to a decent place by the sea, then you should try going to Cornwall, his part of the world. The place was rammed with some of the prettiest coastal towns and villages you could imagine. Compared to them, Brighton really was nothing special. And then, there was the beach; it was full of pebbles, for one thing, and only a stone's throw from the main road. He used to laugh at the thought of Londoners wasting a day travelling down to Brighton Pier when if they'd only driven a few hours further, they could have seen something really special. Even Devon and bloody Somerset were better places to go.

Finally, and this was the thing that well and truly made Bodhi's mind up about never living in Brighton, was the surf, or lack of it, to be precise. Sure, there was a little wave just outside of the Marina or the Hot Pipe next to the power station, but without meaning to be disrespectful to the local surfers who raved about them, it was usually wind-generated slop they surfed, and a poor substitute for a man who had been brought up surfing the pristine groundswell of North Cornwall's bays.

No, Brighton was never a place Bodhi intended to call home, and a career in the fire service was something he had never bargained on, either. The whole thing had pretty much happened by accident, which kind of made him feel guilty, knowing how hard some people had tried to get into the job, and how many failed attempts it had taken them before they finally got in. Bodhi was accepted on his first time of trying, and he wasn't even trying that hard; he'd just gone along for the ride. But then again, he was a surfer, and that was what surfers did. For them, it was all about the ride.

Before he'd joined up, Bodhi's life had revolved around surfing. He first took to the waves when he was seven, and his uncle, a devotee of the sport who had no children of his own, took him out into the white water on the biggest board he owned. Bodhi was instantly hooked, right there and then. When he managed to stand up and catch his first wave, he resolved that, like his uncle,

he was going to spend the rest of his life surfing. And he did too. Except for the few months of the year when it was too cold for a young lad to get in the water, Bodhi was a regular site on Watergate Bay. It was only a mile from his house, and he used to cycle there with one hand as his other gripped his board.

He could never understand why his dad hadn't followed his brother into the water. He was strong and athletic, and Bodhi was fairly certain he would have been a natural. The man was also a workhouse; he spent all his time on the building site as a bricklayer and was always too knackered to even contemplate hitting the water when his day finished. Bodhi admired his father's work ethic, and elements of it he would end up adopting himself, but, for him, even though he knew how to graft, work was just a way of financing his adventures in the water.

When he left school with no qualifications (why learn when you can surf), Bodhi became a hod carrier for his old man, and very soon, his life took on a pattern that would continue until he found the fire service. He would bust his ass working long days on site through the summer, and proving himself to be a practical young man who could turn his hand to most things. It wasn't long before he was laying bricks himself, or whatever else needed doing. When he wasn't working, he was surfing.

When it grew colder, Bodhi would take the money he had saved over the previous months and head to warmer climes. In the first few years, he stayed relatively local, camping in Biarritz or southern Spain, but as the years went by, he pushed further out to more exotic destinations like Indonesia, South Africa and Australia. It was a simple hand-to-mouth existence, but Bodhi loved it and wouldn't change his lifestyle for anyone. He didn't need money when he had some of the best waves in the world at his disposal.

Then one year, when he was in his late twenties, it all changed. The summer was drawing to a close, and he was preparing for what would be his biggest trip to date. He was heading to Hawaii, the Mecca of the surfing world. He had wanted to go there since

he was a kid. He still had a poster on his wall of the legendary Ken Bradshaw, a beast of a man and a beast of a surfer, hammering down the face of a thirty-foot wave in Waimea Bay. The place was the home of big wave surfing. The home of icons like Gregg Knoll, who had turned up there one summer in the sixties with a bunch of friends and spent every day out in the break, perfecting their surfing in the day and sleeping on the beach and getting drunk in the evenings. Bodhi was going to go to the place where surfing royalty was made. He was going to the North Shore.

About a month before he was due to leave, Johnny-Boy, one of his surfer buddies, told Bodhi he was going to East Sussex at the weekend as the fire service were holding an open day for candidates. Bodhi knew Johnny had been trying to get into the job for years, it was all he ever talked about. He had applied to join all the local brigades, but it was only East Sussex who was taking on at that time. It could be another year or two before Cornwall or Devon started employing. Johnny didn't fancy going all the way there on his own, and wanting a little moral support, he invited Bodhi along for the ride. Bodhi agreed right away. He wasn't doing anything that weekend, and the chance of a wave was zero, so fuck it. He decided to go and help out his friend.

He didn't know why he took his sports kit along with him, maybe it was fate. Bodhi was a pretty reflective kind of dude, and while he wasn't even sure if such a thing as fate existed, he was into the whole Karma vibe. Once, he had gone out with a yoga teacher who had told him that Bodhi was actually a Buddhist term and referred to the truth or enlightenment of men. So, perhaps when Johnny-Boy picked him up that Saturday morning, Bodhi was just playing out the role the universe had planned for him since the dawn of time. Or maybe, he just wanted to get involved; he wasn't one for being a spectator.

Being healthy surfer types, both guys nailed the fittest tests, and even though he was no academic, the written tests were pretty straightforward too. You just had to prove you were fairly literate for the English section, and the maths, luckily for him, was based

around practical things he could relate to. It was the whole 'If a tanker holds five thousand litres of oil, but is losing 120 litres a minute, how long will it take for it to be empty?' kind of vibe.

Two weeks later, the successful pair had to return for their practical, role-based tests. Again, they both stormed most of the challenges. Running out lengths of hose, although tricky until you got the knack, had been no real obstacle for them. They both flew through the strength exercises, carrying various pieces of equipment and hauling them aloft, and both were fine on the ladder tests, neither having a problem with heights. It was only when they were made to go through the rat run; a series of tunnels that were only just big enough to crawl through, did Johnny's problems begin. Wearing full fire-kit and breathing apparatus, he had to go through the run in complete darkness in less than five minutes. Two minutes into the exercise, Johnny became aware he was more claustrophobic than he'd ever considered. The instructors had had to open the side panel and let him out when he started freaking out after getting stuck going around a tight corner. Bodhi was in and out of the run in the quickest time of the day.

Luckily, Johnny took it well when he found out Bodhi had been offered a job. The interview had taken place a week later, and he had come out of it smelling of roses. His training was due to start a month later, two weeks after he was meant to be flying to Hawaii. Bodhi always said that he fell into the job, but there must have been something about it that made him give up on the biggest trip of his career. Maybe he recognised in himself that he was going to be a good firefighter, perhaps even better than he was a surfer, and that was saying something. Bodhi's dedication meant he was one of the best surfers in Cornwall, which basically meant one of the best in the country. If he'd wanted to, he probably could have made a half-decent living on the pro tours, but that wasn't his style. Surfing for him was about being out there doing what you love, not competing against your mates for a cheque and trophy.

Training school wasn't a problem for him. Okay, some of the classroom stuff may have tripped him up now and then; he was surprised by how much science was involved, but he struggled through. On the fire-ground, though, he had no equal. His time on sites had equipped him with the practical mind and can-do attitude that most firefighters longed for. Unsurprisingly, at the end of the sixteen weeks, he was awarded the Silver Axe, and unlike in Jo's case, the other recruits were genuinely pleased for him.

So, Bodhi got a job at Brighton, but due to his dislike of the place, he was determined to do what numerous other firefighters before him had done and commute for his four days of work. He would rock up at the station in his prized VW Westfalia camper van, and at the end of his day shifts, he would park it down by the sea and sleep in it. On nights, rather than share the dorms with the others, he would park his van in the spare vehicle bay and sleep there. The commute could be a pain in the arse, but it was worth it to get back to his beloved beach breaks in North Cornwall.

And then, he discovered kitesurfing, and everything turned on its head. Bodhi thought he would never find anything that matched the feeling surfing gave him, but one morning, after waking up stiff of leg and back, he got out of the van and saw a guy in the water being propelled at ridiculous speeds by the giant kite he was harnessed too. Moments later, the man was thirty feet up in the air and he stayed there for what seemed like an age until he came back down to the water with such grace that he barely made a splash. It was right then that Bodhi decided he needed a large serving of what that guy was dishing up.

Unsurprisingly, Bodhi was a natural. It took a few weeks to get the hang of using the kite, but once he had it figured out, he was up and away, literally. In no time, Bodhi was getting some serious airtime, and he loved it. Suddenly, he no longer wanted to go back to Cornwall on his days off, just in case he missed a windy day and lost time out with his kite. The one thing he noticed was

as he was spending less time paddling out through the waves, he was losing some upper body strength. He got around this by sea swimming for fitness, and he also discovered the world of stand-up paddle-boarding, a great workout to keep his core in shape. If the water level was right, he could throw his board off the back of his boat and jump right in after it.

He still loved surfing, he could never get that out of his system, and he still popped back to Cornwall to catch a wave and see his family when he got the chance, but kitesurfing was Bodhi's new religion, and Shoreham was his Mecca. The houseboat couldn't have been in a better location. He could walk out of the front door, cross the small green and main road, and he was on Shoreham beach. The beach was pretty narrow and lacked space, but on a low tide, there was ample room for him and the other kite surfers to set up their gear and launch their kites.

When he came back up on deck, he was wearing his shorty wetsuit and had tied his hair back off his face. Carrying his kite and lines in one hand and his board in the other, he departed his boat and started the two-minute journey to the beach. Mornings like this were ones to be cherished; good wind, a low tide and plenty of sunshine. When you had days like this, it made you wonder what else you needed in life. It was the reason why Bodhi knew he wouldn't have taken the money that night. He already had everything he needed. His life was pretty much complete.

Chapter 19

A Meeting with Management

Jimmy pulled on the handles of the rowing machine so hard, the chain shook as it reached its final destination. He was covered in sweat and not only breathing hard, but wheezing both with exertion and pain as lactic acid filled his leg muscles. He had two hundred metres to go and would finish without dropping the pace if it killed him. That was the thing about Jimmy; he may have put a bit of timber on over the last few years, but he had once been a marine, and that do-or-die mentality was still strong in him. Once he took on an endeavour, he refused to quit, no matter what it did to him.

The gym at the station was only small, so Jimmy's effort was being scrutinised closely by Bodhi, who was somehow standing on the Swiss exercise ball while performing arm curls with a pair of dumbbells. He had been out on the water for nearly two hours that afternoon, but it hadn't stopped him doing some extra work to keep him on the ball, if you'll excuse the pun. Dylan was watching, too, as he hung from the pull-up bar by two fingers of each hand. It was a strength exercise he liked to do to help improve his grip strength for rock climbing.

Wesley didn't like them to use the gym until after nine o'clock usually, but as he had taken nights off at short notice, Jimmy was in charge, and he didn't give a shit what they did. The evening routines had been done, and they'd even squeezed in a Home Safety Visit for an old boy in Kemptown, all by the ripe old time of seven-thirty. Unless they had any calls, Jimmy was happy for them to have a quiet night. Without Jo there to intimidate them with her superior fitness levels, the guys had trooped off to the gym while Harrison cooked moussaka.

Jimmy completed his final few strokes on the rowing machine and swiftly rolled off onto his back. As he cried out in pain, he tried to straighten his legs but they had gone foetal and were not interested in playing any longer. Dylan and Bodhi laughed; they were used to seeing him like this. Bodhi carefully got off the ball and looked at the time on the display.

'7.05,' he said. 'Nearly there, Jim.'

'Fuck,' Jimmy just about managed to answer, his eyes were closed so tight, he seemed to be squeezing out tears.

He had been doing the two-thousand metre challenge for a couple of weeks and had already shaved half a minute off his best time, but he was determined to get under seven before he gave up and found some other stupid labour. As he laid there, desperately paying back his oxygen debt, Lenny walked in. Lenny made a point of never using the gym at work; the light weights that could be found there insulted him. He trained at Cheetahs on Hove seafront, a proper old-school, spit and sawdust gym. Lenny's attitude to training was "Go Big or Go Home," and it wasn't just talk, either. The man lived by the code, and the two prolapsed discs in his lower back were his proof. He could dead-lift, squat and bench-press insane amounts of weight. Lowering his standards, so far as to pick up the meagre dumbbells in the gym were definitely not an option, and as for the running or rowing machines, fuck that. Lenny didn't do cardio.

'You all right there, Jim?' he said. 'Shit yourself again?'

Jimmy held his arm up and waved.

'If I were you,' Lenny said, 'I'd think about getting back to the canteen. That prick Jacobs has just turned up, and Harrison doesn't look happy.'

Ian Jacobs had been a firefighter for as long as Harrison had. In fact, the two of them had gone to training school together, and once upon a time, they had been firm friends. Their relationship had steadily eroded over the years as Ian rose through the ranks of the brigade, but two years previously, it had been destroyed. Ian had spent much of his career at an operational level. He had

been a watch manager at East for over a decade, and his colleagues assumed that was where he would finish his service. But, like a number of officers before him, the urge for promotion hit him at a later date than was normal, but when it had come, he had embraced it with a vengeance.

Ian's rise though the service was swift. In six years, he had gone from riding in charge of the appliance to being the deputy chief of Sussex Fire and Rescue Service. It wasn't the promotions that had caused Harrison to fall out with him. He had no problem with people trying to improve their position, especially when they were still on a final salary pension scheme.

No, what caused Harrison's contempt for his old friend was that just before the last set of strikes, Ian had left the union. Ten years previously, when the firefighters had gone on strike over their pay, he had been one of the strongest advocates for action. He was union, through and through, when he had been an operational firefighter, but since having the management chip inserted, his viewpoint had taken an about-turn. Like many of the other officers, he had refused to go out the doors, claiming that as the army in their ancient Green Goddesses would not be available to provide cover in the strikes, he would do it. He couldn't let East Sussex be unprotected, it went against his conscience.

If that *were* the case and the genuine reason why they had not supported their colleagues, Harrison could understand it, but he didn't see it that way. If management were that concerned with the safety of the city's residents, they wouldn't have banned the firefighters from breaking the picket line and turning out to the most serious calls involving life risks, something they'd done in all previous strikes. He regarded the senior officer's actions as a way of keeping in the chief's good books with a view to ensuring their future prospects in the job. If the officers just came out and said they were leaving the union to further their careers, he would have found it easier to swallow, but the whole guilt thing they were trying to put on his colleagues made Harrison sick.

As far as he was concerned, morals and consciences didn't come into it. Did the officers really believe that going on strike didn't affect the men and women who sat on the fire engines? Harrison had hated every second of being on strike, and he knew his colleagues felt the same way, but it was more than their pensions at stake; it was the very future of the fire service they were trying to protect. Pensions were an expensive burden to any employer. If the scheme collapsed, as many people predicted it would due to the changes imposed by the government, it would suddenly be a whole lot more enticing for private companies that wanted a piece of the action. The privatisation of the service was something that everyone was prepared to fight against.

Normally, Harrison would rather cross the street than talk to Ian, and Jimmy was well aware of this as he walked as fast as his battered legs could carry him to the rec room. He dreaded to think what he would see when he found the two of them together in the canteen.

To his surprise, rather than the chaos he was expecting, Ian was sitting quietly at the table as Harrison kept himself busy in the kitchen.

'Can I get you a cup of tea, boss?' Jimmy said.

Ian held aloft the steaming mug that had been on the table out of Jimmy's sight.

'I'm good, thanks. Harrison is looking after me.'

'Nice one,' Jimmy said, shocked at the statement. He just hoped Harrison hadn't spat in it or worse.

Jimmy looked to the kitchen door. 'You all right in there, mate?'

Harrison suddenly appeared in the opening, wearing an apron that had the outline of a curvaceous woman's body wearing a sexy negligee. It was the same one he always wore when he was cooking.

'All good in here, Jim. Things are always good in my kitchen. It's everywhere else there's a problem.'

Ian looked to the doorway, stood up, then picked up his tea in one hand and his briefcase in the other. 'I know it's short notice,

but as our last meeting got cancelled, I thought I'd give you chaps the presentation on the station closure now, if you don't mind.'

Jimmy did mind. He wanted to have his tea and get some kip, but he didn't feel like the question was a rhetorical one.

'I'll give you guys fifteen minutes,' Ian said. 'Then, I'll see you in the lecture room.'

It came as a surprise to no one that the meeting was a disaster. It was doomed from the first slide Ian had produced. The title of the meeting was Service Transformation: Facing the Challenge, and it had immediately set everyone off. In true management style, rather than tell it like it was, they had come up with a flash name, complete with a colon in the title, that did anything except tell the real situation.

The fight to save their fire station had been going on for nearly eighteen months and had been led with much gusto by Harrison. The Service's budget had been cut by nearly twenty percent, and management had decided that closing East Brighton, as well as a number of retained stations, was the best means to deal with the shortfall. Harrison had argued that the last thing that should be attacked was the front line. The best way to make meaningful savings, he countered, was for the brigades in the South East to amalgamate, reducing backroom staff and admin by a quarter, but more importantly, only relying on one chief and one management team, rather than the five they had now. Obviously, this would take time and effort to set up, but it had been done in Scotland a few years earlier, with the whole country being transformed from nine separate services into one national brigade, saving millions of pounds.

The public had bought into it and had unanimously got behind the campaign to save the station, but it was the fire authority who made the final decision, and after a hard-fought campaign, they had wilted and voted in favour of the cuts. Except management didn't like using that word. In fact, they went as far as they possibly could to avoid it. Say it or not, the firefighters, the guys on the frontline, knew what the closure of their station

meant. A better title for the slideshow would have been Cuts: How to Royally Fuck Up the Fire Service.

The watch had made it painfully clear throughout the presentation about their feelings on the matter. They groaned or laughed as Ian flicked through the slides, first showing how their calls had dropped, and then, how their station not being there anymore should be no cause of alarm for the locals. Harrison had got up and left the room on two occasions, blurting out that he needed to check the food in the oven. He didn't, the others knew that, but they also knew if he'd stayed in the room, he probably would have killed the man standing in front of them.

It had looked like they were going to get though the meeting without it descending it bedlam, when Ian made his fatal error, well and truly fucking things up. After showing them the final slide, which offered a list of support numbers the firefighters at the station could contact if they were being affected by the issues discussed, he closed his laptop that was linked up to the projector screen and looked around the room.

'So, that's it, guys, that's how things are,' he said. 'I know how painful this must be for you, and I also know some of you are feeling let down by management and that we haven't done enough to fight your corner. Now the chief, rightly or wrongly, has come in for an awful lot of slack from you and from the public about the decisions he has made, but I ask you in all honesty, if you were in his shoes, what would you have done in his situation?'

Instinctively, Jimmy looked to Harrison, but before he could make eye contact and attempt some form of warning, the man had already begun.

'I'll tell you what he could have done,' Harrison said. 'If he wanted to know how we felt, he should have come down here and asked us himself. We want to speak to the organ grinder, not the monkey.'

Ian ignored the insult.

'And I'll tell you what else he could have done. He could have stopped pretending that these cuts aren't going to affect the public,

because he knows, and we know, that they will. My family live at the top of the hill out there; it's two and a half minutes from this station. I know that because I've been living there most of my life. Now if he's trying to tell me that having a pump coming from Brighton, which will take an extra five minutes to get here, isn't going to affect their chances of getting out of a fire alive, then he's an even bigger liar than I thought he was. "Fire kills in minutes, smoke kills in seconds." Have you forgotten that logo we used to have written on the back of the fire engines, or is it too inconvenient for you to remember in these times of austerity?'

Ian leant forward in his chair. 'Come on, Harrison. I don't think that attitude is going to help anyone, now, is it?'

Harrison held up his hand. 'If I were you, I'd hold that thought because I haven't even started yet. You senior officers, you're all the fucking same. You haven't got a backbone between you. How dare you make out like you're on our side. None of you have done a thing to protect this service you claim to love so much.'

'That's not fair!' Ian said, his voice rising slightly. 'You don't know what goes on behind the scenes at headquarters.'

'You're right, I don't. But somehow, I can't see you up in the chief's office, fighting our corner. That's not your style, is it?'

'My feelings on this matter are the same as his. He's not doing this for the sake of it. He's as devastated by the closure of this station as anyone else.'

Harrison laughed. 'If he's that bothered about the cuts and the damage it's doing to this service, to his fucking service, then why doesn't he grow some bollocks and speak out about it?'

'What would that do?' Ian said as he reddened. 'Do you think the government would listen to him if he went cap in hand to them?'

'Fuck the government. I'm talking about going to the press, telling them about what's really going on. That's the sort of action we expect from our leader. Instead, he smiles politely and says that everything is business as usual. He makes me sick, and you can tell him that, if you like.'

'Here, here,' Lenny shouted as the others nodded in approval.

'Come on, Harrison. Calm down, mate,' Jimmy said. 'This ain't helping matters.'

'It's making me feel a lot better. You know, a problem shared and all that.'

Ian tried to smile and placed the papers on the desk back into his briefcase. 'I know this was never going to be easy for you. I know how long you've worked at this station and that your dad worked here before you. I know all that, and that's why I wanted to do the presentation tonight. I thought it was best, given our history.'

Harrison laughed, then shook his head. 'Given our history, you should have been out there with us, campaigning to save this station, you fucking turncoat. Just like you should have been out on strike with the rest of us, rather than riding around on that scab lorry with those other bastards. That's what you should have been doing.'

Harrison's words made the room grow quiet. Everyone knew that the word he had just used was enough to get him the sack. They had been told, in no uncertain terms at the start of the strikes, it was no longer the 1980s, and that the staff who decided to work were to be treated with respect and dignity by their colleagues. A firefighter in another part of the country had been sacked for using the word on social media. But Harrison had already overstepped that mark; he had called a senior officer a scab to his face with a handful of witnesses present. The retirement and pension that he was due to receive in less than six months suddenly seemed like a distant memory.

Ian closed his briefcase and, without saying another word, got out of his chair and left the room. Jimmy followed behind him, already pleading Harrison's case. The others just sat there, staring at Harrison, not knowing what the hell to say to a man on death row.

'I've got to give it to you,' Lenny finally said. 'That well and truly pisses on anything I've ever done wrong in this job. Looks like you're the daddy now.'

Chapter 20

Return of the Mac

'Careful!' Lenny yelled at the two children charging towards him.

One of them was dressed much like him in a mini-firefighters outfit, except it was black instead of the beige style that Sussex adopted. In the child's hand was a plastic axe that must have come included in the set. His friend, for no reason that Lenny could see, was dressed as Thor.

'How much longer is this going to last?' he said to Jo, who was helping a little girl direct the hose reel at a wooden house. Its windows and doors spun around when they took a direct jet of water.

'Chill out, Len,' she said. 'It's only been going for an hour, and it's all for a good cause.'

'Yeah, well, their parents need to start upping their game. This ain't a crèche.'

It was the station open day, and this year, Red Watch had been unfortunate enough to catch it. Not that it was that bad, really. The day could actually be quite enjoyable when taken in the right spirit. But the thought of hundreds of kids descending on his place of work was too much for Lenny. One child was more than enough for him. He didn't need to look after the rest of the town's too.

The open day was great PR for the station. Not only was it good for the community to see what firefighters did when they weren't drinking tea and playing pool (the staff were well aware that some people had this idea about them), but it was also an excellent way of making some money for the Firefighter's Charity. For years, it had been known as the Benevolent Fund, but the

name had been changed when its patrons became aware that most people didn't know what those words actually meant anymore.

The charity did vital work in looking after firefighters and the families of firefighters who had been injured or killed. It ran a number of state-of-the-art facilities that dealt in the rehabilitation of all sorts of injuries ranging from spinal care for people who had suffered catastrophic injuries, to counselling for those affected by depression or post-traumatic stress. Unfortunately, these things were common for professionals who had to bear witness to some of the worst examples of human suffering.

Although they had all bitched about the open day being on their shift again (they had caught it two years earlier), the Watch had thrown themselves into it. Wesley had taken to the microphone as the fire safety team did the chip pan demonstration; showing what happens when you pour water onto an oil fire. The kids squealed at the resulting fireball that was so hot, it warmed their hands and faces.

Being a waterman, Bodhi had opted to be the one pelted with sponges that kids paid fifty pence a time to hurl at him. Considering the water was freezing, and the sun hadn't revealed itself, he had taken it all in good spirits. Jimmy was policing the line of children that climbed into the back of the fire engine, tried on a helmet or BA mask, and then had their picture taken by their proud parents. If they hung around too long or started putting their dirty little paws on things that weren't intended for them, he politely shooed them off.

Even though it was Dylan's annual summer leave, he had turned up with Felicity, and the two of them had done an impressive job selling raffle tickets for a bunch of prizes that local businesses had generously donated. It was at times like this, despite the cuts and all the bullshit that was going on, they truly became aware of the high esteem they were held in by their friends and neighbours.

The only person on the Watch that wasn't present was Harrison. Usually, he would have been in charge of the barbeque, but this year, a couple of the Green Watch boys had generously

given up their free time to do it. Harrison had been suspended on full pay while the investigation into his outburst was taking place. The preliminaries had already been done; they just had his interview to go before a final judgement was made. The others tried not to talk about it, because they all knew what the outcome was likely to be. Their friend, the person they had all gone to in their own time of need, was more than likely fucked, and there was nothing any of them could do about it.

As Jimmy gently chastised a little girl for trying to switch on the hand-held radio she was holding, he was suddenly alerted by the feel of someone firmly squeezing his bum. He turned around to see Jen standing there smiling at him.

'Hello, sexy fireman,' she said. 'You look just like Mr July on my hunky firefighter calendar.'

Jimmy laughed. 'I'm pretty sure he had more hair than me and less of a gut.'

George walked up to him and gave his father a friendly punch in the stomach. 'You need your gut, Dad. It's armour against my super punch.'

Jimmy rubbed the boy's head and tried not to show his discomfort, his son was getting strong. At least he'd stopped trying to punch him in the balls; that phase had been a painful six months.

'Can we go in the fire engine now, Dad?' Becky said.

Jimmy looked into the back of the engine at the little boy trying to rip the BA mask away from its air-hose. Jimmy picked him up and handed the boy to his soppy father who had been too polite to tell him not to destroy property that belonged to someone else.

'Go on then, you two,' Jimmy said. 'Climb on.'

'How's your morning been?' Jimmy said to his wife as the kids fought over possession of the radio.

'Not quite as busy as yours, by the looks of things, but we've been pretty full-on. George went to football practice, Becky had her ballet, and then, we went home and took the dog for a walk on the cliffs.'

'Sounds like I've had it easy,' Jimmy said. 'Is your mother still coming around this afternoon?'

'Yep,' Jen said. 'You know she never misses a Saturday afternoon with the kids.'

'It's nice for her to be around them,' Jimmy said, meaning it. 'It takes her mind off things, I reckon.'

Jenny's father had died two years earlier of prostate cancer, and three months earlier, her mum had discovered that she had it in her bowel. She had ruled out chemo before it was even suggested to her. She'd had a good life, but she was tired and was ready to meet up with Ted again, wherever he may have been.

'She's asked if the kids can stay at her house tonight. Becky's desperate to go, and George is up for it, too, as long as he can take his tablet, but I haven't said yes yet. You know what they can be like when they're excited.'

'Let them go,' Jimmy said. 'She won't put up with any nonsense.'

He looked around and seeing that no one was paying them any attention, he leant in and hugged his wife, then lowered his hand down for a cheeky squeeze of her arse.

'Plus, if you play your cards right, you may get to have some one-to-one time with Mr July.'

'That's the best offer I've had all day,' Jen said.

'All right, Jim,' he heard a voice say that made him quickly retract the offending limb. 'This must be your lovely family.'

He turned around to see Mac smiling at him. He was holding an untouched ice-cream cone in his hand.

'Can I get the kids one of these?' he said, holding it up.

Jimmy stood there, momentarily unable to speak. 'No, they're good thanks,' he finally said.

'Who's this, then?' Jen asked, clearly unaware of the intensity in her husband's face. He looked like he was ready to kill the man, while being terrified of him at the same time.

Mac reached forward and shook Jen's hand. 'I'm an old mate – me and Jimmy go way back.'

'Mac used to be on Green Watch at Central. He was my boss back in the day.'

'Ah, that's nice,' Jen said. 'So, you were one of the ones who moulded my husband into the man he is today. I don't know if I should thank or slap you.'

Mac laughed and place his hand on her shoulder. 'You should definitely thank me. That's a fine fella you've got yourself there.'

Jen looked at him hard before speaking again. 'You know, I thought I knew all of Jimmy's work mates. I never missed a night out as long as we could get a babysitter. I'm sure we've never met before.'

'Mac retired not long after I joined the Watch, and before that, he never really was one for social events. Ain't that right?'

Mac laughed again, 'That's right. I was the grumpy sod on the Watch, and I tell you what, I don't miss it, either. Firefighting's a young man's game.' He paused and focused his attention on Jimmy. 'And it can be dangerous, too, if you're not careful.'

Jimmy looked into the back of the cab at Becky trying to rip the helmet that George was wearing off his head. 'Come on, kids,' he said. 'Time to go now before you get Daddy into trouble.'

Unlike the other children before them, the two of them got off the engine without a fight. Like most firefighters' kids, they had spent so much time at the station that sitting on the back of the fire appliance was no big deal to them anymore.

Jimmy turned and kissed his wife again. 'I'll see you later love, I won't be late.'

'Are you trying to get rid of us?' Jen asked. 'We've only just got here.'

Jimmy tried his best to laugh, 'Don't be silly, it's just that I'm planning to do an extension for Mac once the job I'm on is finished. We just need to talk shop for a few minutes.'

'That's right,' Mac interrupted. 'If I can't make the most of my pension now, then what's the point. You can't take it with you.'

'My thoughts exactly,' Jen said, then turned her head as something caught her attention. 'Oh, look, kids, there's Uncle

Bodhi. Who wants to go and throw a freezing cold sponge at his face?'

'Me!' Becky yelled.

'Can I throw one at Lenny?' George asked his mum.

'Yeah, why not. I'm sure he'll find it hilarious.'

The kids smiled and waved at their father as they ran off to torment his workmates.

When Jimmy looked back to Mac, his face was stone.

Mac seemed oblivious, smiling at Jimmy's family as they left. 'That's a beautiful family you've got yourself there. You're a lucky man.'

Jimmy ignore his words. 'What the fuck do you think you're doing here?'

'I don't know what you mean,' Mac said. 'I've just come to see my local firefighters hard at work. It's lovely to see you guys integrating yourselves in the local community like this. Sort of thing that brings a tear to the eye.'

'I said, what do you want? You're not welcome here.'

Mac looked around at Jimmy's colleagues; each doing their best to entertain the kids. 'So, where's the old boy?'

'Retired,' Jimmy's answer was curt. He didn't want Mac knowing about Harrison's plight.

'Sensible man. Like I said, it's a young man's game.' Mac leaned into the fire engine and studied the inside. 'You know I've never been in one of these. What's the chances of coming out for a ride with you?'

'Zero fucking chance, that's what.' Jimmy checked himself when he heard how loud his voice had risen, he didn't want the kids hearing him swearing. 'I ain't telling you again,' he said in little more than a whisper. 'Go now before I do something I regret.'

The smile that Mac met him with was filled with more than a little sympathy. 'Come on now, Jim. Don't start all that nonsense again. I told you before what happens to tough guys, or have you forgotten our last conversation?'

Jimmy held his tongue. He remembered the words they had shared at the racecourse.

'All I need is a very quick chat. Yours and the rest of your mates, that is. Do you think you can arrange that for me?'

'What's it about?'

'I'd rather not get into it now, if you don't mind. Be a dear and speak to your boys. Tell them it's got to be tonight. Let's say half six, after you've finished work. You can even choose the venue. I can't say fairer than that, can I?'

Jimmy shook his head. 'I imagine there's nothing fair about a man like you.'

Mac shrugged.

'Seven o'clock, The Queen's Head in Kemptown. You've got ten minutes, then that's us done for good.'

Mac held up his right hand with his fingers extended. 'Five minutes, that's all I need.' He took a lick of his ice-cream, then turned and headed out of the yard. 'Catch you later, Jim. Enjoy the shenanigans.'

Chapter 21

Rendezvous

At ten-to-seven, they walked silently towards their destination. The young man that approached the group moved with a slight, but certainly not exaggerated, swagger. As he passed them, Dylan, who was leading the group, turned and looked to the others.

'Did you see that?' he said.

The others said nothing, knowing what his next words were likely to be.

'I'm telling you,' he said. 'I'd get so much cock action if I were gay. The boys love me.'

'What do you mean *if*?' Lenny said.

Dylan rolled his eyes. 'I'm getting married next year, Len.'

Lenny snorted. 'Big deal. Elton John was married.'

'To a man.'

'Nah, before that. Back in the eighties, he got hitched to a German woman.'

'He's right, Dyl,' Jo said. 'Plenty of gay men get married to women. It's nothing to be ashamed of.'

Dylan laughed. 'I'm not ashamed. I'm quite comfortable with the idea of being a dick magnet.'

'Drop the last word from that sentence,' Lenny said, 'and I'd say you were spot on. What do you think, Jim?'

'I'd say you lot need to stop fucking about. Have you forgotten who we're about to meet?'

The fire station was situated close to a part of the city known as Kemptown. Something else based in Kemptown was the city's gay quarter. Although Brighton was the gay capital of the country, most people who visited were often surprised when they were

not immediately greeted by the view of thousands of same-sex couples openly displaying their love for each other. The truth was, Brighton, for the most part, was pretty much the same as any other city in the UK.

It was only in Kemptown, or more specifically one street in Kemptown, where it became obvious that the city had a healthy gay scene. It was situated just north of and parallel to the sea. It began its life in St James Street just above the pier and finished on St George's Road, the best part of a mile away. This was the place where the gay bars, sex shops and bespoke clothes boutiques could be found. There was a rainbow flag hanging from almost every building. Kemptown was easily one of the most fun, vibrant parts of the city, even if it wasn't as big as most people expected.

It took about ten minutes on foot to reach the bars in Kemptown, and it was a journey worth taking in pursuit of a decent pub. There were a number of places closer to the station that they could get a drink in, but they all had the feel of a working men's club. The Queen's Head had much better beer, a better atmosphere, and perhaps more important for them on this particular evening, it was busy enough that no one would pay any attention to the conversation they were soon to have with Mac.

When they reached the bar, the group were confronted by a bouncer, who looked like he was only in his early twenties at the most, but was built like a cruise liner.

'Bouncers at seven o'clock on a weeknight,' Bodhi said. 'Bit much, aye, Len?'

Lenny eyed the slab of meat in front of them. 'You can never be too careful. There's always a few pricks around who want to start trouble. Even in a gay pub.'

As they approached the entrance, the man stepped into the doorway, blocking their view of the pub's interior. 'Sorry, gentlemen, but this is a gay bar. There's nothing here for you.'

Lenny stepped forward so that his eyes were level with the boy-hulk's chin. 'I fancy a pint, not a blowjob. Now, step out of the way, there's a good boy.'

The bouncer blinked. He hadn't been expecting resistance; his size was enough to deter most people from arguing with him. He cast his gaze from Lenny to Bodhi, then nodded at the surfer's lower extremities. 'He can't come in dressed like that.'

Bodhi was decked out in his usual outfit of board shorts, flip-flops and a hoodie. The joke went that you knew it was cold when Bodhi was no longer wearing shorts. You knew it was really cold when he had shoes on his feet. It wasn't particularly funny, but it did sum up his fashion sense pretty well.

Wesley joined Lenny on the upper step and spoke before the doorman said anything else. 'What my compatriot is trying to say is we're meeting a good friend of ours inside. We're not here to cause any trouble, I can assure you.'

'No,' Lenny said, looking at the bouncer. 'What I'm saying is, in five seconds, I intend to walk into that pub. Get in my way, sunshine, and you'll see what happens to silly boys who think they can look after themselves.'

Bodhi put his arm on his friend's shoulder and gently pulled him back. 'Come on, Lenny. Chill out, bud. It ain't worth getting worked up over.'

On hearing the name, the bouncer's face changed, and some of the colour seemed to drain from it. 'You're Lenny. You mean Lenny the bouncer?'

'Yep. Lenny the bouncer. How's that working out for you?'

The boy quickly held out his hand, looking like he'd shrunk at least two inches, 'Sorry about that, mate. No harm intended. I was just doing my job.'

Lenny reluctantly held out his hand. 'Do it better next time. You've got a lot to learn.'

As they shook hands, he moved the boy to the side, then led the rest of the group into the pub.

Mac was sitting at the bar with a glass of orange juice in his hands. When he saw them come in, he smiled like they were a group of old friends he hadn't seen for years. Before he could say anything, the barman was already on them, taking their order.

'We'll have six bottles of San Miguel please,' Jimmy said. 'We're not planning on staying long.'

'You know, for a fruity joint,' Mac said as the barman got their drinks, 'I was surprised to see so many people drinking pints. I was expecting more cocktails and umbrellas.'

'That's rich coming from a man holding an orange juice,' Jo said.

Mac held up his drink and studied it. 'Yeah, just the juice for me. It took twenty years and two marriages to make me realise that me and alcohol are incompatible.'

'So, you're an alky, then?' Jimmy said.

'Yeah, I guess you could say that. But now, I always abstain. I don't give out much advice, but that's one thing I would offer; know your limits.'

'That's great,' Jimmy said. 'So, what do you want from us?'

Mac laughed. 'That's why I like you. You're direct.'

'That right, I am. So, what the fuck do you want?'

'I need your help again,' Mac said, 'for the last time.'

'Fuck you.'

The barman gave Jimmy a look as he placed the bottles on the bar, as if he wasn't use to such aggressive talk in his presence.

'Sorry,' Dylan said as he paid the man. 'My friend has a mouth like a sewer.'

Jimmy nodded to the empty table by the window, and it was there that the little gathering took themselves. After they had sat down, Mac spoke again.

'All I need is the loan of you and your fire engine for a very short period of time.'

Jimmy shook his head. 'It's not going to happen. I thought we said last time we were through with you.'

'That's what *you* said. I said no such thing. But I am giving you my word that this will be the last time you will ever hear from me.'

'What do you want us to do?' Wesley asked.

Jimmy shot him a look. He had made it clear before they had left the station that he was to do all the talking.

'I can't exactly get into it right now. All I can say is, it's not going to take much of your time, and I'll make it more than worth your while. It'll literally be a five-minute job.'

Lenny looked to Dylan. 'I reckon he means figuratively.'

Jimmy took a swig of his beer and shook his head again. 'We don't want your money. In fact,' he picked the sports bag he had brought with him off the floor and dumped it at Mac's feet, 'you can take that with you too. We haven't touched a penny of it.'

There had been a few grumbles when the others found out he had kept the money hidden from them, but considering the information they had failed to disclose to him and Bodhi, none of them could say too much. Even Lenny had reluctantly agreed that the only way they could sever their ties to Mac was to give him back the money.

Mac looked down at the bag and shrugged. 'Fine, I'll take it back. Doesn't mean it changes anything.'

'Can't you do this on your own?' Dylan asked. 'What do you need us for?'

Jimmy gave him a stare that was twice as venomous as the one he had previously directed at Wesley. They weren't there to get into a discussion.

'So, maybe, some of you *are* interested in what I've got to say.' Mac said, spotting his opportunity. 'Maybe you should tell that to your friend here. Perhaps he hasn't got your best interests at heart, after all. And to answer your question, yes, I could do this on my own, but having my good friends in the fire service on board would make it a lot easier for me. But if you're not interested, you're not interested.'

'That's right,' Jimmy said. 'We're not interested.'

Mac looked to the others. 'Is that right? Is he speaking for all of you or just himself?'

They looked at each other and then at Jimmy.

'That's right,' Dylan said. 'We're not interested.'

'You sure? It'll be a piece of cake.'

'He's sure,' Bodhi said as Jo nodded.

'I'm out too,' Wesley added.

'And what about you, big man?' Mac said. 'You don't want to play, either?'

Lenny thought about it. 'Nah. It's like you said; I know my limits.'

'Fine,' Mac said, all chipper-like. 'Then, it looks like this is the end of a beautiful relationship.' He finished his juice and got to his feet. 'It was lovely to see you all again, but I've got a lot to do, so if you don't mind…'

Jimmy kicked the bag towards him. 'Don't forget that.'

Mac bent down and picked up the bag. 'Some people would regard that as ungrateful, but not me. I like to see people with standards. Sometimes, I wish I had them myself… Anyway, take care of yourselves, kids. I'll see you around.'

'No, you won't,' Jimmy said.

When Mac had left the bar, Lenny slugged back his beer, banged the bottle on the table, then looked at the others. 'Right then, you fuckers, who wants a proper drink?'

Chapter 22

Close to Home

'So, that's how you're planning to make your fortune is it, Len?' Jo said. 'That's fucking genius, that is.'

It was the morning after the night before. After Mac's departure, with the exception of Jo who had a race that weekend, the Watch had got well and truly battered. Like all the best nights out, it hadn't been intended. The whole evening was spontaneous and had ended with them crawling out of the pub at two o'clock that morning. Usually, the Watch would only go out after the second day shift, as they knew they had the rest of the following day to recover before starting back on nights. On this occasion, they had to be back in work a few hours later. Until Lenny had opened up about his get rich quick scheme, the Bullshit Hour had taken place almost in silence.

'Listen,' Lenny said, 'it's gonna work, I'm telling you. Big Gay John at Central told me all about it. There's a big market for used firefighters' clothing.'

'But you're not talking about clothes,' Dylan corrected him. 'You're talking about selling your dirty underwear on the internet to men. And you're still trying to say you're not gay.'

Lenny shrugged. 'The pink pound is where it's at, man. All I've got to do is take a picture of me in my grundies and then send it along with the goods and, hey presto, that's fifty squid for a pair of kegs.'

Jo screwed up her face. 'That's disgusting. What if they've got skiddies in them?'

'Even better. John reckons the dirtier, the better.'

Jo puffed out her cheeks like she was stopping herself from being sick.

'Where your plan falls down,' Jimmy said, 'is that I assume this is a pretty niche market. What are you going to do once all the weirdos who want your filthy underpants have bought a pair?'

Lenny wagged his finger at his interrogator and smiled. 'That's the clever bit. You keep selling to them. I mean, there wasn't just one Action Man, was there? You had Scuba Action Man, Jungle Action Man, fucking Arctic warfare Action Man. See what I'm saying? You diversify. I'll do pics of me in pants that I've worn at a fire, pants that I've worn at an RTC or animal rescues. I'll even do pants that I've worn after a heavy session in the gym. The only limits here are my imagination.'

Dylan laughed. 'Yeah, your massive imagination. That's something that always impressed me about you, Len.'

Bodhi removed his face from his hands and, for the first time in half an hour, looked around at his colleagues. The booze had hit him harder than the rest of them; he wasn't used to drinking heavily. Bodhi's body was his temple, and it had been well and truly violated.

'Nah, that's not the problem,' he muttered. 'There's a bigger fly in the ointment here.'

'Look out,' Lenny said. 'It's alive!'

'These guys you're planning on selling this shit to, they're gay, not mentally ill. No one's going to want your filthy y-fronts. Maybe if it was your mate PB's underwear, they'd be interested, but not yours.'

Lenny shook his head in disgust at the mention of the man's name. 'Fuck him. What those men are looking for is a bit of rough. Come to think of it, that's what the ladies want too. Everyone wants a piece of Lenny.'

Bodhi tried to smile. 'If you say so, bud.'

'I do,' Lenny said as he slowly pulled himself to his feet. 'Now, if you don't mind, I'm off for a massive shit. That beer has ruined my insides.'

'Thanks,' Jo said. 'I don't know what I would have done without that knowledge.'

After Lenny had left, Bodhi buried his face back in his hands while Jimmy sipped at his coffee. Neither man wanted to make conversation, but Jo was sober and bored, and thought nothing of disturbing their attempts at peace and quiet.

'Is Wesley still being sick?' she asked.

Jimmy nodded.

'That must make for a nice scene, then,' she said. 'Him puking his ring up in one cubicle as Lenny spray-paints the other with his ass.'

Still enveloped in its hiding place, Bodhi's head shook back and forth. 'Please don't,' he said, 'or I'll be joining them in the sink.'

Jimmy couldn't help but laugh. 'I bet Dylan is still tucked up in bed, the lucky bastard.'

'Even if he hadn't been drinking, he'd still be in bed,' Jo said. 'That boy is one idle son-of-a-bitch. You'd think he'd have grown out of his student ways by now.'

'He might as well make the most of it,' Jimmy said. 'Once they get married and have kids, he's gonna have a rude awakening. If he thinks getting up on nights is bad, then he's got a whole world of pain coming to him.'

Jo shook her head. 'No thanks. I'd rather do an Ironman than go through that.'

They were shaken out of their stupor by the bells going down.

'I'll get the turnout sheet,' Jo said, jumping on her feet and jogging towards the Watch-room. 'You two drag your asses to the pump.'

'Cheers, Jo,' Jimmy answered as he pushed himself out of his seat.

When he got to the engine, Jimmy cursed himself for getting so drunk. He'd forgotten that he was driving that day, and while he was pretty sure he was under the limit by now, he knew what he had done was unprofessional. When Wesley dragged himself into the appliance, he was green and looked like he hadn't yet finished the business of emptying his stomach.

'We've got a fire – persons reported!' Jo shouted as she jogged towards the appliance with the printout. The computer on the fire engine that would normally have provided them with such information was temporarily broken, and so just like the old days, they had to rely on a runner to provide them with the news.

Jo's words completed the job of sobering Jimmy up. When driving on blues, a driver had to be extremely aware of their surroundings. Even though they could go through red lights, they still had to give way to vehicles who may not have heard them, or had panicked at the sight of the oncoming fire appliance. "Drive to Arrive" was the phrase that the driving instructors liked to quote to their students, and they were wise words too. There was no point getting into a crash or putting other road users at risk to get to an incident twenty seconds quicker. Saying that, when it was a persons reported, the drivers would push things harder than if they were attending a fire alarm or a bin fire.

'Where to, anywhere nice?' Jimmy asked.

Jo stared at the sheet. 'Um, 64 Union Lane, Saltdean.'

She handed Wesley the tip-sheet then quickly put on her leggings and tunic.

'Fuck!' Jimmy said, when the words had registered. 'That's my fucking house.'

He jumped out of the driver's seat, took his fire-kit out of the front locker and proceeded to put it on.

'What are you doing, Jim?' Wesley asked. 'You're meant to be driving.'

'It's my house,' Jimmy said as he pulled his braces over his shoulders. 'I know my way around it. I'm wearing BA.'

'Are you sure that's a good idea?'

Jimmy looked into the front of the cab as he threw on his tunic. 'It's not a discussion.'

As he finished dressing, Lenny strolled across the bays, trying to do his belt up as he walked.

'Come on, Len!' Jimmy shouted. 'Let's fucking go, now!'

'All right, all right,' Lenny moaned. 'I was trying to wipe my fucking arse, if that's okay with you?'

'No, it's not,' Jimmy shouted back. 'My fucking house is on fire!'

'Fuck,' Lenny said, and ran as fast as he could toward the lorry. He'd already worked out why Jimmy was sitting in his designated position and without saying another word, Lenny jumped into the driver's seat. After quickly turning to make sure everyone was where they should be, Lenny turned on the blues and twos and headed out of the doors.

The route to Jimmy's house was pretty much straight along the seafront road until you cut into his housing estate some four miles away. It was a six or seven-minute journey for a driver that was pushing it, and Jimmy knew without asking that was exactly what Lenny would do. He was one of the best drivers on the Watch, and no one would get them there any quicker and still have them in one piece at the other end.

In his mind, Jimmy raced through his conversation with his wife that morning. After she had taken Becky to school, she was meant to be going to her friend Alex's house for a coffee and catch-up while the kids played together. If she *had* gone, she should still have been there, but the call was a persons reported, maybe she had decided to stay home. What if they *were* in, what if his poor little boy was there. Jimmy knew all too well the effects of smoke on a child as young as George.

'Wesley, get on the radio and find out if they know anything else!' Jimmy shouted over the jumble of the engine.

Wesley passed the message over the radio. The reply was almost instantaneous; they had received no further information on the incident.

Bodhi, sitting in the middle of the appliance, patted his friend's knee. 'It'll be all right, Jim. It's probably just a mistake.'

Jimmy shook his head. 'You don't know that. How can you?' He craned his head forward to see what was making Lenny slow down.

'Get out of the fucking way!' Lenny yelled at the car in front that had panicked at the sound of the sirens. Rather than pull over, it had stopped in the middle of the road. Lenny had to wait for the oncoming traffic to pass before he could overtake.

'Silly old fucker,' he said as the appliance flew past.

They turned into Jimmy's street three minutes later. It was doubtful if Lewis Hamilton could have got them there any quicker. As they approached his house, Jimmy craned his head in search of smoke, but he could see nothing. When they stopped, he jumped out of the lorry and, as fast as his BA set would allow, ran up to his front door and pounded it with the side of his fist. He was about to step back and kick the door in when Jen opened it. She had George scooped in her arms.

'What the bloody hell is going on, Jim? You trying to scare us to death or what?'

'I thought you were going to Alex's place.' he said, reaching in to stroke his son's head.

'She decided to come here instead, if that's all right with you?'

A red-headed woman with a short bob emerged from behind Jen and gave him a sheepish wave.

'Sorry, love,' Jimmy said. 'Someone's been playing silly buggers. I thought the house was on fire.'

'Really? Someone put a hoax call in on us. Cheeky bastards… Well, as you can see, we're all okay here. Thanks for being our hero, though.' She stepped forward and kissed her husband on the lips.

Jimmy gave her a kiss of her own, then lifted George out of her hands and continued to kiss him on the top of his head until the boy got bored and pushed his dad's face away.

After Jen had made them a cup of tea, she did the usual thing of lambasting Bodhi for not getting himself a woman and settling down. Jimmy saved his friend by taking him out the back to discuss his plans for an extension while the others kept the kids occupied.

Half an hour later, the four of them made their way down the drive towards the motor where Lenny was waiting in case they received another call. Jen had brought him out a cup of tea and some chocolate biscuits to keep him happy.

As they were walking, Jimmy suddenly had the distinct feeling that he was being watched. Looking across the road he saw Mac sitting in his car, who responded by offering them a friendly wave.

'Motherfucker,' Jimmy said as he picked up pace and headed towards the vehicle.

Bodhi grabbed him by the shoulder and pulled him back. 'Don't, Jim, not here. That's just what he wants.'

'I'm going to kill him. No one threatens my family.'

'Come on, Jimmy,' Wesley said. 'Just get back in the lorry, and we'll go back to the station. He's not worth it.'

Before Jimmy could reply, Mac started the car and drove out of the street.

'What the fuck's he playing at?' Jo asked. 'I thought we were done with him.'

'We are,' Jimmy said, 'but it looks like he isn't done with us.'

No one said anything on the way back. They collectively decided it was best to let Jimmy seethe in silence rather than attempt to pacify him. It was only when they pulled up outside of Jonathan Bogarde's colossal mansion, that Lenny piped up.

'Jesus,' he said. 'If only Dylan was here to see this.'

The others looked up the hundred-yard driveway to see the man himself standing on the doorstep of his home. His wife, a woman at least half his age, was in the process of taking their young son out of the back of their vintage Aston Martin. They both stopped what they were doing to stare at the fire engine that was obscuring their view of the sea.

'They've finally fucking moved in after all this time,' Lenny said as he gave them a wave. Neither bothered to return the act. 'There goes the neighbourhood.'

'Fuck him,' Jimmy said, staring at the road ahead. 'We've got bigger things to worry about.'

Chapter 23
Ambush

Jo waved her friends goodbye and slipped out of the pub after spending an hour nursing her orange juice. She hadn't had a drop of alcohol since she'd been there, but then again, neither had most of the others. Running training with the Triathlon Club took place every Tuesday night on Hove Lawns; a mile-long patch of grass sandwiched between the beach and the main road. The dozen or so athletes that turned up every week went through a series of drills as hordes of sun worshipers making the most of the evening rays sat on their rugs, wondering why these lunatics didn't just come and join them for a beer and barbeque. But these sessions were designed to improve the runners' efficiency, and if it meant they had an easier and faster run after swimming a mile and cycling twenty-four, it was a price they were willing to pay as they practised their high-knee drives and lunge walks.

After enduring the stares of the normal people who weren't driven by an overly keen competitive streak, the runners dragged their sweaty bodies into The Lion and Lobster. The aim of the visit was to debrief what they had been doing that evening, but more often than not, it turned into an opportunity for them to discuss their new purchases and do their best to create envy amongst the others.

For a sport that was made up of three relatively simple activities, it was amazing how much money some of the athletes were willing to spend on their hobby. Some of them owned bikes that were worth more than their cars. They had the newest and most high-tech GPS set-ups, ultra-lightweight rain jackets that were invented by NASA and helmets that were so aerodynamic they made the wearer look like a giant sperm. Having plenty of income that she

was free to dispose of, Jo was only too happy to get on board the shopping train, but unlike some of them who belonged in the "all the gear, no idea" category of athletes, she was a champion at the sport and felt that the purchases were entirely justified.

As she walked home, Jo became aware of someone close enough to her, she could clearly hear their footsteps. She looked around and on the other side of the road saw a slight young man wearing a scruffy looking hoodie and tracksuit bottoms. He had been staring at her, but as soon as she caught his eye, he spun around and pretended to look in the window of the shop that sold scented candles and overpriced toiletries. Yeah, right, she thought, wondering when the greasy looking urchin had bathed last. She walked another fifty or so yards then turned and saw that he was still hanging around behind her. It didn't bother her too much; it wasn't even eleven o'clock, and there were plenty of people around. She also felt like she had two important things going for her. If for any reason the guy did give chase, she was one hundred percent certain she could outrun him. Secondly, she was pretty confident if he did get hold of her, she could beat the living shit out of him. She'd lived in London for nearly a decade; little shits like him didn't bother her.

Half a mile later when she was nearly home, she turned again to see if her stalker was still there, but there was no sign of him. She'd been checking every couple of minutes, and while he had hung around for a while, his pace had gradually dropped. On her past two observations, the man had disappeared. Nevertheless, she still had felt it necessary to take this one last cursory glance. The muse that she lived in was part of a beautiful regency building set off the main road behind a row of newer flats. It was a quiet, peaceful area, but to get to it she had to walk down a dark unlit alley that led her from the new world to the old. If he had followed her, that was not the place that she wanted to meet him, regardless of how much she fancied her chances.

As she walked through the alleyway, she put her hand into the rear pocket of her ultra-breathable running tights

and hooked out the keys to her flat. She felt the two keys on the fob, trying to differentiate between the square one for the front door and the round one for the rear, and as she rubbed her thumb against one, she dropped them on the floor. After picking them up and swearing at herself for being so clumsy, she looked up to see two men standing between her and the front door. One of them was only small, probably no bigger than the runt who had followed her earlier, but the other one, the one that sent a shiver down her spine, could have been Lenny's bigger, meaner brother. She turned to face the way she had just come from, only to find her stalker blocking her exit; clearly, he hadn't given up his pursuit.

She'd already decided that she was going to go through him rather than his two friends when she felt a hand on her shoulder. She turned so quickly that the smaller man's hand moved away like it had received an electric shock.

'You're fast, ain't you, girly?' he said.

'What the fuck do you want?' she answered, trying her best to sound vicious, but she could already feel the fight leaving her. It wasn't the one talking that bothered her, he was a podgy-looking fucker with bad skin and a pale complexion, but the other one, the lump, he just stood there with no readable expression, saying nothing. The man terrified her.

'All we want,' the smaller man said as he walked her backwards towards the wall, 'is for you to be one hundred percent sure that you made the right decision yesterday. Ain't that right, Frank?'

He looked at the monster standing next to him who gave him the tiniest of nods.

'I mean, we all know that sometimes girls mean yes when they say no.'

The guy in the hoodie had now joined them.

'Yeah, I bet this one's a right cock tease.' He put his hand between her legs and rubbed at her crotch.

Jo responded by grabbing his shoulders with both hands and driving her forehead into the fleshy part of the man's nose.

The sound of the bone cracking was sickening. Her knee came up into his groin a split second later, sending him crashing to the floor.

When the other small guy grabbed hold of her for a second time, she turned on him, stabbing the key at his eye socket. She had done Krav Maga classes when she was in London, and one of things they taught was that in real life you do whatever you need to do to keep safe, and if that meant gouging a man's eyeball out then that's what you did. She would have, too, if the big guy hadn't stepped forward and grabbed her by the throat. She instantly let the other man go, all she could think about was where her next breath would come from. Before the answer came to her, he slammed her head against the wall, almost knocking her out.

When her eyes managed to focus again, the man loosened his grip just enough so the blood that filled her ears subsided for a second, allowing her to hear what he was saying.

'See, that was silly,' he said. 'We were just here to put the frighteners on you. Give you a little scare an' all. But now you've hurt my mates, I've got to do something about it. If I didn't what sort of friend would that make me?'

The one clutching his face looked at his friend with his good eye and tried to smile. 'This may ruin things, but I'm going to fuck this bitch up.'

He slapped her hard across the face. It stung, but had shocked her even more. Suddenly, she felt like crying.

'Sorry, darling,' the big man said, as a tear ran down her cheek, 'but this is going to hurt.'

He started to draw his fist back like a piledriver waiting to strike the earth, but before he could deliver the blow, he dropped to his knees like someone had taken his legs out from behind him. Which, in fact, they had.

Facing Jo was Bodhi, who had stamped down on the back of the guy's knee with all his might. The smaller man turned to see who was foolish enough to take on his giant friend and was met with a lightning-fast three punch combination that knocked him out before he had even hit the floor.

The big lump dragged himself to his feet, groaning as he did so; the stamp to the leg had served its purpose well.

'You're going to regret that, pal. I swear to God.'

'Sure I am, bud,' Bodhi said, brushing his hair from his eyes.

Both men ignored Jo as they circled each other. The big man was heavy on his feet, struggling to put any weight on his front foot while Bodhi was up on his toes, moving back and forth with the grace of a ballet dancer.

As they moved in on each other, the huge man threw a big right hand, but Bodhi had already seen it coming and dropped his right shoulder so the punch sailed past his head. He quickly rotated his upper body and drove a crisp left hook into his opponent's ribcage. The impact made the bigger man take a sharp intake of air as he moved a half-step backwards.

When Bodhi smiled at him, the man frowned and launched himself forward to throw another punch. This time, Bodhi stepped to his left and, at the same instant, kicked him in the side of his injured knee, causing it to buckle again.

As he staggered forward, Bodhi spun around and threw his other leg up, catching him on the temple with a brutal roundhouse kick. It was the sort of thing that if you saw Jean-Claude Van Damme do it in a film, you'd say, "yeah right, that wouldn't work in real life," except it did. Bodhi was testament to it. Just like his friend, the man was out cold as soon as the kick made contact. He went down with his arms by his sides, unable to protect his face from the concrete.

After surveying the devastation he had caused, Bodhi turned to Jo and motioned his hand toward her hair like he was about to stroke it. Jo saw it coming and slapped it away.

'Piss off,' she said. 'I'm not a baby. I don't need you to look after me.'

Bodhi leant in, bringing his lips to hers. 'You're not a baby,' he said, breaking away from the kiss. 'You're my girl.'

Chapter 24

Panic at the Disco

With his hand resting on the boy's back, Lenny guided the troublemaker out of the club. Now that he was on his own and away from his friends, the bravado the kid had initially displayed had vanished. Separated from the mob, all the fight had gone out of him. For Lenny, who had done this a million times before, it was like taking a well-trained dog for a walk. From his position just off the dance floor, he had watched as the boy had put his hand up a girl's skirt and got a good squeeze of her arse. Lenny had been on him in no time. He didn't put up with shit like that; he had a daughter himself, for Christ's sake. One day, she would have to deal with assholes like him. The thought of it made Lenny shudder, and he took it out on the boy as he pushed him out of the exit.

'Try that again,' he said to the lad who only just managed to stay on his feet, 'and you'll be seeing my not-so-nice side. Understand?'

The boy nodded and walked off down West Street, trying his best to look like he wasn't bothered by what had happened.

Lenny shook his head and stepped back into the club. At the fire station, he may have been a loud-mouthed pain in the arse, doing his best to rub any form of authority up the wrong way, but in the club, he was a very different animal. He had worked on the doors almost as long as he had been a firefighter. It seemed a natural second job for a man his size and often available to work the unsocial evening shifts. He was good at it, too, very good, and that wasn't just down to his natural attributes.

Lenny knew how to handle himself. He had never done martial arts, or any of that shit, but he could take a punch, and

he knew how to put his weight into one, too, which meant something when you were pushing eighteen stone. Added to that, despite many trying, no man had ever got out of one of his infamous headlocks. But what set him apart from so many of the other meatheads who plied his trade was that Lenny understood violence or, to be more exact, the threat of violence. He had learnt early on in the game that it wasn't what you did that made you effective at the job, it was what you didn't do. It was what was implied in the threats that he issued to rogue punters that made him so effective.

He had learnt if you hit someone, it usually only made a bad situation worse. Let's say, you had a bunch of skinny eighteen-year-olds looking for trouble; you hit one of them, and it all kicked off. One-on-one, they weren't worth a second look, but you get seven or eight of them working together, and like a pack of hyenas, they could take anyone down, even Lenny the lion. The other thing was, when most people took a punch, they generally crumbled and did whatever they were told to do, but there were others who it awakened something primal in. Some people got hit, tasted their own blood and realised that, actually, it wasn't as bad as they thought it would be, in fact, they kind of liked the feeling. Those were the people you didn't want to be taking on. No, the trick was to do nothing and get them to do the job for you.

When people got into such situations, that's when the adrenaline kicked in, stimulating the fight or flight urge. They did either of those things and that was fine, that was what millions of years of evolution had programmed them to do, but if you could get them to do neither, which was what Lenny was so good at, then the adrenaline dump the body experienced would leave the potential troublemaker in a bad, bad way. It left them feeling like their stomachs were about to fall out of them, and turn even the meanest opponents into quivering wrecks. Basically, he'd have them frozen with fear.

Lenny's trick was to stay calm, say as little as possible and get the aggressors in a state where they were suddenly second guessing

just how tough they actually were. By the time he was through, they were usually fit for nothing. In his time, he'd convinced black-belts, boxers and cage fighters into believing that should they mess with him, he would paint them over the nightclub walls.

It hadn't always been that way. When he'd first started on the doors, he had been set up by the other bouncers as part of his initiation. Brighton Rugby Team were in the club where he was working, and after getting beaten earlier that day by their rivals Hove, they had gone out and got well and truly bladdered. The men were pissed, and pissed off at losing, and if anyone was unfortunate to get in their way, they were quick to feel the team's wrath. When they started throwing punches at a couple of poor guys who had stood too close at the bar, the other bouncers thought it would be funny to test Lenny's mettle and send him in alone. He'd only been working there for a few weeks and not wanting to disappoint, he had taken on the challenge, charging into the dance floor and launching himself at as many of them as possible.

The fight that developed from his moment of madness was legendary. Doormen still talked about it nearly twenty years later. It had ended with Lenny sitting in casualty surrounded by half-a-dozen rugby players he had sent there with him. They spent the next couple of hours trying to persuade him to play for their team, but he was having none of it; there were far too many rules for his liking, and he would take football over egg-chasing any day of the week. He was still friends with a couple of them.

Returning from the disposal of the troublemaker, he noticed a guy on his own, standing in front of the vending machine that was filled with multi-coloured lollipops. It was a strange thing to have in a nightclub, but the punters seemed to like it. The man had his back to him, but from the way he was slumped over the machine, Lenny could see that he was pissed up. The drunken guy put his hand into his pocket, and after fumbling around for a long time, came out with some coins that he fed into the machine. After

trying to turn the handle, he smacked it with the palm of his hand as he yelled profanities at the inanimate object. Lenny rolled his eyes as he made his way towards the disturbance. It was only ten o'clock, and he'd already thrown out two people. It looked like town was full of arseholes, and he was in for a busy night.

He tapped the man on the shoulder with just enough pressure to show that he wasn't kidding. 'Come on, fella,' he said. 'I think it's time to go.'

The man spun around with a speed that belied his drunken state and looked up at Lenny's eyes that had suddenly grown wide. 'You should have said yes,' he said, just loud enough for Len to hear.

As Lenny's arm fell away from his shoulder, the man pushed past him and headed rapidly towards the exit.

Lenny turned and watched him go. 'That was weird,' he said quietly to himself, then looked down to see a rapidly growing red stain on the front of his shirt. 'Really fucking weird.'

As he fell to his knees, he noticed a fresh blob of bubble-gum stuck to the floor and wondered why anyone would think it was a good idea to put carpets in a nightclub.

Chapter 25

Truth or Dare

Bodhi's mobile phone going off woke him up the next morning. He reached across Jo's naked body and grabbed it off the dresser.

Jo looked at the clock, closing her eyes in disbelief when she saw what it had to say for itself. Bodhi was used to getting up at this time, his body-clock was dictated by tides and wind speed, and if they were in his favour, he'd be up, regardless of the hour. Jo, on the other hand, loved her bed more than most of the men she'd had relationships with.

'What prick is calling you at half-six in the morning? Tell them to fuck off.'

Bodhi looked at the phone then put his finger to his lips. 'Shh, it's Jimmy.'

The warning did its trick; Jo instantly stopped moaning.

'All right, Jimbo, what can I do for you?'

There was a pause. 'Shit, is he okay?'

Another pause, then he sighed. 'That's good, yeah. I'll head up there for visiting time.'

He nodded, paused, then nodded again. 'Okay, I'll see you tonight. I think we need to talk.'

He put the phone back on the dresser and turned to Jo. 'Lenny's been stabbed.'

Jo sat up in the bed. 'When? Where? Is he all right?'

'At the club last night. Someone stabbed him in the stomach. Jimmy said he's all right and that they missed all the important bits. That's what happens when you're a big bastard.'

'Jesus Christ,' Jo said. 'I keep telling him he needs to stop working in that fucking place. Too many dicks with something to prove.'

'Jimmy thinks it was Mac's boys who did it. It makes sense, considering what they did to you.'

Jo shook her head. 'Fuckers.'

Bodhi smiled the way that someone did before they said something the other person wouldn't like. 'You know, we're going to have to tell them what happened to you, and when we do, it's going to come out about the two of us.'

Jo shrugged. 'Tell them, if you like. They won't believe you.'

And she was probably right too. If there were two people who the Watch would never have put together, then it was most definitely Jo and Bodhi. The two of them were polar opposites, at different ends of the scale. While Bodhi was so laid back, he was almost horizontal, Jo, who despite chilling out massively since she had joined the Watch, had a pole so far up her ass that the only position she could adopt was vertical. But then again, what was it that people liked to say? Opposites attract.

When they'd first met, there was an obvious chemistry there. Jo was attracted to the fit, healthy, suntanned guys, and Bodhi had always had an eye for slim girls who liked to stay in shape. The problem was that when they got to know each other, that initial attraction quickly wore off. Jo hated his "whatever" attitude to life; she didn't think he was capable of taking anything seriously. The way he was happy to go with the flow, without considering the pros and cons of his actions, drove her nuts. To her, Bodhi was an empty vessel, the only thing that seemed to excite him in any way was his stupid obsession with the sea. It was like nothing else was of any relevance to him, and it pissed her off royally. She also hated the fact he was the messiest person she had ever met. Watching him set the table at work almost made her want to throw up.

Bodhi's feelings were pretty much mutual. He was a disciple of the mañana attitude towards life. If you were too rigid, the water could snap you in half. The only thing to do that made any sense was to bend and go with the flow. Jo, on the other hand, was constantly trying to adapt and change things to her liking, and if she didn't have anything to worry about, she would worry about that.

After their initial desire to fuck each other's brains out had worn off, the pair quickly developed a healthy mutual dislike. It had become a standing joke on the Watch that when doing the crewing for the next tour, Jimmy had to plan it meticulously to ensure they were not seated together on the back of the appliance.

But then, it happened. At the previous year's Christmas drinks, they had both got ridiculously drunk, and over numerous beers, shots and cocktails, they began sharing looks over the table like they had done when they first met. No one had thought anything was going on when they got a taxi home together that night. Firstly, they were too drunk to care, second, even if they were still sober enough to take it in, there was nothing strange about the action; they both lived in roughly the same direction and so sharing a taxi made sense. Thirdly, and most important of all, it was Jo and Bodhi, for fuck's sake; they hated each other.

And that's how they went at it that night; like two people who hated each other, ripping each other's clothes off to get to the goods. Angry sex with someone you wanted to punch in the face (this was from Jo's perspective) and give yourself to completely, at the same time. That was a long and sleepless night for the both of them.

Since that night, they'd managed to keep their relationship secret from the Watch and maintain the charade that they disliked each other. It wasn't that they were ashamed, you only had to look at either of them to understand why someone of the opposite sex would find them attractive. It wasn't even down to the huge amount of piss-taking that would be had at their expense, either. They'd both been firefighters long enough to know the others would hammer them for this deceitful little show of theirs. No, the real reason was, once it came out they were a couple, the idea of them staying on Watch together would be frowned upon. There were a number of boyfriend/girlfriend relationships in the job and a couple of marriages, too, but they tended to be between people on different Watches or different stations. None of them actually worked together, day-in day-out. It just wasn't the done thing.

The other thing was, they were both well aware when it did come out, even if they did decide to buck tradition and continue to work together (there was no rule to stop them), it would change the Watch dynamic. No more would the Watch be able to take the piss out of one of them when the other was on leave. No more would they be able to moan about how Jo needing to chill-the-fuck-out in Bodhi's presence, no matter how many times he told them he was okay with it. No more would Jimmy or Wesley be able to slag Bodhi off in front of the others for looking like a scruffy son-of-a-bitch or for not bothering to complete his Personal Development Record, despite Jo insisting she agreed with them. Once the truth came out, the Watch would be changed forever, and both of them had accepted if and when it happened, one of them would have to put in a transfer request. The problem was, neither wanted to go.

That was one of the reasons they'd discussed breaking up. Did they really want to have to change Watches, and maybe even stations, if their relationship wasn't destined to last, and it was a just a bit of fun they were having? The other, more serious hurdle in their relationship, had been Jo not telling Bodhi about the money. When he found out she had been keeping it from him for three whole months, the usually laid-back surfer was more than a little furious. He could understand why she had withheld the information, and that part of it was a desire to protect him, should they ever be found out, but since he'd learned what had happened, the trust in their relationship had been seriously dented.

Funnily enough, he had been going to her place the previous evening to break things off. What with everything that was going on with Mac, the last thing everyone needed (including him and Jo) was more drama. That was until he'd seen those men trying to harm her. That was when he truly realised just how much he loved her, and when she witnessed him taking down her attackers, Jo's love for him was sealed.

'Seriously,' Bodhi said. It was a word he rarely used, so Jo knew he had made up his mind. 'We've got to tell them tonight.'

'Fine,' Jo said, leaning across to wrap her arms around him. 'Let's tell them. In a way, I'm looking forward to them knowing I'm going out with a super-hot surfer dude.'

'Yeah, right,' Bodhi didn't have a vain bone in his body. He didn't care what he looked like or what other people thought about him, he was a one-woman man… well, two, if you counted the sea. As long as they both liked him, that was all that mattered.

'*Yeah,* right, and now I find out you're a fucking ninja as well, you've suddenly become even more attractive. I didn't think that Bruce Lee kick-ass shit would be your cup of tea. Aren't you surfers meant to be the peaceful, hippie types?"

Bodhi shrugged. He usually was a karma loving, live-and-let live, cool as a cucumber type, but there was also another side to him, one that he did his best to keep tucked deep down inside himself, locked away from his friends and loved ones. See, Bodhi had discovered at a relatively young age that there was only one thing in the world that made him feel as alive as he did when he was taking on a big wave, and that was fighting.

It had happened when he was fourteen, and one of the older boys started some shit with him on the beach after accusing Bodhi of dropping in on his wave; a cardinal sin in surfing. He hadn't; the boy was an asshole and a bully, jealous that someone three years younger than him was twice the surfer he would ever be. He caught the smaller boy with a couple of hard punches, breaking his nose and leaving him sprawled out on the sand. He was about to leave the beach in victory when Bodhi wiped the blood from his nose and sprung to his feet, launching an attack of his own that ended with him pounding on the older boy until his friends had to save him from becoming sausage meat.

Bodhi joined the local karate club the next day, drunk on the feeling that the encounter had left him with. These days, karate gets a bad rap from the mixed-martial-arts fighters. Most of the karate guys who have entered the UFC have had the shit kicked out of them by wrestlers and jiu-jitsu guys who have quickly taken them down and submitted them or beaten them to a pulp.

But the reason for their failure wasn't because of the shortcomings of karate itself, more the devolution of the art by the host of McDojos that made their money selling black belts to kids who had watched *The Karate Kid* one too many times.

Bodhi's sensei didn't buy into all that bullshit. He taught Shotokan Karate; the one-punch, one-kill, no fucking about method, that made the tap-tap shit that most teachers were doing look like toddlers fighting in nursery. Just like with his surfing, Bodhi was a natural. His balance, sense of timing and speed meant he was one dangerous motherfucker.

It wasn't just at karate he excelled, either. On his way to a surf trip in Bali, he had stopped off at a dingy Thai-boxing gym in Bangkok and spent three months learning how to fight dirty with his knees and elbows. He was a total bad ass when he left that place, but the skills he had learnt over there were kept in the locker. When you knew you could kick someone's ass, it took away the urge to fight them. Up until the previous night, that mindset had worked well for Bodhi.

'So, are you prepared for the shit they are going to give us when we 'fess up?' Jo said. She was all too aware of what was to come.

'To be honest,' Bodhi said, 'I'm just fed up of living with secrets. It'll be good to have it all out in the open.'

'In that case, there's something else I think I should tell you.'

'Yeah,' Bodhi answered, smiling. 'Hit me with it.'

'I'm pregnant.'

Chapter 26

Hang-ups

Dylan took a deep breath and let one hand off the wall. He was halfway through the climb and about to take on the overhang that jutted out from above his head. He knew what he needed to do; he had done the climb (or problem, as they were known in the sport) in sections but never completed it in one go. He just needed to adjust his left leg by pointing his toes outward rather than in, then push off, keeping his hips tight to the wall and reach up with his right hand. The next hold was a good one; it was deep enough to get his fingers into and, if necessary, hang off as he got his legs into a better position. The trouble was that the section before had been a pinchy one, involving small holds and him using up much of his finger strength.

He flexed his digits, trying to get some blood back into them, then went for it, driving off his legs and stretching up to grasp the blue hold that looked way too far for him to possibly reach. There were only two more moves left before he got to the top, and knowing he was almost out of steam, he powered through them, grunting with the effort. With both his hands on the final hold that was large, but pebble shaped and smooth with little to grip, he breathed out again, this time much heavier, then made his way back down the wall.

He had never been good at sports in school, he was far too clumsy for football or rugby, and things hadn't got any better as he got older. When Jo saw him fall over himself as he tried to play volleyball in the yard, she had remarked that he was cursed with physical dyslexia. Lenny's assessment of his abilities was far less diplomatic. 'The boy's got spaz feet,' was how he had summed up his efforts. It didn't bother Dylan; he had no interest in team

sports, anyway, and knew, despite his lack of coordination, there were things that mattered to him that he was very good at.

If Bodhi was a master of his craft, then so was Dylan of climbing. The man was like a human spider. Born in the Peak District, he felt like it was his destiny to climb. If he wasn't out on his mountain-bike looking for new single-track trails to take on, then Dylan could always be found on the face of a rock. His father had taken him climbing almost as soon as he could walk, and he had fallen in love with it from the off. His relocation to Sussex had meant a different approach to the sport due to the geography of the area. Bowles and Harrisons were good sandstone challenges, but both were over an hour's drive from Brighton, and not having a car most of the time, they were only of use to him if he could find a partner to drag along.

Luckily, Brighton was rapidly becoming the place to be for indoor climbing, with three or four decent indoor walls located within cycling distance of Dylan's flat. Most exciting for him was the massive indoor bouldering centre in Portslade that allowed him to free climb without the need for a partner, ropes or climbing equipment. The wall was only twenty-foot high with heavy mats at the bottom to protect the climbers if, and when, they fell. Dylan loved the feel of free climbing, and while he wasn't exactly scaling El Capitan, the drop was still enough to get your heart racing if you came off. In bouldering, it was just him against the wall, and that was how he liked it.

Climbing was also something he did when he needed to think or clear his head, and following the news of Lenny's stabbing, he felt like his brain needed a good clean out. All morning it had been filled with only one thought; what if they came for him? Lenny was tough, he'd grown up around violence, it was a part of his make-up. Dylan, on the other hand, had never been in a real fight. Even his sister could get the better of him when there were kids. He was a pacifist and would seek any alternative other than fighting to solve his problems. What would he do if someone tried to do something similar to him? It was a thought

that unnerved him. No, scratch that, it was a thought that fucking terrified him.

Dropping the last few feet of the wall onto the mats, Dylan looked down at his battered hands. He'd gone at it hard, and his hands were a state. The skin on his fingers was ripped, and the calluses on his palms looked ready to follow at any time. *Finish on a high*, he thought. *You've been trying to conquer that route for weeks*. He spat in his hands and rubbed them together, trying to get rid of what was left of the chalk on them and looked across to the guy on the wall next to him.

The man looked to be in his mid-thirties and was decked out in jeans and a T-shirt. It wasn't exactly climbing wear, but that wasn't unusual for bouldering. Unlike the more traditional climbers, many of the youngsters turned up in their skinny jeans and lumberjack shirts looking like they had just stepped out of a coffee shop. Dylan didn't buy into the look, not only was he aware that these kids dressed much cooler than him, but also, he was a real Sweaty Betty. He liked to wear a vest and cargo shorts when he was on the wall. The less he had on, the better.

The reason the guy next to him had caught his eye was his style. Dylan had been keeping an eye on him since he had turned up nearly an hour earlier. The guy was sticking mainly to the orange climbs which all rated "4c"s through to "5b"s. It was an intermediate level that either required some technical proficiency and understanding of what you were doing, or else you had to be fit, strong and agile enough to heave yourself up the wall. In other words, you got through it with sheer brute force. The man to Dylan's right definitely belonged in the latter category. He was short and sinewy with knotty little muscles and not an ounce of fat on him. If he could only learn some technique, Dylan thought as he watched the guy struggle with the final move of the problem, he would be a pretty decent climber.

As he stopped to catch his breath, the man's knees shook like he was doing an impersonation of Elvis. It was a situation all climbers found themselves in at some point. Before his legs gave

way, the man stretched out with his left hand for the hold directly above. He managed to get his fingertips to it but unable to get any purchase, he dropped to the mats below, making a loud thud as he came down. A few other climbers looked around to see what the disturbance was, but the man held up his hand to them, letting them know he was okay.

He looked across to the person observing him and smiled. 'That was harder that it looked.'

Dylan smiled back. 'It was a pretty good effort, if you don't mind me saying.'

'Cheers. Maybe next time, eh?'

'Definitely,' Dylan said. 'You just got to keep at it.'

The guy took in the route he had just climbed, moving his head from the bottom of the wall to the top, then across to Dylan. 'Got any tips?'

'Yeah. For that last move, swap your feet around and push off your left instead of your right. It'll make you a couple of inches taller, and you should be able to reach the hold.'

Dylan was cautious about giving advice to others. He was one of the better climbers at the centre, but he didn't want to look like he was lording it over the others, patronising them with little snippets of wisdom. If they asked, however, he was always happy to help. The man nodded. Dylan could see he was completing the move in his head. It was something he often did himself; visualising a climb and the moves it entailed before doing it. The brain needed a warm up as well as the muscles.

'You know, I'm sure I know you from somewhere,' the man said with a smile after staring at Dylan for a second too long.

'Yeah?'

'Yeah, definitely… You're not friends with Carl, are you?'

Dylan though about it then shook his head. 'Can't say I know anyone called Carl.'

The man tutted. 'No, I'm sure I know you from somewhere.' He paused then clicked his fingers and pointed at Dylan. 'That's it, you're a fireman.'

'That's right,' Dylan said, intrigued.

'I knew it, I never forget a face.'

Dylan went to speak but the man cut him off. 'It's Dylan, right? Your girlfriend's name is…' he clicked his fingers again. 'Felicity! That's it, Felicity. She's an accountant, yeah?

'Yeah,' Dylan said, 'that's right. Look, this is a bit embarrassing, but I just can't remember who you are.'

As he spoke, the man dug his hand into his pocket and brought out his mobile phone. A big no-no in climbing, Dylan thought, but refrained from saying. Not only could it go off and distract himself and others, but perhaps, more importantly, if he fell, the phone could easily be wiped out. The man fiddled with the phone for a few seconds then turned it around to show the screen to Dylan. On it was a picture of Felicity coming out of their flat.

'That's her, right?'

Dylan looked at the picture. 'How did you…?' and then, he stopped talking as the realisation hit him.

The man's smile had disappeared when he spoke again. 'We've asked you nicely once. Don't make us ask again. The right answer is yes, got it?'

Dylan nodded.

'Say it, then.'

'The answer is yes.'

The man's face broke out into a broad grin once more. 'There we go, see… easy.' He held his hand out for Dylan to shake. 'Nice to meet you and thanks for the advice.'

Not knowing what else to do, Dylan extended his own hand that was gently squeezed, not crushed as he had expected.

'See you soon,' the man said with a wink.

Dylan watched as he left the building, then ran to the toilets and threw up.

Chapter 27

Baby Daddy

Bodhi was almost home, sitting stationary at a set of traffic lights, when the beeping of the car behind roused him into action. He waved an apology to the driver as he took off. Looking around at his environment, he became aware he had no recollection of how he had got there. It was a similar feeling to driving on blue lights after being woken up in the wee hours.

He had spent the morning talking with Jo, or listening to Jo would have been more precise. What he had actually done is sit in silence for the most part, nodding and offering words of support when he felt it was needed. The gist of the conversation/speech was this; there was no way on earth she could have a baby.

She was too old; she'd be forty on her next birthday. Did he realise, she had asked him, what percentage of children born to older women had Down's Syndrome (*she* didn't, it turned out, but she knew it was pretty high). And then, there was Bodhi. He was only a year younger, and while the age thing wasn't such an issue for fathers, it was more his emotional immaturity that bothered her. He was a man-child, interested in only the things that excited him, everything else she said, quoting him, "was just background noise." The man lived on a boat for crying out loud.

Then, there were the triathlons. She'd worked so hard to be where she was at this point; number three in the country for her age group, and she believed she'd only get stronger. By the time she reached the over forty category, she was fairly certain she would be number one. *Then,* there was her career. She loved her job, and the thought of giving it up for the length of time she knew it would entail, was a killer.

Unlike in most other jobs, due to the nature of the work, the moment that a woman knew she was pregnant she was meant to notify the brigade who would immediately take them off the run and onto light duties. It also meant that they couldn't wait for the twelve-week window to be closed before they let the cat out of the bag. If she had the baby, she would have to have the full nine months off work doing mind-numbing paperwork, followed by at least another six months off to look after the child. That meant the best part of a year and a half off the run, and the thought of that drove her crazy.

Finally, and this was the crucial thing in her mind, there was Jo herself. She didn't want to be a mother. She didn't even like kids. If she did have it, she'd only end up resenting the child for dragging her away from the job that she loved, and ruining her chances of sporting success. She didn't think it fair for the kid to have that burden hanging around their necks for the rest of their lives. No, she was pretty certain that if she had a child, and even if it was healthy in the physical and mental sense, emotionally it would be well and truly screwed.

Even though he hadn't said much, Bodhi agreed with her. Not the bit about her being a potential bad mother, he was fairly certain if she did have the child she'd be great at it, just like she was great at everything else she put her mind too. But other than that, he was onboard with her thinking. He also agreed with her sentiments about him. She was right; he was basically a childish, selfish motherfucker. She often told him that he loved the sea more than he could ever love another human being, and while he had always laughed at the notion, part of him thought she was probably right.

He left the van next to the kids' park and walked up the steep bank that brought him out on the river path that accessed the houseboats. When he walked up the self-made wooden bridge that linked his boat to the land, Vera, his seventy-year-old next-door neighbour was there to meet him. He loved Vera; she was a free spirit like himself and young at heart. When she was in her

twenties, she had worked at the fairground, driving a motorcycle along the wall of death.

'That was one hell of a party you must have been having last night,' she said. 'Right old racket coming from your place.'

'Sorry about that, Vee,' Bodhi said, his heart sinking at the thought of what had happened.

'Don't be sorry,' she said with a cheeky smile. 'Just remember to invite me next time. You know what a party animal I am.'

Bodhi tried to smile back, and walking to the entrance, quickly saw that the keys in his hands were now redundant. The door had been kicked in and was hanging off its hinges.

When he stepped inside, the place looked like a war-zone. The handmade kitchen that he had spent so long creating was now a pile of firewood in the middle of the floor. The tables and sofa had been flipped over, his books and CDs were strewn across the place, and the TV screen was smashed on the other side of the room to where it normally sat. He guessed that it must have been the same men he had beaten up the night before. They must have dragged themselves up, he thought, dusted themselves down, then come here to get their revenge.

The pile of human shit in the middle of the floor showed that one of them had probably lost his nerve while in the act. He had laughed when a copper had told them once how burglars would sometimes drop their pants and take a dump at a victim's home. It wasn't them being malicious to the homeowner, it was just the adrenaline build up was so big, something had to give, and in most cases, it was their anal sphincter. As he turned his nose up at the smell, it didn't seem so funny anymore.

Before he could go into the spare room and inspect his beloved boards and kites, he noticed a can of petrol sitting on top of what had once been a bookshelf made of scaffold planks. He walked up to it for further examination, half expecting to see a note from the offenders but there was nothing. The message was clear; next time, we'll burn your boat to ashes.

Chapter 28

Decisions, Decisions

Jimmy's lip curled as he sniffed the air. He had a look of pure disgust on his face. 'I'm telling you,' he said, 'I can still smell it. There's human shit on me.'

He took his hand off the steering wheel and quickly inspected his arm before re-focusing on the road.

They were on their way back from helping an ambulance crew rescue a bariatric patient who had fallen off his toilet and become trapped between it and the wall. A bariatric, for those not in the know, is a morbidly obese person whose weight puts them at risk of serious health issues. In this case, the middle-aged man was pushing thirty stones and so big that it had been almost impossible to move him. It was one of those days they could really have done with Lenny being there, but as he was still in hospital nursing his wounds, they'd had to manoeuvre the man with only four of them present. Jimmy had even had to leave the appliance to give them a hand.

The only way to move the casualty was for one of them to get down there and manhandle him. Being the strongest, the job fell to Jimmy, and so he'd had to wrap his arms as best he could around the patient and do what was necessary. The thing was, the man hadn't managed to do his business before he fell off the toilet, that came after, when he was lying helpless on the ground.

'Good thing Harrison wasn't there,' Jimmy added as an afterthought.

When it came to amputations, decapitations, or anything else particularly gruesome, Harrison wouldn't blink. He was the one who usually became the dedicated casualty carer if they got there before the ambulance. Shit and puke, on the other hand, were his

worst enemy. Just the smell was enough to make him retch his guts up.

'Your efforts were much appreciated,' Wesley said to his driver. 'We would have been stuck without you there.'

'You could always have made up,' Jimmy said. 'If we ain't got enough people, there's no point killing ourselves. It's either that, or they try and cut more pumps 'cos we're not busy enough.'

Wesley nodded as he took in Jimmy's words. 'You're probably right. I'll remember that next time.'

'Hopefully,' Jimmy said, sniffing the air again, 'there won't be a next time.'

He took a quick look over his shoulder at Bodhi and Jo in the back. They were staring out of their respective windows in silence.

'Hey, you two!' he shouted to them. 'I hope you're not getting it on back there. I don't want the windows steaming up.'

'Fuck you, Jimmy!' Jo shouted back.

When they'd started the shift, the two of them had revealed all. After discussing Lenny's predicament, they had told the others about their relationship over the past six months, culminating in the attack on Jo, and Bodhi's boat being ransacked. It was fair to say that the others were gobsmacked. Mid-conversation, they had got the call to assist the ambulance crew, and so the opportunity to rip the piss out of them had not yet been taken. The lovers sat ignoring each other as they waited for the firing squad to take them down.

'Can I ask you something?' Wesley whispered. He knew that if he spoke quietly, the noise of the engine would drown out their conversation from the not-so-happy couple.

'What's up?' Jimmy said.

'I was just thinking about what happened to those two yesterday. What happened to all of you.'

'Yeah,' Jimmy said, slowing down as he approached the fire station.

'Why do you reckon they didn't do anything to me?'

Jimmy looked across to Wesley then back to the road as he turned onto the station yard, 'I don't know, maybe because your

family lives so far away. Perhaps they couldn't be bothered to follow you all the way back to Milton Keynes to keep tabs on them.'

'Maybe,' Wesley said as he pressed the button on the remote control that lifted the station barrier arm. 'Or maybe it was because they thought I didn't need convincing. Maybe they knew I would do anything they wanted me to do. I didn't need my arm twisting.'

'Don't be soft,' Jimmy said, even though he had thought exactly the same thing. 'You're being paranoid.'

'No, I'm not, because they're right. When you told Mac to go fuck himself at the pub, I was ready to go along with whatever he wanted. So, tell me, Jim, what does that say about me?'

As Bodhi and Jo got out of the vehicle, Jimmy looked across the cab again.

'Listen, Wes,' he said, 'no one said being a leader is easy. If you want to do it, you need to stand up and prove yourself. Show Mac he was wrong… show me I was wrong.'

Wesley nodded. 'I'll try.'

After they took off their boots and leggings, the four of them headed to the canteen where they were met by Dylan, drinking a cup of tea as he waited their return. He was still on his annual leave and should have been at home with Felicity, but after the previous day's events, he had come in to find out what the fuck they were going to do. When he saw them, a smile spread across his face.

'Hi, lovebirds,' he said.

Jo instantly turned to Jimmy. 'That didn't take long.'

Jimmy shrugged. 'Seriously, what did you expect?'

'Don't be like that,' Dylan said. 'I think the two of you make a lovely couple, I really do.'

'Is that right?' Jo said.

Bodhi just stood there, saying nothing. He was too cool to get heated up about such things.

'Yeah, it is. The two of you are beautiful together. I think it was your destiny to be lovers.'

He stood up, walked toward them and took one of Jo's hands in his own. He then turned to Bodhi and linked hands with him too. He looked like a vicar about to read out their marriage vows. 'I'm so happy right now I could cry,' he said. 'Let's sing, and tell the world how much you two love each other.'

Jo snatched her hand away then used it to whack him on the shoulder. 'Shut up, knobhead. All the shit that's gone on, and that's all you can think about?'

'Jesus,' Dylan said, rubbing his shoulder. 'What do you expect? I mean, you and Bodhi, for fuck's sake. I can't believe you devious little buggers kept it quiet for so long.'

'Sorry, bud,' Bodhi said. 'We shouldn't have lied to you guys.'

'Yeah, well, if my girlfriend was a crazy bitch, I probably wouldn't have told anyone about her either.'

Before he could protect himself, Jo punched him in the stomach with enough force to send him back to his chair. 'Right,' she said, 'if we've finished fucking about, do you mind if we discuss this goddamn mess we're in?'

Half an hour later, their minds were made up. None of them were happy about it, in fact, they were deeply fucking unhappy about the whole thing, but if it meant the safety of their loved ones, then they would do whatever it was that Mac wanted of them. They hadn't needed to consult Lenny; he had already told Jimmy what he thought that afternoon when he'd visited him in hospital. He'd also informed him that he'd be back in work by the start of their next tour in five days' time.

Lenny had one of the worst sick records in the brigade, and such an injury would normally have led to him dragging it out for as long as possible and getting in at least a month's worth of sick leave. But this time, he wanted to get back as quickly as possible. He hadn't even informed his employers of his injuries. If they were going to do this thing for Mac, then Lenny needed to be there; he couldn't risk the Watch having a temporary replacement shipped in for him. If that happened, it would be a disaster, dragging even

more people into the massive fuck-up they had found themselves in. The Watch would have to cover for him as he'd still have his stitches in, but if they kept him solely on driving duties for a few weeks, he was pretty sure it would work out okay.

'So, we're all agreed, then?' Jimmy said. 'We're going to do this thing.'

'What I'd like to do,' Bodhi said, 'is find this prick and kick the living shit out of him, but given the situation, yeah, I agree.'

It was unusual to hear him issuing such threats. If Bodhi didn't have something good to say about someone, he normally chose to say nothing at all.

Jimmy nodded. 'Listen, mate, I ain't happy about it, either. He threatened my family, too, remember?' But as it is, I don't see what other choice we've got.'

He picked up his mobile phone and held it up for the rest of them to inspect. 'Yeah?' he said, checking for final confirmation.

'Just do it and get it over with, Jim,' Jo said. 'It's like you say. We've got no choice.'

Jimmy looked at the card Mac had given him and punched the numbers into his phone. It rang twice before someone picked it up.

'Is that Mac?'

'It is indeed,' the voice said. 'Glad to hear from you, my friend.'

'You're not my friend. You're a fucking piece of shit, is what you are.'

Mac chuckled. 'Funnily enough, you're not the first person to have come to that conclusion… now, do you have anything else to say, or did you just phone up to hear my voice?'

'We're in,' Jimmy said after a pause. 'We'll do it.'

'That's good, Jim,' Mac said.

Even though Jimmy couldn't see him, he was certain the man was smiling.

'That's real good.'

Chapter 29

A Debt Repaid

As instructed, Bodhi pulled the fire appliance off the seafront road into the Roedean Café car park. Mac was already there waiting for them in his Bentley.

'Are we sure about this?' Bodhi asked. 'I can drive off, if you want. It's not too late.'

'Yes, it is,' Wesley answered from the OIC's seat. 'Let's just get it done.'

They came to a stop alongside the other vehicle, then waited for Mac to emerge.

It was another two minutes before he stepped out of the passenger side. He nodded at Jimmy sitting in the back of the lorry, riding BA. Jimmy responded by opening his door to its full extent, but rather than get out, he sat and waited. Mac looked around, checking that no one else was observing them, then patted the car's roof. The rear door swiftly opened allowing a smaller man to get out. He took a couple of quick steps up into the fire engine, squeezing past Jimmy. As soon as he was in, Jimmy closed the door.

Mac approached Wesley's window, looking up at the man in charge. 'You know what you're doing now?'

Wesley nodded.

'And just remember, all you've got to do is get him inside. Once he's in, your job is done.'

'I know, I remember,' Wesley said with the merest hint of frustration in his voice.

Mac leaned a little closer to the appliance. 'I meant what I said yesterday. Once this is done, you're out, for good. A promise is a promise.'

He looked to the back of the vehicle where Jimmy was staring daggers at him. If the window was open any further, he probably would have stuck his arm out and grabbed the man by the throat.

'Just make sure you get him in,' he said to Jimmy. 'I can trust you to do that, right?'

Jimmy turned his head forwards. 'We're firefighters. We can get in anywhere.'

Mac smiled. 'See, I knew you were the right people for the job.' He glanced at his watch before returning his gaze to Wesley. 'You ready?'

Wesley nodded again. 'Do it quick before we get another call.'

Mac took out his phone, pressed a few buttons, and held it to his ear. He waited a few seconds before speaking again. 'Fire brigade, please. I think there may be a fire in my neighbour's house.'

Wesley rolled up his window and turned to Bodhi. 'Let's go.'

The man who had just joined them, sat in the middle, rear-facing seat. He was opposite Jo, but it was Dylan his attention was focused on. He was seemingly oblivious to her and Jimmy's stares.

'How you doing, cliff-hanger?' the new passenger asked.

Dylan looked, but was unable to make eye contact with their passenger.

'You should see this guy on the climbing wall,' the man said, now looking to the other two. 'He'd give Spiderman a run for his money.'

Jimmy nodded at the fire-kit on the floor of the vehicle. 'Get that lot on quick. We'll get the call in a sec.'

As he finished talking, the speaker on the computer activated, letting them know they were being called to action. Needlessly, Wesley looked at the screen where the nature of the call and address were displayed. He turned to the rear of the cab. 'Guess where we're going.'

The journey was carried out on blue lights and at a fast pace. Bodhi was known for not hanging about on his way to calls. To give credit to their new recruit, he did a good job of getting his

leggings and tunic on as the vehicle accelerated along the coast road.

When it came to the roundabout at St Dunstan's, the hospital for blind war veterans, the vehicle rocked from one side to the other as Bodhi skilfully negotiated it. The partly dressed man had to reach forward to steady himself and, in doing so, ended up only inches away from Jo's face.

'Hi there.'

Jo's response was stony. 'Put on your seatbelt. Be a shame if you had an accident.'

The man sat down, zipped up his tunic, then did as instructed. He looked down at himself then held out his arms, displaying his new look like a proud peacock. 'So, what do you think? I've always fancied the idea of being a fireman.'

'Firefighter,' Jo corrected him. 'We haven't all got dicks.'

The man laughed, then looked to Dylan. 'Yeah, I guess you're right.'

A couple of minutes later, they were at their destination. The house they had arrived at was in Rottingdean, a pretty little village along the coast, filled with very old houses and very wealthy residents. They had come off the seafront and travelled through the village's narrow winding streets until they ascended the base of the South Downs. Suddenly, it felt like they were in the countryside, with the houses being far more spaced apart. Each had their own land and, in some cases, fields and stables. Some of these premises were nestled in their own little valleys, far back from the main road with their own private lanes leading to them. It was one of these tracks they were travelling down as Wesley turned to the back.

'So, this is what's going to happen, um…' Wesley said as he looked to the man struggling to clip up the strap on his fire helmet.

'Call me Al,' he said, 'like the song. It's not my name, but if you feel it makes us closer, then go for it.'

'Okay…Al,' Wesley said. 'When we go in–'

'When *we* go in,' Call-Me-Al said, pointing at Jimmy. 'My boss said he wants him to come with me.'

'But I'm in charge.' Wesley tried not to sound like the little boy who didn't win pass the parcel on his birthday.

'No offence,' Al shrugged in a way that suggested he didn't give a shit if he was offended or not, 'but that's what my boss wants. And what he wants he tends to get, but you guys already know that.'

'Don't worry, Wes,' Jimmy said. 'We'll be fine.'

He could hardly say he was happy about the situation, but he'd rather it was him than Wesley.

'I do all the talking,' he said to Al. 'You just stand there and keep your mouth shut, got it?'

Al nodded. 'And once we're inside, *I* do all the talking. You just stand there and keep your mouth shut. I'm just going to get what I came for, and then, we're gone.'

That was the brief that Mac had given them. They were there to get something that belonged to him, something he considered to be of great value. All Al had to do was scare the owner into revealing the item's location, get hold of it and get the hell out. The whole thing should take less than five minutes.

The appliance came to the end of the track where a twenty-foot-high security gate stopped them from going any further. Metal railings as high as the gate wrapped themselves around the grounds of the property. Beyond the gates, they could see an old farmhouse that had been expensively renovated and extended, and judging from its size, home to at least six bedrooms.

'Right,' Jimmy said, opening the door. 'Let's do it.'

Al threw up a *Dad's Army*-style salute and followed him off the lorry.

Jimmy punched the buzzer on the wall, and as he waited, glanced up at the CCTV camera on top of the gate staring straight at them.

'Don't worry about that,' Al said. 'This guy won't go telling tales.'

Jimmy shook his head and was about to come back with something when the intercom kicked in.

'Yes,' a crackly voice said.

'Hello, sir,' Jimmy answered. 'This is the fire brigade.'

'What?' the voice said. Its owner didn't sound particularly impressed by the disturbance.

'Yes, hello, sir. This is the fire brigade. We've been called to reports of a possible fire at your premises that we need to investigate.'

'No fire here,' the voice said abruptly. It sounded of Eastern European descent, Jimmy thought, similar to Adam, the Polish cleaner at the fire station.

'I understand that, sir, but we need to be sure of that for ourselves before we can leave.'

'I said there's no fucking fire,' the voice said. 'Now piss off.'

Jimmy looked at Al who nodded encouragement at him. 'Like I say, I appreciate that, sir, but I am legally obliged to investigate any reports of fire, and if you do not let me in, I will have to call the police to assist us, as you *will* be breaking the law.'

The intercom grew quiet for a moment then crackled back into action. 'Okay, wait.'

As they stood there, watching the lights at the front of the property turning on, Al looked to Jimmy. 'Is that true?' he whispered.

Jimmy shrugged. 'More or less.'

Thirty seconds later, two large men in what could have been matching tracksuits came out of the house and walked towards them.

Jimmy glared at Al. 'You said there was going to be one person, maximum.'

Al gave a shrug of his own. 'I didn't say anything. That's what Mac said, and he does have a habit of telling porkies. Anyway, don't sweat it. One person, five people; it don't make any odds to me.'

'It does to me. The more people who are here, the more people see me with you.'

'Seriously,' Al said, 'just keep this up. You're doing great.'

The guards approached, standing less than five feet from them on the other side of the gate. They both looked like they could have worked alongside Lenny in the bouncing profession. One was taller with short cropped hair and a goatee beard, the other was wider with a razor-shaven bald head that was decorated with tattoos.

'Look,' the taller one said in his guttural accent, 'everything is okay. There must have been some kind of mistake.'

Jimmy gave the man a friendly smile. 'Listen, mate, I'm sure you're right. But if I don't come in and investigate, and then something does happen, it's my job that's on the line.'

'But I say to you, there is no fire. Someone must be taking the piss, you know?' He attempted to smile back, but Jimmy could see this was a man to whom smiling did not come naturally.

'I know what you're saying,' he said holding his hands up, 'but like I say, it's more than my job's worth, and if you don't let me in and have a quick look around, then I've got to get the bloody police down here and the next thing you know, three hours have gone by, and we'll still be here, taking up space on your driveway.'

The taller man looked to his bald friend.

'Seriously, fellas, it will take two minutes. I just need to confirm there's no fire, then I can piss off and leave you to it.'

'Okay,' the man nodded, 'but just you.'

Jimmy wore the same "I'd like to, but…" smile again.

'Sorry, guys, but I've got to take someone in with me. It's a legal thing, just in case anything was to happen. It takes away the whole "he said, she said" situation should we end up in court.'

The mention of the courtroom was enough for the man to back down.

'Okay,' he said, 'but quickly.'

He reached forward and pressed the button on the wall. After a short pause, the gates opened inwards making the man and his partner step back out of their path. Jimmy quickly walked through the gap with Al following behind. The guards made them stand

there and wait until the gates had closed before leading them into the house.

When they got inside, it was clear that the property had retained none of its farmhouse charm. Everything was either white or wooden and minimal in its nature. Jimmy hated it.

'So, where do you want to start?' the bearded man asked after shutting the door. It didn't look like he was going to change his mind, lighten up and offer them a cocktail before they left. His partner had still not uttered a word.

'Kitchen's probably the best place,' Jimmy said. 'That's where most fires happen.'

'Follow me,' goatee said, and the four men fell into single file as they walked down the hall.

After a dozen or so steps, Jimmy heard a dull thud behind him. He turned around to see the big bald guy lying face down on the floor with a hole in the back of his head. Al was standing behind the prone finger with a gun now pointing in Jimmy's direction.

'No!' Jimmy shouted as he braced himself for the impact, but when Al took his next shot, it was the bearded guard behind Jimmy who grunted like he'd just been kicked in the bollocks. As the man staggered backwards clutching at his chest, Al closed the space between them, letting off another three shots. When the guard finally hit the floor, Al stood over him delivering one last shot to his head. There was virtually no sound; the pistol he was using had a silencer attached to it. Jimmy had never heard one before, they didn't bother with such things in the marines, but it sounded just like they did in the movies. Sometimes, Hollywood did get things right.

Jimmy's eyes were ready to pop out of his head when he looked back at Al. 'Cool, huh?' the man said.

'What's going on down there?' a voice from upstairs yelled. Like that of the guards, it sounded distinctly Eastern European.

'That's our man,' Al said, wiping at a spot of blood on his tunic.

Apart from everything else going around his head at that moment, Jimmy now had to factor in getting Jonesy's fire-kit clean before he returned to work in two days' time.

'Who's there?' the voice asked again. 'I've got a gun, and I will fucking use it.'

Al laughed. 'Course you will, sunshine,' he said to himself as he walked towards the stairs. 'Come on, Jim, this should be good.'

Not wanting to be left with the two bodies, and not knowing what the fuck else to do, Jimmy did as he was told and fell in half a dozen paces behind the assassin. Just as Al mounted the stairs, the door to Jimmy's immediate left opened, and another equally big guard walked out. When he saw Jimmy, the man reached for the pistol in his belt, but as he brought the gun up to aim, Jimmy used both his hands to grab hold of his pistol arm and wrench it up towards the ceiling. Before the guard could implement his superior strength, Jimmy drove his knee up into his guts, and as the guard buckled, he flipped him over his hip, judo-style. When he was lying on his back, Jimmy locked up the man's wrists and pushed his elbow back the wrong way until the pain made him drop the pistol. It was a move he had been taught when he was in the marines that the men had dismissed at the time. They carried assault rifles, they'd said to each other, when the fuck were they going to be wrestling guns out of people's hands?

Jimmy looked down and shared a look with the man he had just bested. He felt the need to say something to him, and maybe he would have, if Al hadn't appeared in front of him with his pistol aimed at the man's head.

'Thanks, Jim. I'll take it from here.'

Before Jimmy could protest, Al shot him twice in the head; the good ol' double tap, the preferred execution method of any decent hitman. Jimmy staggered backwards like he been shot himself. He went to throw up, but nothing came out, gagged again unsuccessfully, then spat on the floor. He went to say something to Al, then stopped, realising there was nothing he could say.

Al nodded towards the upstairs landing. 'Come on, we're not finished yet.'

'Yes, we are,' Jimmy said. 'I'm going back to the lorry.'

Al raised the pistol and pointed it at Jimmy's head, 'Look, pal, I'm grateful and all for what you just did, but you try and leave now, and I'll put a bullet in you too. Then, when I'm done here, I'll go outside and shoot your friends. Now, is that what you want?'

Jimmy shook his head. 'You wouldn't do that.'

'Wouldn't I? What, you think I haven't got it in me? Look in my eyes and tell me you think I haven't got the balls. Please, I double dare you.' He glanced up the stairs again. 'Now, you coming or what?'

Without waiting for a response, Al turned and started up the stairs. When he was halfway up, Jimmy began his ascent.

They found the short fat man sitting on his bed, shaking like a shitting dog. The lime blue silk dressing gown he was wearing had fallen open at the waist, allowing his visitors a full-on view of his shrivelled cock and balls.

'Jesus, Freddie,' Al said. 'Put it away. I've got enough shit in my brain without having that memory floating around in there.'

Freddie looked down at himself then feebly tried to cover his privates which although small, stubbornly refused to go back into captivity.

'Please,' he said. 'I'll give you whatever you want. Just don't kill me. I beg you.'

Al give him a sympathetic smile, 'Honestly, man, if I had a pound for everyone who'd said that to me...'

'Please,' Freddie said, as the sobs started to rise up through his chest. 'Drugs, money, whatever you want. I'll leave the country... Just let me go.'

When Al shook his head, Freddie turned his attention to Jimmy. 'Please, you won't hear from me again, I promise.'

Al also turned to Jimmy. 'What do you think, Jim? Should we let him go?'

'I thought we were just here to collect a package,' Jimmy said. 'Why kill him?'

'He is the package. Now, do we kill him, or take him back alive? It's your choice.'

Jimmy thought about the difficulty of getting yet another passenger on his fire engine, and the risk they were running if they got caught, but when compared to the other option of watching the man be killed in cold blood, there really was no choice. 'I say we take him back alive.'

Freddie burst out crying, shaking his head both in relief and disbelief that he was going to walk out of this situation in one piece. He put his hands together like he was praying and directed them to Jimmy.

'Thank you, my friend. You won't forget this. I promise–'

He was cut short by Al putting a bullet in the centre of his forehead.

'Don't be sad, Jim,' he said as he looked down at his pistol and unscrewed the silencer. 'He died with hope in his heart and a smile on his face. What more can any of us ask for?'

They drove back to the rendezvous point in silence. The others recognized the look on Jimmy's face as he opened the door. It was the same mixture of shock and despair that most firefighters had following a particularly nasty job, the kind where you saw kids die in front of their parents and you were helpless to do anything about it.

When they got back to the car park, Al got out of the appliance and gently patted Jimmy on the shoulder as he squeezed past him. He looked the same as he had when they'd first picked him up after stripping out of the fire-kit. Mac was standing next to his car, holding the rear door open like it was him being employed as the driver and not the big guy who sat in front of the steering wheel.

When he got in the car, Al gave him a curt nod, letting him know that his work was done. After closing the door, a smiling Mac turned back to face the fire engine when Jimmy's fist crashed

into his face. He bounced off his car before landed on his arse on the tarmac.

The door of the car opened again, and Al leaned out, letting Jimmy see the pistol he had pointing at him.

'Leave it,' Mac said, holding his spare hand up, the other was busy wiping a trickle of blood from his upper lip. 'We're good here, aren't we, Jim?'

'You should have told us what you were going to do,' Jimmy said. 'We deserved that much.'

Mac used the car's door handle to pull himself up to his feet. 'You wouldn't have helped me if I did. Your job is to save lives, not take them. And if there *was* any other way, I would have used it, but since our falling out, that bastard Freddie has locked himself away in that little fortress of his like a goddamn hermit… If it makes you feel any better, the guy was a real piece of shit, even by my standards. No one is going to miss him.'

'I don't care if he was Adolf fucking Hitler. You shouldn't have involved us in any of this shit.'

Mac wiped the dust from his arse. 'It's over now, you'll be glad to hear. Our partnership has officially been dissolved. You boys won't be hearing from me again.'

'Too fucking right, it is,' Jimmy said. 'If I ever see you again, I swear to god, I'll kill you. Understand?'

Mac inspected the blood on his fingertips. 'To show my gratitude, I'd like to offer you boys something for your contributions to my business affairs, but I'm guessing you wouldn't accept it, right?'

'There's only one thing I'd accept from you,' Jimmy said, 'and that's the promise that you stay the fuck away from us.'

'Receiving you loud and clear,' Mac said, walking around the vehicle. Before getting in, he turned to face Jimmy again. 'Have a good life, fellas. I'm going to miss you.'

Part Three

Chapter 30
In the Dark

The classroom was hot and airless; conditions that could send even the most willing pupil to sleep. If it weren't for what he was being primed to do, Jimmy would have let himself nod off half an hour earlier.

The scrawny young man with bad skin who stood in front of the class, gestured at the whiteboard. Sketched onto it was a simple plan of the BA chamber.

'What we want to see,' said Plug, 'is the usual things: good door procedures, good comms between the team and good branch control. We don't want to see you steaming the place up and losing your visibility. Lastly, don't forget your personal search. We've failed people up here because their BA shuffle wasn't up to scratch. It sounds a lot, but it's just your bread and butter stuff. You chaps are more than up to it.'

Jimmy wondered how the fuck he would know what the bread and butter stuff was. The boy had only been in the job for a handful of years, and from what he'd heard from the guys at Hove, his own BA skills left a lot to be desired. By all accounts, he was the type of person you had to calm down before they went into a job, because they got into a panic and started flapping. But here he was, in his new role as BA instructor at the Service's training centre, telling the class stories of the many jobs he'd been to.

Most of the other people on the course were retained firefighters who'd only done a few years themselves, and had eaten up his tales of daring-do, but Jimmy knew otherwise. He'd been tempted on a number of occasions to butt in and embarrass the boy, but all he wanted to do was get the course over with, pass his BA for another two years, and get back to station.

'One last thing, guys,' Plug said – there were no women on this particular course. 'Just remember that we're not in there to try and trip you up. We want you to pass this course; just treat it like any other job. Do what you do in the real world, and it will be fine. Easy for me to say, but enjoy it.'

Yeah, Jimmy thought, *it is easy for you to say*, because despite his attempt at reassurance, none of them would enjoy it. If you asked any firefighter their honest opinion of the two-day BA refresher course, they would all tell you the same thing; they fucking hated it. Most of them would rather go into a raging house fire with flames pumping out of every window than go up to the training centre and be assessed on their abilities. It wasn't that they weren't up to it, quite the opposite, in fact. Most firefighters prided themselves on their abilities in BA. What they hated was knowing that while they were fumbling around in the dark, searching for casualties and the source of the fire, an assessor, also clad in BA, was following them around, using a thermal imaging camera to critique their every move. They may not have been able to see him, but he most definitely could see them.

It had been two weeks since their final encounter with Mac. For the rest of the Watch, life had returned back to normal almost immediately. The police had visited the station the following night and questioned them after one of the victim's neighbours had reported seeing a fire engine arriving there on blue lights, but Wesley had told them it was just a routine call that had turned out to be a false alarm. Jimmy knew Al had wiped the CCTV before they'd left the scene of the massacre, but they still needed the police to accept their version of events. The relief when the officer bought into it could be seen in all of them. This, added to the knowledge that Mac was permanently off their back, meant the mood around the canteen table had lightened considerably, and apart from the impending investigation into Harrison's outburst, all was good in the world for Red Watch.

All except for Jimmy. None of the others had gone into the house that night. None of the others had watched four men be struck

down in cold blood. None of them had had to wrestle with a man in a fight for their own lives, then seen that same man's brains blown across the floor. Jimmy had, though. Jimmy had witnessed it all, and while the others might have been fine, he was about as far away from it as he could imagine. The only other time he could remember feeling this way was after the death of his friend Baashi, nearly thirty years earlier. He hadn't seen any action in the forces, but he'd spoken to plenty of his friends who had. He also knew many firefighters who'd dealt with some truly horrendous incidents that had affected them deeply, and the symptoms he'd been displaying in the privacy of his own home were very similar to what they had gone through. He was suffering from post-traumatic stress.

In front of anyone else, he was fine, but anytime his wife and kids weren't around, he'd find himself bursting into tears for no apparent reason. He could have been doing the dishes or watching football on TV when suddenly, this pang of grief crept up on him from nowhere and hit him like a punch in the guts. The next thing he knew, he'd be sobbing like a baby, trying to work out why he couldn't shake this thing off and why the deaths of four people who meant nothing to him were tearing him up like it was. He'd been drinking hard, too, when Jen went to bed, hammering the whisky like it was going out of fashion. It hadn't helped. It just made him get to sleep easier, but the problem was, when he was sleeping, he dreamt about what happened, and his powers of recall became even more vivid. The last thing he had needed at that time was a goddamn BA refresher.

Jimmy and his partner sat in front of the BA chamber watching as one of the instructors untangled the hose reel that a team had just brought out. They hadn't managed to locate the casualty, and on exiting the building had quickly ripped their masks off as they bent over, trying to catch their breath. Judging from the way their fire-kit was steaming off, Jimmy guessed they had done exactly what they were told not to, and put way too much water on the fire, making conditions inside even worse for

themselves. He thought it was doubtful either of them would pass the course.

The BA chamber was made up of metal shipping containers that had been welded and bolted together to create a building that vaguely resembled something they may encounter in real life. It was three containers wide by three high and subdivided internally into a number of rooms and stairways. Each room had a number of doorways which could be opened or locked, meaning the route the wearers took could be changed easily. Trying to remember the layout from the last time you did your course was a waste of time, as it would certainly have changed since then. And even if you did know your way around, it didn't mean you wouldn't get disorientated and lost in the dark.

Technically, you shouldn't be able to lose your way out of the building. If you went in following the right-hand wall, you just turned around and came out with your left hand on the wall. Easy, right? Or if that wasn't working, you just followed the hose reel back out. What could go wrong? Plenty, actually. Following the hose often became a real ball-breaker, especially if there was a pile of it on the floor that you had to negotiate. More often than not, you'd start working your way through it and realise you'd gone the wrong way, and it had led you back to the branch you were holding, rather than to the exit. As for the other method, that was fine, if you were still thinking straight, but usually, by this stage, the BA wearers would be tired and suffering from heat stress.

Heat stress was something few firefighters admitted to getting, but in reality, most had experienced. When your body gets too hot, it starts to work hard to try and cool itself down and keep your core temperature at a safe level. Things like critical thinking and decision making become secondary for your brain, which is more interested in keeping you alive, and so simple tasks suddenly become difficult. You got tunnel-vision, concentrating on only one thing and not thinking of the bigger picture. Doing something as seemingly straightforward as reversing your searching technique becomes a complex and demanding task that is often too much

for the fatigued BA wearer. This was the real reason firefighters didn't want to work until they were sixty, which they all would now be, since the government had changed the rules of the game. Jimmy was a fit guy, yet he, like most others, already found the course to be a real ball breaker. The thought of dragging himself through the BA chamber fifteen years in the future sent a cold chill down his spine.

These were the things that were running through Jimmy's head as he waited for his turn. His partner, a guy called Dean Waters, known to his mates as Shallow, was, with the exception of Jimmy, one of the few old hands on the course. He was a whole-time firefighter in Hastings, and while Jimmy hardly knew the guy, he'd heard enough about him from the brigade grapevine to know the man was a first-class prick. In the last day and a half, Jimmy had barely said a dozen words to him.

The instructor finished laying out the hose and gave Jimmy and Shallow the thumbs up, letting them know they were good to go. Silently, the two of them went to work, putting on their masks, gloves and helmets. As they did their buddy checks on each other, Plug came out of the chamber and addressed them, making sure they understood their brief. Jimmy, as number one, checked the hose, letting off a couple of quick pulses as he adjusted the cone of water. He handed his tally to the Entry Control Officer, checked his air pressure and went to the chamber door with his partner in tow. Knowing the procedure, Dean knelt against the door with his hand on the handle and waited for the sign. Kneeling next to him, Jimmy nodded.

'Crack!' he shouted.

As the door of the chamber opened, he aimed the branch at the ceiling and let off a quick pulse, then watched to see how it reacted with the smoke. 'Open.'

The door opened, and the two of them disappeared into the darkness.

By the time they got to the third floor, they were already feeling it. Dean had done most of the hard work in dragging the hose up

the stairs, and he'd done a pretty good job of it too; they hadn't got snagged up once. Jimmy had helped him where he could, but his job was to lead the search and keep hold of the branch, spraying occasional gas-cooling pulses into the air. After going through door procedures again and entering the large room on the third floor, a strange thing happened to Jimmy. As he got his hand on the wall and began his search, suddenly, it wasn't a dummy he was searching for anymore as he swept out with his foot. All he could think of now was the man he had watched being shot in the head.

'You okay there, Jim?' he heard Dean shout. He had gotten away from his partner and should have waited until they were in contact before continuing the search, but Jimmy's mind was now filled with thoughts of the dead man. As he searched in the darkness, he felt himself panicking. He no longer wanted to find the casualty; he had no interest in seeing the man's destroyed features again. Jimmy reached the corner of the room, turned and walked ten steps, then found the other corner and turned again.

'Where are you, Jim?' he heard Dean say. 'You need to wait up for me.'

Jimmy did as he was told and stayed in place until he felt Dean's fingertips make contact with his.

'Sorry,' Jimmy said. 'I thought I found a casualty.'

'Okay, just slow down a bit. I can't see a thing in here.'

If he detected Jimmy was off his game, Shallow was dealing with it diplomatically.

They continued searching the room, but Jimmy's thoughts were preoccupied by the faces of the men whose lives had been ended that night. He felt something on his face and went to wipe it off but his finger bumped off his BA mask. What he thought was a piece of dirt was a tear trickling down his cheek. When they turned at the next corner, Dean spoke again.

'Hang on, Jim. I think we've just done a full search of the room. We should have found a door by now.'

Jimmy knew he was right; the point being reinforced when he felt the open doorway from where they had entered the room. From the plan on the whiteboard, he knew there were two rooms on the third floor, and somewhere, he struggled to recall its exact location, was a door that linked the two. Unlike in a real property where the walls were made of brick and plaster and the doors of wood, here in the chamber, everything was made of metal, and so it was quite possible to run your hand across a door, and, unless you found the handle, you'd be none the wiser.

'We're going to have to go around again,' Jimmy said, becoming aware of the heat. Not only was there a casualty in the other room, but there was also a fire raging in one of the cribs that demanded to be extinguished. The door to the adjoining room may have been closed, but the metal walls were radiating heat from the fire directly onto them.

The second search of the room proved just as fruitless. Maybe if Jimmy was actively searching for the door handle, he would have located it, but all his mind could focus on was the dead men he now saw in every direction that he turned. When they had completed another full lap and got back to the open door, Plug, who had been silently watching it all through his Thermal Imaging Camera placed his hand on Jimmy's shoulder.

'Okay, Jimmy,' he said. 'I've seen enough now. You can make your way out.'

Usually, Jimmy would have protested and demanded that he stay in until he'd located the casualty, but on this occasion, he seized on Plug's words. Exiting the room, all he was interested in doing was getting out of the darkness and the ghosts that haunted it.

Chapter 31
Revelations

'Fuck, man. I was sure that was going to be the one,' Dylan said to the rest of their watch as they sipped their teas and coffees. 'I thought I was going to rescue a baby *and* get my picture in the paper.'

They had just returned from a persons reported in a block of flats where they were greeted by the fire alarm going off and a screaming woman who told them her friend and her little boy were trapped inside. Dylan's heart had been in his mouth as he and Jo went under air, but he had managed to stay composed, not panicking when the woman yelled at him to get inside and save the baby.

It turned out the woman and her child had gone out over an hour earlier, leaving an egg boiling on the stove. When the water had evaporated in the saucepan, the egg had started to burn, setting off the alarms and stinking up the BA crew's fire-kit.

As they left the building to get the fan to clear the smoke out of the flat, a photographer for the Argus, the local newspaper, turned up. He had been on his way to work when he spotted the fire engine and thought he'd stumbled on a scoop. Regretfully, Dylan had to inform him there was nothing worth reporting.

'Careful what you wish for,' Bodhi advised him. 'It's all well and good if you make a rescue, but kids don't last too long when their lungs are full of smoke.'

Dylan reddened up at his own comments.

Seeing this, Bodhi changed the subject. 'We still going to that school, Wes, or has that job screwed up our timings?'

'Unfortunately, we are. The teachers have asked if we can talk to the kids about the Great Fire of London.'

Lenny shook his head. 'What the fuck do we know about the Great Fire of London? We're firefighters, not fucking history teachers.'

'Piece of piss,' Jo said. 'Sixteen-sixty-six, Pudding Lane. Samuel Pepys burying his cheese in his garden.' She looked across to Dylan. 'See, college boy, I know my shit too.'

The conversation was interrupted when, through the window, they saw a red fire service vehicle driving into the yard at way too fast a speed. They were unable to make out the identity of the driver.

'What the fuck does that bell end think he's up to?' Lenny said to no one in particular.

'It must be Nobby,' Jo answered. 'Only he drives that badly.'

Seconds later, their question was answered when Jimmy burst in the room. 'Right,' he said, his face was red, the way it normally looked when he was about to lose his rag. 'It's time we had a little chat.'

Lenny looked at his watch, 'Fucking hell, Jim, they haven't kicked you off the course already, have they? It's not even twelve o'clock.'

'Yeah, they have,' Jimmy said, his voice joyless.

Lenny had meant it as a joke. Jimmy was a solid BA wearer, and no one had thought for a second that he would be coming back with anything other than a pass. To Plug's credit, he had taken him away from his partner before informing him of the inevitable. Shallow had wanted to say something, but he'd seen in Jimmy's eyes that the best thing for his health was to keep his mouth shut. He had been meant to stay and wear BA again in the afternoon so Shallow could be assessed as a number one, but Jimmy had booked sick then and there, telling them he had twisted his knee and was unable to continue the course.

Wesley walked out of the toilet, still adjusting his belt as he looked up at the unexpected arrival. 'All right, Jim? Aren't you supposed to be at the training centre?'

'Yeah,' Jimmy answered. 'I am.'

Wesley shrugged like the answer was perfectly acceptable and sat down next to Jo.

'So, what's up, Bud?' Bodhi asked.

'What's up,' he said, 'is I've had enough of this shit. It's time we put a stop to it once and for all.'

'What shit?' Jo asked.

'That bastard Mac threatening us and our families,' Jimmy said, 'that's what I'm talking about. It's time we got things sorted.'

'It is sorted,' Lenny said. 'He's gone. The prick's out of our lives for good.'

'Really? 'Til when? What happens next time he needs a favour?'

'But he promised,' Dylan said.

Jimmy shook his head and laughed. 'Grow up, for fuck's sake. Do you really think that bastard is going to stay away from us just because he said so?'

'I'm not being funny, Jim,' Lenny said, 'but is this about Mac or you failing your course?'

'I don't give a shit about my course. What I care about is there's a psychopath out there who had you stabbed, tried to attack her,' he nodded at Jo, 'and threatened to kill the rest of us. That's what this is about, Len. You may not think that's a problem, but I fucking well do.'

Lenny shrugged. 'It was just for show. He was trying to scare us. Seriously, Jim, I honestly think we're better off leaving him well alone. Being stabbed wasn't much fun, and I'm no expert here, but being killed is even less of a giggle, I reckon. We fuck with this guy again and Dead Watch won't just be our nickname.'

'So, what do you propose?' Dylan said.

'Please,' Lenny laughed, 'don't tell me you, of all people, agree with this tough guy bullshit.'

'Jimmy's right,' Dylan said. 'The man's a bully, and bullies don't stop until someone makes them. If we don't do something about it, he'll be back, and when he is, he'll want his pound of flesh.'

‘Damn right he will,’ Jimmy added.

Lenny turned his attention back to the man who’d just spoken. ‘Come on, then, let’s hear you out. What exactly are you proposing?’

Jimmy looked around at the faces of the people sitting in front of him before he spoke again. ‘I say we take him down.’

Lenny’s fingers and thumb formed a pistol shape as he pointed them at his own head. ‘What, you mean, *take him down*?’

Jimmy shook his head. ‘Don’t be stupid. I mean follow him, find out who he is, where he lives, where he takes his drugs to, all that shit. Then, when we’ve got enough evidence, we drop a call to the police and make sure they find him with his stash. He’d go down for a long stretch, and no one would even know it was us that did it.’

Lenny rolled his eyes. ‘Jesus, Jim, who do you think we are, The Famous Fucking Five? So, let’s say, we do it, and he finds out that we’re onto him. What do you think he’s gonna do? Like you said, the man’s a psycho. This isn’t the A-Team. These fuckers pack real bullets, and they can shoot straight.’

‘And you think I don’t know that?’

Lenny put his palms up in the air when he realised what he’d said. ‘Sorry, I didn’t mean that.’

Jimmy nodded, acknowledging the apology. ‘I’m not just shit-stirring here, Len. I genuinely think that motherfucker has no intention of dropping this. He’s going to keep pushing and pushing us until one or more of us is in jail or dead. He’ll squeeze us dry – it’s what people like him do.’

‘I like the idea,’ Jo said ‘especially after what those twats tried to do to me. As far as I’m concerned, they’ve got it coming to them.’

Jimmy looked to Bodhi. ‘What about you?’

‘It’s like she said. After what they did to her,’ he shrugged, ‘I’m up for anything.’

‘Ah, fuck it,’ Lenny said. ‘Who wants to live forever anyway?’

Jimmy’s gaze rested on Wesley next.

'It doesn't look like I've got a choice, does it?'

'Yes, you do,' Jimmy said. 'We only do this if we *all* agree to it. We've got to be one hundred percent sure.'

Wes looked up at the ceiling and stroked his chin. 'I guess it's time I took responsibility for my mistakes… I'm in.'

'So, what's the plan?' Jo asked. 'How are we going to keep tabs on him? We know nothing about the guy, and if we try contacting him again, he's going to know that something's up.'

Jo's words set their minds in motion as they thought of a solution to the problem. Before anyone could break the silence, a familiar face appeared in the doorway Jimmy had charged through minutes before.

'Is this a private meeting, or can anyone join in?' Harrison said.

'Fucking hell,' Lenny replied. 'I thought you were dead.'

'That's what I miss most about this place,' Harrison said. 'The warm welcome I get from my friends.'

'Colleagues,' Lenny corrected him with a smile.

'So, other than a cup of tea, what can we do for you?' Wesley asked.

Harrison pointed his bony finger at Dylan. 'You could lend me him for five minutes, if that's okay.'

'So, how's things at home?' Dylan asked.

He was at a bit of a loss as to what else to say. He loved Harrison, but had no idea why the man would want to speak to him. Wesley had used the opportunity to get the rest of them into the bays where they would carry out the daily routines. The canteen had been left empty for the two of them to talk in private.

'You know what,' Harrison said, 'things are great. Better than they have been for a long time. Janet's doing well, she's taking her meds, and at times, it feels like I've got the woman I married back. Just goes to show what a bit of time away from this place can do for you.'

'That's good to hear,' Dylan said, trying not to look uncomfortable.

Some of the guys were happy to tell all about their situations at home, but not Harrison. Usually, he kept his cards close to his chest; he never so much as mentioned his son anymore, so hearing this admission, especially away from the others, felt strange to him.

'And what about the investigation?' he asked. 'You got a date sorted out for that yet?'

'Funnily enough,' Harrison said, 'that's what I've come to talk to you about. It's booked in for next Thursday, and Matt Finch, the regional rep, has offered to represent me.'

'That's good.' Dylan said. 'I've heard he's tough.'

'He is that. A right tenacious little bastard when he gets going.'

'That's just what you need, someone who'll keep at them until they back down.'

'Yeah,' Harrison said, 'except I don't want him.'

'Why not?' Dylan asked. 'You said he was the best man for the job.'

'No, I didn't. I said he was good at what he does. I think you're the best person for the job.'

'You, what?'

'I'm asking if you'll represent me at the investigation.'

Dylan rubbed his head the way kids did when they couldn't answer a maths question. 'I can't represent you. I wouldn't know what I was talking about.'

'Why not? You're clever, articulate, you know me as well as anyone in the service, you'd be perfect.'

'But I'm not a union rep.'

Harrison brushed it off with his hand. 'That can soon be sorted out. We'll get the rest of the Watches to vote you in, and the job is yours. I can guarantee that, for all their bluster, there's no one else who wants to do it. By the weekend, you will be the union chair for this station.'

'But that's your job.'

Harrison shook his head. '*Was* my job. I've spent long enough in the role. It's time I passed it on to new blood.'

Dylan scratched his head again. 'So, what's brought this on?'

'Three things. Firstly, I could get sacked next week, so it may be inevitable. Second, having time away from dealing with all this union stuff has been a weight off my shoulders. I think that's why things have been so good between me and Jan. For once, I've been able to put her first instead of this bunch of 'erberts. And thirdly, because I think it will be good for you. I meant those things I said about you, but you're also a lazy bastard who runs a mile anytime anyone tries to give you any responsibility.'

'Thanks,' Dylan said.

'No problem. I won't lie, it's not an easy role, in fact, sometimes, it can be bloody infuriating. When things are going wrong, you'll get the blame for it. When things are going right, they'll say they did it off their own backs. If you try to get people to help you with campaigns, they'll run a mile, but you'll be the first person they call on when they've got themselves in trouble. Most of the time, it's a thankless job, but you know what, I wouldn't change a thing. I'm glad I did it, and I think in twenty years' time, you will too.'

Dylan shrugged. 'I don't know, it's a big ask.'

'Yeah, you're right, it is. And I wouldn't be asking if I didn't think you were up for it. It'll be good for you, I promise.'

'All right,' Dylan said. 'Let me think about it.'

After doing the practical tests on the hydraulic cutting gear, Wesley and Lenny headed to the office. They needed to discuss how Lenny was going to be able to do the job until his injuries had fully healed. Jo, in the meantime, had taken herself off to the gym to squeeze in a quick 10k on the running machine before lunch. As she shook her legs out in preparation for the punishing pace she was about to set, Bodhi slipped into the room. He looked nervous, like he was spying on her in the shower.

'Do you mind if I have a word?'

Jo glanced at her watch. 'Can't we leave it 'til after lunch. I haven't got much time to play with.'

'I'd rather we did it now, if you don't mind.'

Jo rolled her eyes. 'Make it quick, then.'

'First of all, I want to know why you've been avoiding me.'

'I haven't,' she said, bending down to touch her toes. 'I've just been busy.'

'I thought you wanted to make this quick,' Bodhi said. 'Rather than spend the next five minutes doing the whole "yes, you have, no, I haven't" thing, why don't you just be honest and tell me what's really going on here.'

Jo grabbed her knee and pulled it towards her chest, 'I don't know what you're talking about.'

'It's the abortion, right? You went and got it done on your own, didn't you?'

'No,' Jo answered, bringing her knee down and her ankle up behind her so it made contact with her bum.

'Yes, you did, I can tell. Look, I know you're independent and all that shit, but this wasn't just about you. You should have involved me in it too. Don't you think I deserve that much?'

Jo stopped stretching and turned to face him, 'Look, Bodhi, I haven't had the abortion yet, okay? I just don't want to talk about it right now.'

'Then, when *are* we going to talk about it!' Bodhi shouted, shocking the pair of them. It was rare for him to raise his voice above a whisper. 'You know you haven't got forever. There's a time limit on these things.'

'I'm keeping it,' she said quietly.

'You're what?'

'I said I'm keeping the baby. I've thought about it non-stop since I found out, and I'm going to keep it. I'd like you to be involved, but if you don't want anything to do with us, then I'll understand.'

At first, Bodhi couldn't say anything. It wasn't that he didn't want to, he just didn't know where to begin.

'So?' Jo finally said when the silence became too much. 'What do you think?'

'I think,' he said, 'that's a brilliant idea.' And then, it crashed down on him like a wave he'd paddled for and badly mistimed; he meant it too.

Chapter 32
Blood Brothers

Even though it was summer time, the south-westerly wind was whipping up off the beach onto Marine Parade. Lenny and another man stood next to their cars watching the waves crash against the legs of the pier. It was funny to look at Paul. He was shorter than Lenny, with less bulk and hair, but they both shared the same look that instantly marked them as blood. Even though he was less imposing than Lenny, Paul was more intimidating. There was something in both of their eyes that represented danger, but while in Lenny's case that may have meant a kicking behind the nightclub, with Paul, his gaze suggested if you got on his wrong side, things could end up much, much worse. And that was how things had to be in his line of business. It wasn't just about the threat of violence; it was the repercussions if those threats were to be ignored that mattered.

'So, after twenty years,' Paul said, staring intently at his brother like he was trying to work out exactly what it was about him that was different, 'you finally break this vow of silence we've got going.' He put his cigarette to his mouth and inhaled deeply. 'Fucking hell, bruv, you must have really fucked up this time.'

'Look, Paul,' Lenny said. 'I'm not asking you to get involved. I just want to know if you do business with him or not.'

Paul nodded, like he hadn't already heard the request. 'That's the thing, though, you may not be involving me, but if I tell you what you want to know, then it is going to affect me, isn't it? You take down my main supplier, which is why I assume you want this information, and it means I've got to go sniffing around for a new source, which is going to cost me a lot of time, money and

effort. Now, tell me, considering the nature of our relationship, why the fuck should I do this for you?'

Lenny stared at his brother for a long time before answering. 'Forget it,' he said, turning to get into his car. 'I knew this was a waste of time.'

'Wait!' Paul said as Lenny played with the door handle.

Lenny turned to see his brother looking at him like he had done when he was a teenager, watching the younger boy's back.

'How deep are you in this?'

'I'm not out of my depth yet.'

'Good,' Paul answered, 'because, seriously, it's not that I don't want to help, but this is a guy you do not want to fuck with. I'm guessing you know about that Albanian who got on the wrong side of him… This hasn't got anything to do with that, has it?'

Lenny shrugged. 'Kind of.'

Paul shook his head. 'Fuck… Listen, I know you're not going to believe this, but I care for you, always have, always will. If this guy has got a beef with you, then you need to take him out before he takes you out. If you can't do it, then I can get someone else to. I'll make sure it never comes back to you.'

'Nah, that's not my way.'

Paul smiled. 'I know.'

'I couldn't do it,' Lenny said after a long pause. 'I couldn't kill him. I know what that meant for you, but I haven't got it in me. Deggsy was our friend, even if he did rat us out.'

'It's okay.'

'I know I should have done him in, I could have stopped you going to prison, but I was a kid. I didn't have it in me, still haven't. I'm sorry.'

'You've got nothing to apologise for, you stupid bastard. I never should have asked you to do it in the first place. I know that now. I have done for a long time. I'm your brother, I was meant to look after you.'

'You did look after me. You never grassed me up, and you did more time because of it. I'm grateful to you for that.'

‘Don’t be,’ Paul snapped. ‘If you’d listened to me and rubbed him out, they would have collared you for it in no time. You’d have done fifteen years because of my actions. I never should have dragged you into any of that shit.’

‘Yeah, well,’ Lenny said, ‘what chance did either of us have? We’re Johnsons. It’s in our blood.’

‘That don’t make what I did right though, does it?’

Lenny leant against his car and took in the sunset. ‘If that’s how you feel, why didn’t you say something before? You could have gone through Mum. We didn’t have to do any of this. Twenty years is a long fucking time.’

‘I was ashamed,’ Paul said, blowing out a stream of smoke. ‘Plus, I thought you were better off without me in your life.’

‘You’re a fucking idiot,’ Lenny said.

Paul laughed. ‘And what about you? I don’t remember any olive branches coming from your way.’

Lenny kicked imaginary stones at his feet. ‘I guess I was ashamed too.’

‘You shouldn’t have been. You know they say that people change when they have kids? Well, it’s bollocks. It’s killing someone, that’s what changes you, in ways you couldn’t even imagine. Not listening to me that day was the smartest thing you’ve ever done… Look, I don’t know much about him. All I’ve got is a contact number. I don’t even know his real name, I just got the same one he gave you: Mac. What I’ll do is arrange a meeting. I need to stock up anyway. I’ll give you a call when it happens, and you can take it from there.’

‘Is it going to be a real pain in the ass for you if he goes down?’

Paul shook his head. ‘Not really. The guy’s a tight arse. The Albanians were good for me. The competition brought the prices down to a place I liked. Since they’ve gone, the greedy bastard’s started to take the piss again. I’ll be glad to see the back of him. If he starts talking to the cops, they’ll find nothing on me, I can promise you that. I’ve learnt from my mistakes.’

Lenny pushed off the car and held out his hand.

His brother looked at it with suspicion before reaching out with his own. 'I was thinking, how about this Sunday we eat at Mum's house at the same time? One o'clock sound good?'

'Sounds great. Just break it to her gently. We don't want her having a heart attack.'

Before getting in his car, Paul turned to face his brother again. 'I know you said you're going to do this your own way, but just in case things don't work out, do you need a piece?'

Lenny thought about it then shook his head. 'Nah, I'd probably just end up blowing my own cock off.'

Paul laughed. 'Yeah, you probably would. See you around, bruv.'

Chapter 33
Mac

It turned out that Mac was his real name, well, kind of. Paul was good to his word. He arranged to meet up with his dealer three days after the brothers' reunion. Lenny had been there, too, along with Jimmy and Bodhi, watching from a distance as the exchange of money and narcotics took place. Mac had chosen the location; the race course car park, the same place he had met with Wesley and Jimmy to take back possession of his money.

His real name was Neil MacDonald. They had found that out by following him out of the race course, staying just far enough away to avoid arousing suspicions. The journey had taken them north on the A23 up to Crawley. Lenny had cursed his petrol gauge as they made the trip; he wasn't expecting to do any real miles that night. They tailed Mac back to his home; a large mock-Tudor detached house in a respectable suburb just outside of town.

Early the next morning, they returned and followed his Nissan pick-up as it made its way to his place of work, a few miles away. That was where they discovered his real name, on the sign outside his yard; MacDonald and Son Building Services. He didn't have sons, as far as they had been able to tell in the time they had been following him, just twin teenage daughters who luckily got their looks from their mother, a glamorous big-haired woman with at least ten years on her old man.

They saw nothing for the first few days that made them suggest there was anything untoward about him. Every day, he left the house at eight o'clock sharp, dropping the twins to their sixth-form college before heading to the yard. Some days, he'd leave after an hour or two to visit the job that seemed to be consuming most of the company's time. The large Victorian

house in the middle of town was, from the looks of things, being converted into flats. Jimmy reckoned that if he'd got it for the right price, and knowing the persuasive skills of Mac that he most likely had, there was a tidy profit to be made. After work, he would go straight home to his wife, doing nothing that came close to resembling criminal activities.

It was only on the fifth day of watching him that they saw something that piqued their interest. He left the house the same time as every other morning, but after dropping off the girls, rather than heading to the yard, the car turned in the road and headed back on itself.

Riding in Jimmy's car (they had swapped motors every day to stop Mac from getting suspicious), they tailed him as he drove back down the A23 to Brighton. They didn't know why, but there was a feeling amongst the firemen that this would be the day.

When Mac pulled up on the seafront and got out of the car with a briefcase in his hand, they were even more certain they were onto something. After standing next to his motor for less than thirty seconds, he was approached by a young, good looking guy in a suit that looked like it cost more than the amateur spies earned in a month. With no more than a nod, the briefcase swapped hands and just as quickly as he appeared, the younger man strolled off towards town. Mac got back in his car and quickly drove off, but his stalkers were no longer interested in him, it was the other man who had seized their attention.

After less than a minute's walk, he stopped next to a brand-new Audi T4, slid the case into the passenger side, then got in and drove away.

'That's it,' Jimmy said, banging on the steering wheel. 'We've got the bastard now.'

It was nearly six o'clock when office wanker, as he quickly came to be known, finally left the building on North Street. That morning, he had parked his car outside one of the high-ceilinged buildings on Regency Square and disappeared inside with the briefcase.

Two minutes later, they saw him standing at the window of a first floor flat, staring out at the sea. Five minutes after that, he re-emerged and, carrying his Gucci man bag, walked swiftly towards the town centre.

With the rush-hour morning traffic having ground to a halt, Bodhi got out of the car and followed him on foot, hanging just far back enough to not look like a wallet snatcher. He tracked him to his place of work, a twelve-storey building, housing a mix of new media start-ups and more traditional companies. Bodhi knew the place well; he'd done a familiarisation visit there with the crew when it had first opened three years earlier. He knew that without a swipe card he would be unable to get past the guard on the lobby desk and discover which office their man worked from. It didn't matter; they knew where he lived. Lenny had wanted to break into the flat and find out what was in the case, but Jimmy told him it was unnecessary. All they had to do was wait, and they'd soon find out who the man was and what the fuck he was up to.

That night, from the interior of Bodhi's van, they sat watching his flat, trying to get an idea of their new friend's habits. Jimmy had decided to stay home and spend some time with Jen and the kids. Neither of them minded; they were just happy he still had a life to go home to.

'See this is what I should get myself,' Lenny said as he sat in the back of the Westfalia, checking out the kitchen and fold-out bed set-up.

'I could park it outside the club and then bring the chicks back and bang the shit out of them. They'd love it.'

Bodhi peered in the back and smiled at him. 'Sure they would, big man, sure they would.'

It was eight o'clock, and they could see the lights go on from behind the curtains in office wanker's flat.

'Do you think he's going out tonight?' Bodhi asked. 'Or do you think he's got company coming over? He looks like the type who likes to be seen, to me.'

Lenny shrugged. ‘Maybe he’s just going to have a pot noodle and a wank.’

A hand-holding, twenty-something couple walked towards the building and stood outside the front door.

Bodhi pointed at them with a lazy finger. ‘I wonder if they’re here to see our boy?’

Lenny spun around on his swivel seat just as the love-birds entered the building.

Seconds later, the shadows reflecting on their man’s curtains told Bodhi that he was right. This was the beginning of a steady stream of at least a dozen visitors, mainly young and mainly good looking.

‘Looks like our boy is in for the night,’ Lenny said. ‘I think we might as well fuck the fuck off.’

Bodhi turned the key in the ignition and put the van into reverse. ‘I think I’m inclined to agree, bud.’

‘Hang on a fucking minute,’ Lenny said as another couple walked toward the house. ‘You’ve got to be fucking kidding me.’

When they had gone inside, Lenny and Bodhi stared at each other, not knowing quite what to say.

‘Please tell me,’ Lenny finally said, when he managed to find his words, ‘what the fuck Dylan and Felicity are doing here.’

Chapter 34

Party Time

Felicity watched Dylan's reflection take an age to button up his shirt.

'Please can you at least try and pretend you're happy about going tonight.'

Dylan's eyes diverted from his button holes to her image in the doorway behind him. She was naked, with the exception of her knickers, and the towel wrapped around her head that made him think of an Indian Princess. He forced the worst possible attempt at a smile from his lips.

'I know how you must be feeling,' she said, 'but don't you think it's time we moved on. You can't keep dragging up what happened in your mind otherwise it's going to drive you crazy… We've got to be mature about this.'

Dylan stopped what he was doing, one button short of his goal and turned to face her. 'I'm sorry if I'm still feeling a bit awkward about going to your boss' home and having to pretend that nothing happened, even though we all know what you got up to with him. But I guess that's just me; immature.'

Felicity walked up to him and stroked his hair. 'Let's not go through this again. You know I'm sorry, and you know I regret what happened. But it's not him I love, and it's not him I want to marry and spend the rest of my life with.' She leant in and kissed his lips. 'You're the person I want, never ever forget that.'

She smiled and did up the last button on his shirt. 'We're not going for him. We're going because everyone else at work is going, and if I'm not there, then people *will* be talking. Don't let one mistake spoil what we've got.'

'When you put it like that,' Dylan said as he tucked in his shirt, 'we should get going. The line between fashionably late and rude is a thin one.'

Even though he had met most of them before, the demographic of Felicity's office never failed to surprise him. Most of her workmates were young and good looking, the opposite of what he'd imagined an accountant to look like. It shouldn't have surprised him; if Felicity was gorgeous, then there was no reason that others in her profession shouldn't be too. There were a handful of older, more normal looking people in the office, who weren't part of the beautiful people clique, but none of them had turned up. Whether their self-consciousness had prevented them from attending, or they hadn't been invited in the first place, Dylan was unsure.

Then, there was Nick, the most preened peacock of them all. He was tall and good looking with a head of thick black hair and a muscular upper body. It was only the skinniest of skinny jeans he wore that gave the hint that his workouts focused solely on his chest and arms. His baby-chick legs looked like they had never attempted a set of squats.

Dylan had tried his best to mingle, smile and laugh in all the right places, but he couldn't get it out of his head that he was hanging out in Nick the fucking Prick's overpriced apartment. He was counting the minutes until Felicity was ready to leave. Hopefully, it would be sooner than later.

An hour into the party, he saw his chance at a brief escape. He had been politely nodding along to Dan, a Doctor Who obsessive, when the man excused himself to go to the kitchen for a refill without even asking Dylan if he wanted one. Seizing the opportunity, he sneaked through the open door onto the balcony for a moment of solitude. It was cold out there; the wind came off the seafront and smacked him straight in the face, but he didn't care, he was away from *them*. He could see why the apartment earned its price tag; the unobscured view of the beach and the carcass of the burnt down West Pier made it prime Brighton property. Away from the beach on the street below, his attention

was drawn to a van that looked almost identical to Bodhi's. In fact, he was almost certain it was Bodhi's.

'Hey,' a voice behind him said, 'do you mind if I join you?'

Dylan turned to see Nick the Prick step onto the balcony, not waiting for an answer. God, Dylan hated him. If he wasn't bigger than him and he wasn't so shit at fighting, he would have punched the arsehole in the face. On the street below, the van started up and revved off down the road. It even sounded just like Bodhi's motor.

'Hey, man, how are you doing?' Nick said. His voice, like everything else about him made Dylan's skin crawl. He sounded like one of those models in the aftershave adverts who told you that life was for living.

'Great,' was the best Dylan could muster.

'Listen, fella,' Nick said with a smile, 'I just wanted to say that I really appreciate you coming here tonight. I know it must have been hard after what happened between me and Felicity.'

Dylan shrugged. 'Yeah, well, these things happen when drink is involved.'

Nick looked at him for a second too long before speaking again. 'No, really, it took a lot of guts to come to the house of the man your fiancée cheated with. Not a lot of men would do that.'

If he *were* a fighting man, Dylan probably would have headbutted him in the nose at that point rather than do what he did, which was nothing. 'I'm here for Felicity's sake, Nick, not yours.'

Nick returned the smile, only with far more enthusiasm, then laid his hand gently on Dylan's shoulder. 'Thanks for coming anyway. It's great to see you.'

A fighting man would have finished him off there and then.

'Listen, let's just give it another half hour, then we'll go.'

Felicity squeezed Dylan's hand, then put her other hand on top of his for good measure. It was two hours after his encounter with Nick on the balcony. He'd wanted to leave, but he sucked it up, avoided telling her what had happened, and tried not to look too lost every time she went to socialise with her friends.

'I'm proud of you tonight,' she said, giving him a wink.

He didn't know what to make of that. He knew he was a bit awkward in certain situations, but thanking him for managing to spend an evening in the presence of a group of adults without embarrassing himself suggested he was more of a social misfit than he'd realised.

They were standing in the doorway of the spare bedroom, and with no one around them to witness it, Dylan wrapped his arms around his fiancée and kissed her lips.

'As I've been such a good boy,' he said, seizing on her words, 'maybe I'll get a reward when I get home.'

Felicity jumped as his hand moved up her skirt. 'Maybe. Now move your hand before someone sees.'

Dylan gave her bum a squeeze before letting go.

'Cheeky!'

They turned to see Felicity's friend Amy standing next to them. 'Dylan, you dirty dog, I didn't think you had it in you.'

'There's a lot you don't know about my man,' Felicity said, pulling him closer to her. Dylan's face had turned scarlet.

'Hey, listen, sex machine,' Amy said. 'Any chance I can borrow your woman for ten minutes? We're making mojitos in the kitchen.'

'Of course. You ladies go and have fun.'

'Is that all right?' Felicity whispered in his ear. 'I don't have to.'

Dylan laughed like the idea was ridiculous, even though he desperately wanted her to stay. 'Don't be silly, I'll be fine. You go make cocktails, and I'll see what the men are up to.'

In the lounge, four of those men were sat on the sofa huddled around Nick who was holding out his mobile phone for all to see. As they were facing the opposite direction, none of them had noticed Dylan's arrival. When he got closer, Dylan could see they were watching a video of a blonde woman with massive breasts going cowgirl on top of some lucky guy. After a few seconds of her tits bouncing up and down, the camera spun around to show the identity of the person below her. Dylan almost winced as Nick

smiled and gave a thumbs-up to the camera he was holding. It was only after the high-fives and pats on the back had finished that they became aware of Dylan, who had now manoeuvred himself into their view.

Nick looked up and smiled at him. 'Dylan, take a seat, my man. Me and the guys were just talking about you.'

He gestured to the grey velour armchair that Dylan happily accepted. He hadn't sat down all night, and his legs were killing him.

'That's funny,' Dylan said, already feeling the anger from their earlier encounter building up in him, "cos I thought you were watching a video of you banging some girl. Does she know you show it to your friends?'

Nick gave the others a "who the fuck is this guy?" look, then followed it up with a laugh. 'You're a funny guy, Dylan. I'll give you that.'

'I try my best.'

Nick looked to the others before starting again. 'Yeah, we were just saying earlier what a cushy little number you must have being a fireman. What is it, four days on, four days off? You boys must be laughing.'

Dylan shrugged. 'Yeah, it's great.'

'And I bet your ping pong and pool must be pretty awesome too.'

'Not anymore,' Dylan said, trying, but not particularly hard, to keep things pleasant. 'They took them away from us, back in the day.'

He declined to mention that Central still had a rec room that would have put most youth clubs to shame. But that was the exception. What he had said was true for the most part.

'In that case, what do you guys do all day? I read somewhere that there are hardly any fires anymore. I think they said it was because of the way modern buildings are constructed or some shit like that. I wasn't that interested, if I'm honest.'

'That's right,' Dylan said, cutting through the spectators' giggles. 'We do have less fires, and building construction does play

a part in it. But it's also down to us spending a lot of time putting up smoke alarms and educating people about the risks of fire.'

Nick gave him a miniature clap. 'Well done you.'

'And even though there are less fires, it doesn't change the fact that when you do have one, you need us there as quick as possible with the right resources.'

Nick nodded along as Dylan spoke. 'No doubt. You guys do an important job, don't get me wrong.'

'And then, there are the car crashes and other shit we have to deal with.'

'And all the cats you have to rescue from trees.'

'That's right,' Dylan nodded to the guy sitting next to Nick who had interrupted him. Dylan thought his name might have been Dave. 'Don't forget the animal rescues.'

'So, what about that strike of yours?' Nick asked. 'All sorted now?'

'You could say that,' Dylan answered. 'Our pensions are fucked, and we've got to work for at least another five years. Happy days.'

Nick nodded, looked up to the sky, then spoke again. 'Yeah, well, we've all got to do our bit, haven't we?'

'What's that?'

'You know, in these times of austerity. We're all in it together, isn't that what they say?'

Dylan laughed. 'You know something, Nick, there are people out there who I would take that from. Doctors or nurses, maybe. Volunteers at a leper colony, perhaps. I wouldn't mind them taking a cheap shot at what I do. But people like you…' He looked around the room like the sight in front of him was about to make him sick.

Nick sat forward on his sofa. 'Oh, yeah, and what's that supposed to mean, exactly? *People like us*?'

'It means, Nick, that the reason fire stations like mine are having to close, and why hospitals are shutting down and disabled people's allowances are being cut is because the richest people in this country don't bother to pay their fair share of taxes. And your job is to facilitate that. You help them to shirk their

responsibilities, and as a result, the rest of us suffer. Yet, here you are, looking down on me like I've done something wrong. That's what I mean when I say people like you.'

Nick rolled his eyes as his friends groaned loudly. None of them said anything to challenge Dylan; they were happy to sit back and watch the two of them scrap it out.

'Let's have a guess who's a fan of Jeremy Corbyn,' Nick said. 'Come on, Dylan, surely even you're not that naive. What do you think would happen if all these businesses had to pay ridiculous amounts of tax? Not that any of our clients belong in that bracket, by the way. But back to the point, they'd leave the country, that's what they'd do. Now what good would that do us?'

'Then, let them go,' Dylan said, 'because if they don't pay their taxes, then they ain't contributing. If I earn less than thirty grand a year and can afford to pay my share, then I don't see why your rich chums can't do the same. Yeah, I may get a bit of downtime at work, but at least I do a job that contributes to society. I can go home at night knowing that I've helped people. But you lot, the only people you help are yourselves and your tax-dodging clients. So, don't tell me we're all in it together, because we're not. You assholes are part of the problem.'

A broad smile spread across Nick's face as his eyes diverted away from Dylan to a figure standing behind him. Before Dylan even saw who it was, he could feel his blood run cold. He turned around to see Felicity staring back at him. Her arms were crossed, and he couldn't tell if it was the anger or sadness in her face that was winning the fight for domination.

'How long have you been standing there?' he asked.

'Long enough,' she said, before storming towards the door and charging out.

Dylan sprang to his feet and ran after her.

'Thanks for coming!' Nick yelled after him. 'It was great to see you, mate.'

Chapter 35
Nick the Prick

Jimmy looked at his watch then shook his head. 'He's not coming, I'm telling you.'

'He'll be here,' Dylan said. 'I didn't think he would, either, at first, but when I started crying down the phone, I had him hooked.'

Lenny looked at the man in disgust. He was meant to be on leave, but there was no way he was missing out on this. 'I honestly don't think I've ever met such a pussy in my life. You know, my bathroom has got more skincare products in it now than when my ex-missus lived with me, and she was a stripper.'

The morning after the party, Felicity had politely asked Dylan to move out for a few weeks while she thought about things. She didn't care that he'd had an argument with Nick, but what she couldn't get her head around were the things she'd heard him say about the profession they shared. If he felt that way about Nick, then the same must have held true for her. They'd sat up for nearly two hours with Felicity trying to work out how he could be with someone if he held such a dim view of not only her career choice, but also her moral being. It was all too much for her, and after sleeping on it, she ordered him to pack a bag.

Lenny had invited him in, if not with open arms, but an understanding of what he was going through. When his relationship had broken up, he'd spent three months sleeping on the couch in Bodhi's boat, and despite spending all his life living on the coast, he fucking hated water.

Their time together had given Lenny plenty of opportunity to grill his new flat-mate about what the hell he was doing in the apartment of the man they were following. It didn't take long

to come to the conclusion that Nick must have been laundering Mac's drug profits. The question that still remained was what they were going to do about it. Usually, Dylan would have seized on the chance to get one over on Nick, but now Felicity wanted nothing more to do with him, he no longer really cared.

'So now you two are openly dating,' Jo said to the odd couple, 'does that mean you're going to stop pretending you're both straight?'

Even though she was keeping the baby, she'd decided to go against brigade policy and not tell them about the pregnancy. With everything that was going on, she couldn't risk going on light duties and let someone else into their circle. They had way too many secrets for that. She'd also decided not to tell the rest of the Watch. It would only make them over-protective of her the way that men instinctively did. Jo couldn't handle the thought of that.

'Even if he does come,' Jimmy said, looking at his watch again, 'what makes you think it's going to work?'

'It'll work,' Lenny said. 'Let me deal with that.'

'Please don't do anything silly,' Wesley said, 'I just want to remind you that we are at our place of work.'

Lenny laughed. 'Don't sweat it. We've got it all worked out.'

Nick's Audi drove past the window and into the yard. Dylan jumped out of his seat and headed for the door.

'Don't you want me to handle this?' Lenny asked.

Dylan shook his head. 'I got it.'

'Stay cool. We don't want to create a scene out there.'

'No problem. Like I said, I got it.'

Nick was out of his car and walking towards the door when Dylan met him. 'Hey, Dylan… I'm sorry to hear about you and Felicity, but I really don't know what you expect me to do about it.'

Dylan struck him with an ugly looking hay-maker; the punch landing just below his ear.

Nick recoiled, then brought his hand up to the violated area. The look on his face was of shock more than pain. He inspected his hand, making sure there was no blood. 'What the fuck was that?'

'Fuck you, you dick,' Dylan said.

It was fear that suddenly gripped Nick's face as his attention turned from Dylan to the grizzly bear of a man charging towards him. He turned and grabbed at the handle of his car door, but before he could open it, Lenny was on him, wrapping him in a headlock before dragging him off towards the BA compressor room.

'I thought I told you to stay cool,' he said to Dylan as Nick turned purple and gave up any attempts at resistance.

Other than a rack of charged cylinders and a couple of empties that were connected to the compressor, the BA room was pretty much derelict. In the old days, when firefighters were still allowed to get involved in the maintenance of their equipment, the room had also been a workshop. The large vice that took centre-stage on the ancient wooden workbench was the only clue to the room's former existence. These days it only got used if one of the guys had a DIY task they couldn't complete at home. On this particular evening, it had a four-foot length of steel re-bar secured into it that Jimmy had brought in from his garage.

Nick's eyes moved back and forth from the vice to the hydraulic cutters that Bodhi was holding in his hands. He was wearing his full fire-kit with his helmet on and visor down, reflecting the captive's scared image back at him. Nick tried to move, but his legs had been gaffer taped to those of the chair he was sitting on, and his arms were bound behind his back using the same method. Try as he might, he was going nowhere.

'Please, can you just loosen the tape?' he said to Lenny, then seeing the complete lack of sympathy on his face, switched his eyes to Dylan. 'It's cutting off the circulation to my hands.'

'That's probably not a bad thing,' Jimmy said, looking at the cutters. 'It means you'll bleed less when we cut them off.'

'You can't!' was all Nick managed to say.

Jimmy gave him a look that suggested otherwise.

'These little beauties,' he said as he patted the blades of the cutters that Bodhi was holding, 'are what we use to cut people out of cars. They can go through aluminium, cast iron, steel…'

He thought about it for a second. 'Pretty much anything you put in front of them.'

He nodded at Jo who pulled the ripcord on the hydraulic power pack. Nick winced at the roar of its engine. One of the cables that ran from the pack connected to the tool Bodhi was holding. Thankful to get it to work, as the weight was starting to have an effect on him, he twisted the lever on the handle, opening the blades to their full extent.

Turning towards the vice, he put the steel bar between the open jaws, then twisted the lever in the opposite direction. The blades went through it like it wasn't even there. As one half of the bar fell to the ground with a loud clang, Jimmy nodded at Jo who switched off the power-pack. The room fell silent again and filled with the smell of petrol.

Jimmy cast his eyes on Nick. 'You were saying?'

'That's not what I meant,' he said. 'I mean, you're firefighters. You're supposed to help people. You're the good guys, for Christ's sake.'

His response made Lenny laugh. 'That's right, dickhead, we're the good guys. But you, you piece of shit, you're with the bad guys, aren't you? And I'm not talking about those rich scumbags that Dylan likes to get all worked up about. I mean, real bad guys. Nasty horrible drug dealers who wouldn't think twice about killing us.'

Nick shook his head. 'I don't know what you're talking about.'

'Yes, you do,' Dylan jumped in. 'This lot saw you taking a briefcase from that scumbag Mac. So, you better start talking, otherwise you need to consider what sport you want to compete in for the next Paralympics.'

'I don't know anyone called Mac,' Nick said. 'I don't know what you're talking about.'

'Really?' Lenny said. 'Then choose which of your limbs you like least, because one of them is about to go bye-bye.'

Nick struggled, then, as if realising there was no way he was getting out, calmed down and turned his attention to Wesley, the person he saw as most likely to be able to negotiate with.

'This is silly. We both know you're not going to hurt me. Why don't you just let me go now, and I swear I'll never tell anyone what happened here tonight.' He attempted a smile. 'It'll be like it never even happened.'

Wesley stepped forward and offered a smile of his own. 'Let me ask you something, Nick. Do you know how many people go missing in this country every year? Sure, if you don't turn up for work on Monday morning, there'll be a bit of a hoo-ha for a few weeks, but after that, when they can't find your body, do you know what will happen?'

Nick shook his head.

'Nothing,' Wesley said, 'that's what. Absolutely nothing. See, the thing is, life goes on. Not for you, of course, you'll be dead. But for everyone else, they adapt, they get over it, they move on. That's one thing I've learnt since I've been in this job; that the human race is a pretty resourceful and, when it comes down to it, ruthless bunch. There'll be tears at first, but two months down the line it'll be Nick who? And the police won't give a shit. They've got so much on their plates, that when they find your clothes that we've dumped at Beachy Head, they'll be happy to put it down as just another suicide. Now, think carefully, my friend, do you want to give us the information we need, or are you happy defending your not-very-nice mates and becoming another statistic? Make your mind up, because we haven't got all night.'

Nick sat there silently for a moment then shook his head. 'I'm sorry, but I can't say anything. If I do, I'm dead.'

Just then, they were interrupted by the sound of the bells going down. Jimmy turned to look at Wesley. 'I thought you'd taken us off the run?'

'I thought you'd done it!'

The plan had been to phone up control and report a problem with their appliance's brakes. The lorry would instantly be taken off the run until a mechanic came over to take a look at it, and if they were unable to fix it there and then, a replacement from somewhere else in the brigade would be brought in for them to

ride. As the on-call mechanic lived not far from Hastings, they knew that gave them at least an hour to extract Nick's confession. Unfortunately, the call had never been made.

'Right,' Wesley said, as the others disconnected the tool from the power pack. 'Let's get this lot back on the pump. The quicker we get there, the quicker we can get back.'

As Lenny was off-duty, he would be the only one left on station. 'Don't worry,' he said to Wesley. 'I'll keep him company. No one's going to turn up on station, and if they do, they're not going to come back here.'

'With any luck, it'll be nothing,' Wesley said as the rest of the crew picked up the tools and took them back to the appliance.

Jimmy closed the RTC locker and looked back at Lenny. 'Be nice!'

They had been called to an AFA at one of their regular shouts, a centre for homeless people with drug dependency. One of the occupants had fallen asleep while smoking a joint and set light to his bed sheets. A member of staff had got in there quickly and put out the fire using a carbon dioxide extinguisher. They had been lucky; in different circumstances, it could have easily resulted in at least one death, probably more, considering the state of the occupants. On the way back from the call, Wesley radioed control, letting them know about the vehicle's suspected brake failure.

When they got back to the station, they found Nick and Lenny where they had left them. Lenny looked the same as he did when they had gone, but sometime during their twenty-minute absence, a profound change had taken place in Nick. He was white when they entered the room. His jeans were darkened at the crotch and a pool of piss lay underneath his chair. When Dylan approached him, the look of terror in Nick's eyes would have made anyone feel sorry for him.

Jimmy pulled Lenny to one side and whispered into his ear, 'What the fuck have you done to him?'

Lenny shrugged. 'I dunno. I may have told him a few things about what Dylan was going to do to him. He didn't know what

a jealous man our new boy could be until I filled him on the details.'

Jimmy looked across to Dylan's gormless form. Nick peered at him from the corner of his eye like he was confronting the devil himself. 'What, and he believed you?'

'I'm very convincing when I need to be.'

Jimmy turned to Nick, seizing on the momentum shift. 'Right, talk now, or we leave you and him,' he nodded at Dylan, 'to sort this out alone.'

Nick shook his head. 'No, don't. I'll tell you what you want to know, just keep him away from me.'

Figuring what Lenny had done, Dylan tried his best to look tough.

'Okay,' Jimmy said, 'we know who he is, and we know his business. What we need from you is something that we can use against him.'

'I can't,' Nick said. 'He'll kill me.'

Jimmy pointed at Dylan. 'And he'll kill you if you don't. Give us what we need, and we'll make sure your name stays out of it.'

'There's nothing to give you, that's the point of what I do. I put the money through a number of ghost companies, and the next thing you know, it's clean. If I just said, here's a hundred thousand pounds for drug deals, that wouldn't make me very good at what I do, would it? No offence, but even you guys could do that. I make sure the money can't be traced to him. You may not like it, but I'm good at cleaning his dirty money.'

'You must be so proud,' Dylan said.

Nick looked up to him and said nothing.

'So, what you're saying,' Wesley said, 'is Mac is pretty much untouchable. You can't give us anything on him.'

'Like I said before, I have no idea who this Mac guy is.'

The look of confusion on his face suggested Nick was telling the truth.

'Yes, you fucking do!' Lenny shouted at him. 'The old guy with the briefcase. I watched him give it to you.'

Despite the gravity of his situation, Nick somehow managed to laugh. 'Him? He just fetches and carries stuff. The man's a fucking gopher.'

Dylan knelt down so he was eye-level with Nick. 'So, who *do* you work for? I'm not asking again.'

Their captive looked around the room at the faces staring back at him before answering. 'Bogarde. I work for Jonathan Bogarde.'

'Do you think he's going to be all right?' Bodhi asked as they sat in the canteen drinking tea. 'He looked pretty shaken up when we let him go.'

'Fuck him,' Jo said. 'The question you want to be asking is, do you think he's going to go to the police about what just happened?'

Bodhi gave her a sideways glance. 'Easy. There's no need to take that tone.'

'Ahh,' Lenny said. 'They're having their first domestic in front of us. Isn't it cute?'

'I'm serious,' Jo said. 'If he does, we're fucked. We could all go to jail for what we just did.'

'And lose our jobs,' Wesley added.

'Listen,' Lenny said, unconcerned. 'After the things I told him when you were on that call, there's no way he'll be talking to anyone. As far as he's concerned, Dylan here is the worst thing since Hannibal Lecter. He's not going to do anything that he thinks may piss our man off. He wouldn't dare.'

Dylan nodded. 'That's right. From now on, you lot better show me some respect.'

'Shut up, knobhead,' Jo said.

'What exactly did you say to him?' Dylan asked.

'Honestly, you don't want to know.'

'Okay,' Jimmy said, 'that's one problem hopefully dealt with. Now onto a bigger one. What are we going to do about Bogarde?'

Bodhi looked to the others. 'What I want to know is, what the hell he's doing involving himself in drug trafficking? He's a multi-millionaire.'

'That's why he's a millionaire,' Dylan said, 'because the man craves money, and people like him have never, ever got enough of the stuff. That's free market capitalism for you; it breeds people like him.'

'All right, Russell Brand,' Lenny said. 'We get your point.'

Jimmy took the stage again. 'So, back to my question, what do we do about him?'

'I say we should kill him,' Dylan said without missing a beat.

Lenny laughed. 'Nick's gone now. You can drop the tough guy act.'

'I'm serious. Let's just kill him. The man is a boil on humanity's ass. All he's ever done in his awful little life is cause other people misery. The world would be a better place without him in it.'

'Okay, great,' Lenny said. 'So, how do you propose to do it? What are you going to do: shoot him, stab him, throw him in a shallow grave and bury him alive? I can't wait to hear what you've got planned.'

Dylan looked shocked at the suggestion. 'I didn't mean me.'

'No, that's right,' Lenny cut him off, 'you didn't. You meant me or perhaps Jimmy or Bodhi. Someone who wouldn't mind getting their hands dirty. Well I'm telling you now, I ain't killing no one, not if I don't have to. If you want to kill him so much, then do it yourself.'

'Sorry,' Dylan said quietly. 'That was a stupid thing to say.'

Wesley used the silence to intervene. 'Okay, so now we've established that we're not going to kill him, maybe we can decide what we *are* going to do. You know, it's not too late. We can still walk away from this thing.'

'Bollocks,' Lenny said. 'Just because I don't want him bumped off, it doesn't mean I don't want the horrible bastard to pay for what he's done. We've got a bigger fish to catch is all it means.'

Wesley looked unconvinced. 'But this is Jonathan fucking Bogarde we're talking about. He's not any old fish. He's a great white shark.'

'Then, in the immortal words of Chief Bodhi,' Dylan said, 'we're gonna need a bigger boat.'

Chapter 36

Mac Attack

'See you later, Nelly,' Barry the fat plumber said to his boss.

Neil MacDonald ignored him, closing the door of the mobile unit they laughably referred to as the office. He'd had a bitch of a day and couldn't wait to get home. The office stunk of mould and cigarettes and was starting to make him feel nauseous. He'd told the bastards they weren't allowed to smoke in there, but he knew that when he wasn't around, the lazy sods sat inside doing their best chimney impressions. The smell didn't give him the urge to smoke again, he'd given that up over ten years earlier, and just like the booze, he'd put it behind him for good. What bothered him was that it was a representation of the men's dissent, and that, like a load of other problems he'd encountered that day, well and truly pissed him off.

It had started first thing that morning. Vince, his go-to plasterer, had pissed off to Ibiza for a month with his mates without bothering to tell anyone. So, while Vinny boy was dropping pills on the beach, Neil spent two hours phoning around for someone free that day. The only person not booked up was Simple Simon, and his work was bordering on shit. These weren't flats he was converting, they were upmarket apartments that would go for top whack; the last thing they required was Simon's wavy walls. Eventually, he found a guy he knew was up to the task, but wouldn't be available until the following week. And that was just the start of the problems.

One of the apartments that Vince had bothered to complete before fucking off to the sunshine had had its kitchen installed by a Polish guy Neil had taken on recently. He liked the Polish; they worked hard, didn't complain and were happy to take less pay

than their English counterparts. This guy had started working for him as a labourer and was a workhorse. After spending two months mixing muck and lumping shit around, he'd asked for a promotion, telling him he was also an accomplished chippie. Impressed by his attitude, Neil gave him the nod.

It turned out the only thing he was accomplished at was lying. Neil's jaw had almost hit the floor when he saw the finished kitchen. It had a bigger snag list than could be fitted on both of his arms. Like Simon's plastering, it would have been perfectly acceptable in one of Bogey's slum flats, but not in this des-res. It was back to labouring for this Pole, and he could start by ripping out the piece-of-shit kitchen he'd spent the week installing. If he thought he was getting paid, he had another thing coming.

When Neil got in his car, he breathed a sigh of relief that the week was finally over. If only life could be as straight forward in this line of business, as it was in his other, more lucrative one. People didn't fuck about with him like this in the drug trade, and if they did, as the Albanians found out, they only did it once. The one thing that held true for both of his careers was that they were all about reputation. There just happened to be different methods involved in its protection.

The thing that really got to Neil, the thing that wound him up most, was that he even had to be doing the legit shit anymore. Considering the quantity of merchandise he was responsible for bringing into the country, he should have been a rich man. The twenty percent he got for his efforts from Bogey was a fucking joke. But that was the problem when you worked for a man like Jonathan Bogarde. Negotiation was not a word in his vocabulary. Fuck with him and you quickly ended up dead. Neil knew that better than anyone. He was personally responsible for seeing off most of his boss' rivals.

Their relationship had started nearly thirty years earlier, when Bogarde was embarking on his fledgling career as a slum landlord. He'd inherited some money and had bought six flats in one of the most run-down blocks in Brighton. He brought

Neil in to do a job on a couple of them, nothing fancy, just some dirt-cheap work to bring them up to a barely liveable standard. It didn't bother Neil; he was more about muscle than finesse, and it was that muscle that became more and more useful to Bogarde over the years. The building work quickly fell by the wayside as Neil became his enforcer – collecting late rent, evicting tenants, and dealing with any other problems that arose. For a man like Bogarde, those problems were legion.

It was Neil who had come up with the idea over a decade earlier. He knew a man who knew a man who was able to get hold of an awful lot of coke in Spain. He even came up with the idea of bringing it over on their own boats, rather than risk the ferries. It was him who had determined that small and regular deliveries via a number of marinas on the south coast was a safer way of doing business than bringing in bulk shipments on commercial vessels. This way, should they get caught, their losses were minimised, and they could simply bring future product in elsewhere.

It was even his idea to use two boats, one coming from each country, to further reduce the risk of getting caught. If someone was taking too many trips to the continent, it may arouse the suspicions of customs and result in their vessel getting searched. To combat this, Mac had one boat leave Spain with the drugs on board. The crew would then attach them and a GPS tracker to a buoy and discard them in the English Channel. Half an hour later, a boat departing from Brighton, Portsmouth or Southampton would intercept the package. To anyone taking any notice, the culprits would resemble amateur sailors having a jolly on the high seas for a few hours. He'd been running the operation for five years and hadn't yet lost one shipment.

Bogarde had been happy to bankroll the venture, but in doing so, he had taken such a large chunk of the pie that Neil was making a fraction of what he should have been. It was like Dragon's Den, and Bogey was Duncan Bannatyne, taking most of the profit for himself. Neil was the one doing all the work and taking the risk, yet Bogarde was reaping the benefits. By rights,

he should have been rich himself, not a rich person's bagman, not at his fucking age. If it weren't for the likely consequences, he would have gone solo a long time earlier, cutting Bogarde out of the picture altogether.

Neil pulled up outside his house at six-thirty. The thought of having the place to himself for the weekend was enough to make him forget his shitty week. His wife was taking the girls to London for the weekend to celebrate their upcoming eighteenth birthdays. It would cost him a small fortune, but fuck it. It was worth it to get them out of the way for a couple of days. His plan for the weekend was to do precisely fuck-all. Arsenal were on TV the next day, and the thought of a lay-in was far more appealing than a blowjob from a twenty-two-year-old brunette.

He tutted when he got in the house. All the downstairs lights were on, and the heating was blasting. *Fucking women*, he thought, if they had to pay the bills, they'd think twice before making the place look like the Blackpool Illuminations. When he walked in to his living room, the sight that faced him was so strange, it took a few moments to sink in to his already-tender brain.

'How the fuck did you get in here?' he said to the lanky streak-of-piss fireman who sat on *his* chair. No one else was allowed to sit there, not even his wife.

On the sofa, next to him, lounged the one who looked like a beach bum, and Jimmy, the gobby shit who thought he ran the show.

'We're fireman, asshole,' the young one said. 'That's what we do.'

Neil shook his head and dug his hand into his pocket. 'You bastards are going to regret this,' he said as he fished out his phone.

Before he could bring it to his ear, a massive forearm wrapped itself around his throat, cutting off his air supply.

'Hello, mate,' Lenny said as he squeezed. 'How's tricks?'

It was with reluctance that Mac finally opened his eyes. The dream he'd been having was a dozy. The twenty-two-year-old he hadn't wanted a blow job from in the morning had turned up anyway

and was putting on a little routine for him. It was only the slaps on the face that brought him out of his private show, back into the real world.

'What's going on?' he slurred at the gargoyle whose massive hand was poised, ready to strike him.

'It's all right, pal,' the beast answered. 'You've just had a little kip, that's all.'

The words helped get his brain in order, and after rubbing his eyes with the palm of his hands, he began to work out where he was and who the fuck the crowd of people standing in front of him were.

'How long have I been out for?' he asked.

Lenny shrugged. 'Couple of minutes. How long did it feel like?'

Mac rubbed his head, getting rid of the final pieces of confusion. 'Listen to me, you fucking ape!' he yelled, pushing the fog from his brain. 'Get the fuck out of my house now, before I do something that you and the rest of these pricks may not live to regret.'

'That ain't going to happen, bud,' Bodhi said. 'We need words with you.'

Mac shook his head, accompanied by an "I can't believe you're that fucking stupid" laugh. 'What the fuck is wrong with you morons? Have you forgotten what I'm capable of? Can't you remember that no-headed Albanian cunt? I tell you something, you'll be begging for what we did to him by the time my boys are through with you.'

'Do me favour, will you?' Lenny said. 'Shut the fuck up. We've heard enough of your bullshit for now.'

Mac's faced turned red, and his eyes started to bulge. 'Are you stupid, or what? You know that I know everything about you. I know where you live, I know who your families are.' He looked to Jimmy. 'I know where your kids go to school. Why the fuck would you risk their lives by coming here? Don't you love them anymore?'

'Have you ever played trumps?' Dylan asked from the comfort of the rocking chair. In his hands, he was holding a shiny new tablet. 'Because what we've got on you trumps the fuck over what you've got on us.'

He got up from the chair, turned the tablet around, and showed Mac the picture on the screen. After taking in the picture, Mac shrugged his sagging shoulders. 'Who the fuck's that?'

Dylan met his sneer with a smile. 'Good question, glad you asked. This, my friend, is Anton Jashari. And before you repeat your previous statement, I'll fill you in on the details. Mr Jashari here just happens to be one of, if not *the* most powerful gangster in all of Albania.'

Dylan turned the tablet around, got busy with his fingers, then revealed the new image on the screen to Mac. Despite himself, Mac diverted his eyes from the scene for the briefest of moments.

'Pretty rough, isn't it?' Dylan said, 'It's hard to make out exactly what's going on here, but seeing as I read all about it on Wikipedia, I'll fill you in on the details. See, this lot just happen to be part of a rival gang to our mate Mr Jashari. So, what he did was round them all up, and there were sixteen of them mind you, boil them alive, skin them, then he threw bags of salt all over them. This picture is of his still-alive victims laying in a mass grave, just before the JCB filled in the hole.'

He waited a few seconds before speaking again. 'Kind of pisses all over you chopping that bloke's head off, doesn't it?'

Mac's angry red complexion was starting to fade. 'So, what's this got to do with me?'

'Again,' Dylan said, 'good question. Although, to be fair, it's one you probably should have asked before your boy dressed up as a fireman and shot dead his nephew.'

Mac was now looking more of a deathly white on the Dulux paint scale. 'How do you know all this?'

'Google, you dumb fuck. Which is what you should have done before you started off this gangster shit. Now, the thing is, hopefully, it won't come to anything. Anton and his nephew

weren't particularly close, from what I understand. In fact, it looks, although this is just my personal opinion, that Anton had nothing to do with his nephew's little venture in this country. I'm guessing the young Jashari member was trying to cut loose and prove he could do it off his own back, so hopefully, you're off the hook.'

He paused again, giving Mac time to take in his words. 'Saying that… If the elder Mr Jashari were to find out what you had done to a relative of his, then I'm pretty sure he'd feel obligated to avenge his death. I believe you referred to it as "keeping face," if I remember correctly.'

'Are you all right?' Jimmy asked. 'It's just that you're looking a bit pale. Do you want me to get you a glass of water or something?'

'Fuck you,' Mac said, lacking any bark.

'Now, if he *were* to find out what had happened, then it's unlikely that he'd want to cross swords with your boss.' Dylan allowed Mac time to absorb his words.

'Oh, yeah, didn't think we knew about that either, did you? So, like I say, while our man will want to preserve the family name, I doubt even he will want to go to war with our good friend Mr Bogarde. The man's reputation is international. So, the question is, if not Bogarde, who will he take his revenge on? What do you reckon, Mac? Got any ideas?'

'You wouldn't,' was all Mac could say.

'Yeah, you're right,' Jimmy leapt in. 'We wouldn't have a few months ago, but things have changed a lot since you started terrorising our families. Now we think it's time you and yours got the same treatment… Unless you feel like you want to start opening up to us, that is. It's your call, big man. Take your time.'

After a long pause, Mac finally spoke again. 'Want do you want?'

Chapter 37
Raiders

'So, how's things going with Dylan?' Bodhi said. 'Do you think she's going to take him back soon?'

'She better fucking do,' Lenny answered. 'He's getting right on my tits.'

They were leaning against the wall on the opposite side of the street to Jonathan Bogarde's offices. For the headquarters of a James Bond villain, it was pretty unimposing.

'Do you know what happened last night?' Lenny asked.

Bodhi shook his head.

'I had to sit through two hours of the biggest pile of shit I've ever seen. I had to apologise to my eyes afterwards. Tell me something, what do you think a film called *The Cars That Ate Paris* would be about?'

Bodhi shrugged. 'I dunno. Sounds a bit art-house to me.'

Lenny ignored the answer. 'Do you know what I was expecting? *The Fast and Furious* in France, something along those lines. Do you know what it turned out to be? Some weird shit about these inbred motherfuckers who make people's cars crash when they drive through their town, then lobotomise the passengers and turn the cars into fucked-up death wagons.'

'Sounds right up your street,' Bodhi said.

'Sounds bollocks, more like. And you know the worst bit? It wasn't set in Paris, it wasn't even in France. It was some fucking hillbilly town in the middle of the Australian outback… I tell you something, that's the last time I let him decide what we watch.'

Bodhi's eyes narrowed as his brain kicked into gear. 'I think I've seen that film. Must have been twenty years ago. It was pretty good, if I remember right.'

'Then let him move into the Good Ship Bodhi, and you can watch shit films in bed together.'

Bodhi laughed. 'I already did my good deed, if you remember right. It's your turn now, bud.'

Lenny rolled his eyes, acknowledging the responsibility was indeed his.

'Here we go,' Bodhi said, nudging his friend.

They watched as a large man in a black suit and sunglasses headed into the building.

Lenny got out his phone and scrolled his thumb across the screen, 'Nice one. I'll let the little prick know what's going down.'

Dylan jumped when his phone vibrated. He was sitting in the back of the pump with Jo. Jimmy was driving, with Wesley sitting in the OIC's seat. They were parked three streets away from the scouting party. Dylan took out the phone, shaking his head as he read the message.

'What's happening?' Jimmy asked.

'Seriously,' Dylan said, 'the man's almost forty-five. Fifteen-year-old wannabe gangster rappers don't write this badly.'

He tossed the phone over the seat to Jimmy, who spun it around and read the message for himself.

DA DRIVER JUST TURNED UP. BOGARDE WILL BE CUMMING OUT SOON. U BOYZ GET REDDY 4 DA CALL COZ DIS SHIT IS ABOUT TO GET REEL!!!!!

'In the age of predictive texting,' Dylan said, 'it's harder to write this shit than to spell the words correctly.'

Jimmy flashed the message to Wesley then handed the phone to Jo. She inspected it for herself before passing judgement with a shake of her head.

'So, Dyldoe,' Jo said, 'what's it like living with the knuckle dragger?'

Dylan shrugged. 'It's all right, I suppose. I mean, I shouldn't moan, considering he's doing me a biggy.'

'But you're going to anyway.'

'It's just that he's so fucking messy. His gaff makes my old student digs look like a show-home.'

'It's not like you didn't know that already,' Jimmy said from the front seats. 'I mean you've seen the state of his locker.'

'You should take a picture of the squalor and send it to Felicity,' Jo said. 'Maybe she'd feel sorry for you and invite you back.'

Dylan laughed. 'Yeah, that's exactly what I need; a relationship based on sympathy.'

Jimmy looked over his shoulder. 'It's done you all right up 'til now.'

'I don't want to be a killjoy,' Wesley said, 'but can we just focus on what's about to happen? I can't do jovial at times like this.'

'What worries me is if we get another shout first,' Jo said, 'then what are we going to do?'

Jimmy turned both of his palms to the sky. 'I guess we just better pray to the god of calls that there's no emergencies going on in East Brighton today.'

The big guy in the glasses left the building, followed by a man not much shorter but less than half his width. Jonathan Bogarde was rake thin, with short black hair flecked with white streaks. He looked good for his age, something he credited to the numerous hours every week he spent running. It was his obsession, and like most things he turned his hand to, he was good at it. In his younger days, he could breeze a sub-three-hour marathon, and at nearly sixty, he still wasn't far off the pace. Everything about the man suggested he was a predator. His eyes were small and close together, perched above a nose that resembled a hawk's beak. He looked exactly like what he was – a nasty, horrible bastard.

When they got to the bottom of the steps, they turned right and headed for their vehicle. As they walked, a white transit van pulled over and parked at the side of the road, twenty feet ahead of them. Bodhi and Lenny had already crossed the road, and as the men they were tracking got closer to the van, they broke in to a trot. As they jogged, a truncheon fell out of the sleeve of Lenny's jacket which he deftly caught by the handle. At the sound of the

heavy footsteps, the driver turned, but it was too late to protect himself from the blow that crashed down on the top of his skull.

As he hit the floor, Bogarde made to flee, but before he could take a step, Bodhi got hold of him by the elbow and shepherded him towards the doors of the van that Lenny had already opened. It looked like Bodhi was barely touching him, but his captive was helpless to resist. That was the thing about Karate guys; they knew about pressure points and shit like that.

As Bodhi threw him into the back of the vehicle, Lenny scooped the unconscious driver off the floor, dumping him next to his boss in the way a normal person would chuck around their sports bag. With them both in the van, Bodhi ran around to the driver's door and started up the engine. The person that had driven the vehicle to its present location was nowhere to be seen.

Before shutting himself in with the prisoners, Lenny looked around to make sure there were no witnesses. The only person he *could* see was a strange-looking man on the other side of the street. He was decked out in an army jacket, aviator sunglasses and a baseball hat. Across the lower half of his face was wrapped a black and white Yasser Arafat scarf that made his identity impossible to establish. The man's uniform was not dissimilar to that of the demonstrators that were often camped outside Bogarde's office. They had been protesting about his involvement with an Israeli company who owned a factory on occupied land that was once part of Palestine. Lenny nodded at the man then closed the van doors to the outside world.

'I'll kill you for this,' Bogarde spat at him as the vehicle lurched forward. 'I'll find out who you are, and I'll kill you. Then, I'll find out who your family are, and I'll kill them too.'

Lenny laughed. 'If you want to know who I am, just ask your mate Neil MacDonald, you piece of shit. I ain't fucking scared of you.'

Bogarde steadied himself as the van took a left turn. 'Then, you're even more stupid than you look. Let me go, or you're a dead man.'

'Not if I kill you first,' Lenny said, picking up the truncheon. 'Now, give me the key before you get a large slice of what your mate just had.'

Bogarde shook his head. 'I don't know what you're talking about.'

'Yes, you do. Give me the key, or do I need to start breaking fingers?'

'What key?'

'*The* fucking key, that's what. Now don't make me say it again.'

The driver stirred and started to raise himself up. Lenny slammed the truncheon across his back, and he collapsed into a heap once more. He looked to Bogarde and scratched the back of his own neck with the truncheon.

'Do I really have to ask again?'

Three minutes later, the van was back on the street. It crawled up to the masked man still standing in the same place they had left him. It stopped briefly, allowing Lenny, sitting in the passenger seat, the opportunity to hand something to the figure. The man briefly inspected it, then turned and walked toward Bogarde's office.

When he got inside the lobby, he took an object out of his pocket and held it up in the air.

'Justice for Palestine!' he shouted as loudly as he could, then threw it at the security desk.

The area immediately filled with thick white smoke, forcing anyone present, including the intruder, out of the building to the fresh air outside. With the deafening fire alarms adding to the confusion, the man was able to disappear down the street without being noticed. After turning the corner onto the quiet avenue, Harrison took off the hat, scarf and glasses and walked toward the fire engine that had just turned on its lights and sirens in preparation for its short journey. As it passed, it slowed down just enough for him to throw the key to Wesley through the open window.

When the appliance pulled up outside the building, the staff had done what was expected of them and gathered at the rendezvous

point. The fire marshal in her high-viz jacket had valiantly managed to get hold of the register before being forced to flee and was now taking names in between coughing bouts. When they got out of the cab, Jo and Dylan were already under air, and after giving their tallies to Jimmy, who promptly inserted them into the BA board, they made their way to the top of the steps where Wesley was talking to the security guard. In broken English, the man was trying to explain what had taken place and was miming the actions of a grenade being thrown.

'Okay,' Wesley said, turning to address his BA crew, 'there's no fire, so you're not going to need a reel. Just go in there and ventilate. When you're done, we'll get the fan on and pump it out.'

He was saying it for the benefit of the guard and anyone else who could hear. His crew already knew exactly what they had to do.

When they got inside, the smoke was still thick, and they struggled to find their way past the lobby into the offices. Harrison had done his job well. They hadn't wanted to involve him, but if the stunt was going to work, they needed the right amount of people. Like any successful incident, it was a numbers game. Bodhi had already had to book sick in order to help Lenny deal with Bogarde and his driver, but they still needed someone to get the van there and, more importantly, to clear the offices. When Harrison found out who they were going up against, he was more than happy to be involved. He hated what Bogarde represented as much as Dylan did. The smoke grenade had been Lenny's idea. He'd got it from one his bouncer mates, who got it from fuck knows where.

Once inside the offices, it was pretty much smoke-free. The heavy fire doors had done a good job in checking its progress. It wasn't a particularly big area, not considering that millions of pounds were made there every year. It was mainly his property empire that was conducted from these rooms, but numerous other ventures – some legal, some not so much – also took place

within its walls. Bogarde's office was located on the mezzanine, and he was its sole occupant.

Other than a large portrait of himself that sat above his desk, the room was dull and boring, bereft of the extravagance that Bogarde had become known for. From their interrogation of Mac, they had found out that the safe in this room held all of Bogarde's dirty secrets. Every dodgy deal he had ever done, every penny he had cajoled, blackmailed, stolen or made from nefarious deeds were all documented and stored in a little red book, inside a little steel box right there in that room. He'd even documented all the killings he was responsible for within the book's pages. It stemmed from Bogarde's arrogance. It wasn't enough that he had made his money. He wanted to remember, to recall every last penny he had stolen from every last person. Sometimes, when he had time to himself – and it was rare for a man like Bogarde – but when he did, he liked nothing more than to take out his ledger and recall his brutal rise to the top.

Even though Jo and Dylan were in possession of the key that would allow them the most intimate access to Bogarde's private life, it meant nothing if they couldn't locate the safe itself. If Mac hadn't revealed where it was, it was unlikely they would have found it either. As he'd instructed, they moved out his desk, then after picking at a few of the wrong ones, they lifted one of the carpeted floor tiles which revealed a twelve-inch square safe located in the floor. Dylan put in the key, and, to his surprise, the door opened, revealing nothing but a tattered-looking red diary. He took it out and buried it in the inner pocket of his tunic. After locking up the safe, he nodded at Jo, then the two of them put the desk back in place and made for the door. Halfway there, Jo turned and jogged back to the desk.

'What are you up to?' Dylan asked.

Jo ignored him and picked a pen up off the desk.

'Come on, let's go!'

'Chill,' Jo said as she scribbled on the writing pad in front of her.

Dylan walked over to inspect her handiwork. He stared at it for a few seconds then turned to Jo and shook his head at what she had written.

Got you, dickhead!
Love, your friendly neighbourhood firefighters x

'You're so childish,' he said. 'Now, let's get some windows open, and we can fuck off out of here.'

They had to fight their way past the gale-force winds being generated by the positive pressure fan as they left the building. Jo moved her fingers back and forth across her neck as they exited, giving Jimmy the universally accepted "knock it off" signal.

As Wesley went back in with the security guard to oversee the resetting of the fire alarm, Dylan and Jo changed their cylinders and serviced their BA sets double quick. By the time Wesley was out of the building, they were back on the lorry, ready to go.

After clambering into the front of the cab, Wes turned to face his crew. 'Did you get it?'

As Jimmy drove off, Dylan took the ledger out of his tunic and waved it in the air.

'We got the motherfucker.' He sang the last word, his voice getting higher with every syllable until it was high enough to torment animals.

Jimmy banged the steering wheel to the laughter of the others. He looked at Wesley then beeped the horn three times.

'Sorry,' he said, 'but we got him. We nailed the son of a bitch. It's going to be us calling the shots from now on.'

Before anyone could respond, the alarm on the computer went off, letting them know they had a call. Wesley leant across and looked at the screen.

'Get our game faces on, people,' he said. 'We got an RTC, multiple vehicles, persons trapped.'

Chapter 38

Carnage

It *was* carnage. As soon as he got close enough to view the scene, Wesley made pumps four; a request for a further three appliances to attend, along with the police for traffic control. Not that they were needed at that point, the three-vehicle accident had shut down the whole of Wilson Avenue. To make things worse, they were the only pump in attendance, and the ambulances were yet to arrive. From the information on the tip-sheet, Wesley knew that both of Central's appliances had been turned out and should be there within minutes, but with regard to the ambulance, he had no idea. Surveying the chaos, he could only hope it wouldn't be long.

It was all too clear what had happened. Wilson Avenue was a steep hill that rose from the seafront, just in front of the fire station, up to the race course on the peak of the South Downs. A souped-up, ten-year-old Fiesta being driven by a boy racer had decided to overtake the Ford Focus in front of him and ran head-on into a Volvo coming down the hill. The driver of the Fiesta had spotted the oncoming vehicle too late and tried to turn back in, knocking the Focus off the road into a three-foot-high garden wall. Considering the impact it must have taken, the Volvo had escaped the incident relatively intact. The thirty grand the owner had paid for it and its Swedish protective engineering was worth every single penny. The damage to the Fiesta, on the other hand, was catastrophic.

Triage was the foremost thing on Wesley's mind as their pump pulled up in the fend-off position. Until more manpower and the ambulances got there, there was no point in even thinking about the extrication of casualties. For the moment, his priority was

preserving as many lives as he could until the cavalry arrived, then he could worry about everything else. Usually, the crews wouldn't need to be instructed about what to do at an RTC. While the OIC was information gathering and formulising a plan, the others would be setting up a tool dump and stabilising the vehicles. On this occasion, their priorities had changed.

'Jo, Dylan,' Wesley said, 'you two are casualty care on the Fiesta. Just try your best to keep them alive.'

Jimmy was already busy getting out the hose reel and making the scene safe.

When he got off the lorry, other than a cursory glance, Wesley ignored the elderly driver of the Focus sitting in the garden next to the brick wall he had just destroyed. Apart from being a bit shaken up, he looked pretty much fine, and the person attending to him, whether it was the owner of the property or a passer-by, was doing a good job of keeping him calm. Wesley's attention instead had been drawn to the Volvo. The owner, a middle-aged, well-to-do looking man, was sitting upright in his seat being about as calm as he could be, in light of the situation. His face was covered in white powder from where the steering wheel airbag had gone off, protecting his face from almost certain destruction. His wife was sitting next to him, trying to keep a stiff upper lip like her husband, but the tears that fell down her face betrayed her resolve. A female member of the public was knelt next to the passenger door, holding the woman's hand through the open window. Wesley appeared next to the good Samaritan and leaned his head into the vehicle.

'Are you okay, madam?'

The woman tried to nod, then winced. 'I think so. It's just my neck. It really hurts.'

'I'm not surprised,' Wesley said. 'The best thing you can do is to keep looking forward and try to stay as still as possible. No turning around to see that handsome man sitting next to you, got it?'

Despite her pain, the woman let out the smallest of laughs.

'What about you, sir?' he said, looking across to the driver. 'How are you managing?'

The man nodded, and unlike his wife, his vertebrae seemed to have avoided any trauma.

'Somehow, I'm fine. It's them I'm worried about.'

He was referring to the Fiesta that had bounced off his car and sat twenty yards in front of them.

'Me too,' Wesley said.

Before he left, he patted the newest member of his crew on the shoulder, praising the woman for what she was doing and encouraging her to keep talking to them both.

It was the Fiesta that was the real concern. The front of the vehicle, particularly on the driver's side, had taken the brunt of the impact and had reacted like a concertina, folding in on itself. Worse was the deceased young man whose bloodied upper torso had projected through the car's windscreen. The impact had split his skull open, leaking the inside of his head onto the car's bonnet.

When Wesley got to the vehicle, things didn't get any better. Jo had taken the unconscious driver's head and tilted it backwards, ensuring that his airway remained open. The engine block had pushed back into the car, with the steering wheel pressed tight against his chest. It wasn't crushing him, but it was highly likely that the two had collided and internal injuries were almost guaranteed. His legs were in an even worse predicament. The collision had made the footwell pretty much disappear, along with his feet and the lower half of his shins. They would only find out to what extent they were damaged when they had created sufficient space, and considering the state of the vehicle, that was going to be a real bastard.

Despite Dylan's attempt to calm her, the girl in the front passenger seat was close to hysterical. Other than a nasty cut on the side of her forehead, where she must have hit the B-post, she looked fairly intact, not discounting the possibility of internal trauma. It was the sight of her dead friend sticking out of the windscreen, and her boyfriend, the driver, not answering her calls, that was the primary source of her distress.

'Chris!' she screamed in between her sobs. 'Answer me. Chris, fucking answer me!'

'Get a salvage sheet,' Wesley said so only Dylan could hear, 'and cover him up. It may help to calm her down.'

It was only then that he noticed another young man sitting on the kerb with his head hung low like he'd spent the night drinking too much. He'd given up trying to stem the steady flow of blood that was escaping from his nose and instead watched it pool on the road. Wesley took it that he had been in the back of the car, but, unlike his friend, had been wearing his seatbelt. The ambulance crew could deal with him later on, Wesley decided. Triage was brutal sometimes. Turning back to the girl, Wesley leant into her window, speaking loud enough to be heard over her sobs.

'Your boyfriend's going to be okay. He's had a nasty bang and he's unconscious, but he's breathing, and once the ambulance gets here, we're going to have you both out.'

'I told him to slow down,' the girl cried. 'He only got the car last week and was showing off.'

'Let's not worry about that just now,' Wesley said. 'Getting you out of here is my priority.'

'Tell that to Andy,' the girl said. 'He's fucking dead now because of Chris.'

She tried to look across to her boyfriend, but the dead boy's body was acting like a curtain, cutting him off from her. Given his condition, Wesley thought that was probably a good thing.

'You prick,' she screamed. 'You fucking killed him.' She winced at the pain the effort had induced.

'Where does it hurt?' Wesley asked.

With much discomfort, the girl shifted herself in her seat. 'My back, my chest, my neck. The only thing that's not hurting are my legs… Oh my God, I'm not paralysed, am I?'

Wesley reached down and gently pinched the girl's thigh. 'Did you feel that?'

The girl nodded.

'Good, then you're not paralysed. Now, tell me your name; it's rude not to introduce yourself.'

'Nicola,' the girl said. 'My name's Nicola.'

The sound of sirens coming down the hill improved Wesley's mood. It was tapered slightly when he saw that it was both Central's appliances arriving in unison. Not that he wasn't grateful to see them, but if the driver was going to survive, he needed an ambulance fast.

Smudge, the Watch manager, and Billy, the OIC of the second pump, approached Wesley as he stepped away from the girl. He let Dylan go back to looking after her after completing his task of covering up the corpse.

'What's the plan?' Smudge asked. 'Have you got one yet?'

Smudge was an old-school, no-nonsense JO, and it was fair to say he had a less than glowing opinion in regard to Wesley's abilities as an incident manager.

Wesley nodded. 'As you can see, we've got a three-vehicle collision. I'm not worried about the Focus. The Volvo will probably need extrications, but for now, this vehicle is my number one concern. The driver is trapped, with likely crush injuries. The girl, her name is Nicola, she seems to have come out of it relatively intact, but we'll probably have to cut her out just in case she's got spinal injuries. I'm going to sectorise the incident, my crew are going to be sector one, and we're going to work on the driver. Smudge, you're sector two, and you can deal with the girl. Bill, you can make a start on the Volvo, and Hove will assist you when they get here. You'll be sector three.'

He paused and listened for a second. 'That sounds like them now. Any questions?'

Smudge raised an eyebrow then shook his head. 'Nah, sounds good.'

It was actually the ambulance and not Hove that Wesley had heard. They arrived a few minutes later. As he'd predicted, it was a bastard of a job. It was always difficult working at an RTC. When you had crews working with heavy cutting gear, and paramedics

trying to look after multiple casualties, doing everything they can to keep them alive, it was more than a little tricky. People were often stepping or falling over each other, if not careful, in order to achieve their goals. Hands ended up going in between someone else's legs in order to reach what they needed, and people had to constantly move around as the vehicle was being cut, all whilst ensuring the casualties remained perfectly still. This job happened to be no different.

After stabilising the vehicle and managing the glass, the roof was quick to come off. It made life much easier for both the paramedics and firefighters, instantly creating room for them all. For the casualty, the situation was also much improved, helping to alleviate that claustrophobic feeling of being trapped. After the roof removal, Nicola had come out of the vehicle under her own steam, without the need of a stretcher.

Getting the driver out was far trickier. The only way to release his legs was to create extra space by executing a dashboard roll. This involved making a relief cut, then using the telescopic rams, they were able to lift and push the entire dashboard area backwards. Due to the damage that had been caused to the vehicle and the mess it had made of the driver's feet, this was a laborious task. Every time they used the rams to push one piece of the vehicle back, it created a movement that pushed something else in towards the casualty's legs. Cause and effect; it could be a bitch sometimes.

To free his feet up, they'd used a hydraulic, hand-powered cutter to remove the foot pedals. His knees were smashed, he had serious compound fractures in both shins, and all that stopped his right foot from being separated from his leg were a few stubborn tendons. The other one hadn't fared much better; it was well and truly mashed. The paramedics later said it would be a miracle if he didn't lose them both.

Luckily, the steering wheel hadn't been an issue. As soon as they started using the rams, it had instantly moved a few inches, giving the paramedics the space they needed to work their magic.

Somehow, they had managed to get him out of the vehicle in forty-five minutes, ensuring that the Golden Hour (the time from accident to hospital, when it was most likely to recover from serious injuries) hadn't been breached. Other than the damage to his legs, the driver had suffered a cracked sternum, broken ribs, internal bleeding and who knew exactly what else, but he was still alive.

At the end of the incident, when the Volvo owner and his wife were eventually out of their urban tank and all casualties had been whisked to hospital, Phil Collins, who had turned up halfway through the incident as the on-call officer, called all four crews together for a hot debrief. The brigade liked to try and get an initial breakdown of events done as soon as possible, and as they were going to be there for a good while yet, this was seen by Phil as the perfect time.

As was customary in a debrief, Phil gave the floor to the OIC who had arrived first, allowing him to explain the scene he was presented with and what his thought processes were at the time. After Wesley had given his account, the mic was then handed to Smudge followed by Jacko, the Hove OIC. The overwhelming feeling was that it had been a successful job and much praise was aimed at Wesley. Phil had nodded along as they spoke, occasionally looking down and scribbling something on his clipboard. When they had finished, he stepped forward and took centre stage.

'Firstly, I'd like to say that I think you all did really well today. It was a difficult incident given the number of vehicles and casualties involved, but I think you dealt with it very well.' He paused, then turned his attention to Wesley. 'There are, however, a few notes I made that I'd like to discuss, if you don't mind.'

Wesley shook his head.

'I got here at fifteen twenty-two, which was nearly twenty minutes after the arrival of Wesley and his crew. The first thing that struck me was that incident command was not yet set up. By then, there should have been a flag up and the command wallet out with the tally-boards of all the vehicles present.

'I did it five minutes after you got here, Phil,' Jimmy said. 'You watched me do it. You also saw I was pretty busy before that helping the paramedics with their gear.'

Phil looked up at Jimmy, then returned his eyes to his clipboard. 'The other thing I noted is that even though the incident had been sectorised, no one was wearing a sector commander tabard. In fact, no tabards of any kind were worn at all.'

He turned his attention back to Wesley. 'And while we're on the issue of sectors, I felt that as the OIC of the incident, you would have been better stepping back and letting Jimmy be in charge of Sector One. That would have allowed you to have a greater span of control over the incident as a whole. Other than those few points that I did feel let things down slightly, it was a successful job, and all objectives were achieved.'

He gave Wesley the most half-hearted of smiles. 'Well done.'

Wesley returned the smile with the same enthusiasm, then shook his head and laughed. 'Thanks for your comments, Phil, but if you felt things were going that badly, why didn't you take over the incident? You were the senior officer, after all.'

Phil gave him a look. 'Sorry?'

'I mean, if that's how you felt, why didn't you put your clipboard down and get involved? We could have done with a spare pair of hands.'

'Don't take offence,' Phil said. 'I'm just giving you my opinion.'

'To be honest, Phil, I don't really care about your opinion. It's hard to take the words of a man whose first concern, at an incident like this, is why we're not wearing tabards, too seriously, if you know what I mean.'

Phil looked like he was about to erupt. Instead, he put his clipboard under his arm and made for his car.

'I'll speak to you later,' he said as his shoulder brushed past Wesley's.

When he slammed his door and drove off, all four crews broke into applause.

When they got back to the station, Phil's car was already parked in the bays. Jo and Dylan got off the lorry to open the doors up for them, and Wesley turned to follow them out.

'I might as well get it over with,' he said. 'Should I pull my pants down now, or wait 'til I get in the office?'

'Listen, Wes,' Jimmy said. 'I was really impressed with you today. You did everything the way it should have been done. I can't fault you.'

'Thanks, Jim,' Wesley said, 'but I might as well tell you now that my penance is up soon. I can finally go back to fire safety.'

'Right, and you're not going, are you?'

Wesley nodded. 'I think it's best. That is, if Phil doesn't fuck it up for me.'

'Why?' Jimmy asked. 'I thought you were happy here.'

'You said it yourself, Jim, I'm not up to the job.'

Jimmy shooed the comment away. 'Aw, fuck that. I said those things a long time ago. A lot has changed since then. You've changed since then.'

Wesley smiled. 'Thanks for your kind words, but I'm better behind a desk. I don't get judged for my actions there.'

'What are you talking about? Your actions today proved you're more than up to it. If you didn't already have it, you would have gained the respect of the crew, and I don't just mean ours. Everyone there saw what you did.'

'And everyone else in the Brigade? To them, I'm just the guy who ran out of a BA job and left my partner in there. I'll never get their respect.'

'Who gives a fuck? You don't work with them. You're one of us. None of the rest of them matter.'

'They do to me. Now, I better get to Phil's office before he drags me in there.'

He got out of the lorry just as Dylan pulled the roller shutter doors open for Jimmy to drive through.

When Wesley entered the canteen, he was greeted by a cheer from the Watch.

'Make the man a cup of tea, new boy,' Jo said to Dylan. 'Looks like his arse has taken a pounding.'

Wesley smiled and rubbed his behind. 'I've got to say, for a small man, he really has got a massive knob.'

'It was worth it,' Jo said. 'You did yourself proud today, boss.'

'Yeah, good job, Wes.' Dylan held his teacup up to him.

Jimmy and Jo followed suit and toasted their leader.

Wesley smiled at his crew, then looked to his pocket as his phone vibrated.

Throughout the whole incident and his time in Phil's office, it had been ringing pretty much non-stop. He inspected the phone and saw the twelve calls he had missed were all from Mac. Wesley sensed desperation, which must have meant that Bogarde was rattled too. Their plan had worked.

Unable to get through, Mac had finally resorted to leaving a text. It was with a mixture of excitement and downright fear that Wesley read the message:

Call me now. We need to talk!

Chapter 39

The Big Boss Man

Jonathan Bogarde continued to stare at his guests. It felt to Jimmy that the man's eyes were boring into his very being, discovering his deepest, darkest secrets. It was stupid. He knew if he wanted to, he could beat the shit out of the skinny rat-faced bastard, but there was something about their inquisitor that unnerved him. The calm on Bogarde's face couldn't hide the anger that bubbled just below the surface of his skin. They had been facing the man for over a minute, and he was yet to speak. At any second, Jimmy expected him to stand up from behind his desk and explode in fury, and he had every right to.

After taking his precious key, Bodhi had driven him and his driver to Ditchling Beacon, one of the highest points on the South Downs and miles from anywhere. Lenny had unceremoniously lobbed them out of the vehicle, before giving them the finger and returning to town. Jimmy could only guess how they got back to the office as Lenny also made them hand over their mobiles.

When they finally *did* return, Bogarde would have found his safe had been violated and all his dirty little secrets gone. The meeting at his office had been arranged to take place straight after work. It was only three hours since they'd saved Nicola and her boyfriend from the crash.

Eventually, Bogarde gave them a very slow, very deliberate clap.

'You might just possibly be the stupidest people I've ever met,' he said, when the clapping had finished, 'but you've got some stones on you, I'll give you that.'

Jimmy accepted the half-compliment with a nod.

'To assault my driver, steal my book, and dump me in the middle of nowhere,' he shook his head, 'and then, for only the two

of you turn up at my office, even though I specifically requested you all to be here. People say firefighters are crazy; running into a burning building when everyone else is running out, but you gentlemen really take the biscuit.'

Bogarde's clipped accent revealed that, despite being involved in some of the dirtiest businesses out there, he came from good stock and had the best education money could buy. He turned to look at Mac, who stood just behind his shoulder like the guard dog he was.

'What do you think, Neil?'

'If you don't mind me saying, Jon, I think the lot of them have been a right pain in the arse. I should have killed them all I soon as I found out they stole your money.'

Jimmy noted the emphasis on the word *your*.

'Perhaps,' Bogarde said, giving away nothing. He forced himself to smile. It looked all wrong on his thin face. 'So, you've had your fun and you got one over on me… Well done, you. You and your friends have done a great job in well and truly pissing me off, and so I say again, well done, but now, I think it's time we talk about how we make this situation right.'

'You're the drug dealer, you're the murderer. Don't put what's happened on us.' Jimmy felt a pang of fear after speaking, like the first time he decided to stand up to the bully at school.

'Careful,' Bogarde said, sounding less eloquent. 'It *is* my business, and like all good CEOs, I take responsibility for my staff's actions, but let's be clear. I didn't kill anyone. I didn't smuggle those drugs into the country. Other people steer the ship for me. I just happen to own it.'

When his words had sunk in, he spoke again.

'So, this is what I'm expecting. You made a mistake, but it's not too late to rectify it. That book, you could call it a diary, if you like, is of great sentimental value to me, and I really, *really* would be happier if it were back in my possession. So, like I say, you return to the fire station or wherever it is you've got it, get my book and bring it here. Do it by the end of

the day, and I swear on my baby son that nothing will happen to you. I'll also make sure that you and your colleagues are financially better off as a result. Like I said, you've got balls, and that deserves recognition, but there's only so far that that goes. So, you gentlemen do what I'm asking, and we can end this stalemate right now.'

'Excuse me for saying, Mr Bogarde, but I don't see how you consider this to be a stalemate.'

It was the first thing Wesley had said since he'd entered the room.

'As you well know, that diary you kept, and god knows why you would want to document that stuff, I can only assume it's your vanity, but that information could put you in prison for a long, long time. So, if we're going to keep using the chess analogy, then its most definitely checkmate to us, or game, set and match, if you want to mix it up and try a bit of tennis.'

Bogarde made a strange clucking sound in the back of his throat before speaking. 'You know, if you were dealing with most men, then your assessment of the situation would be pretty spot-on. If that *were* the case, and I was most men, you could take that diary to the police and I'd spend the next twenty years in prison trying to avoid the attention of psychopaths and would-be rapists whilst I cried into my pillow every night. But the problem you gentlemen have got is you're not dealing with most men. Unfortunately for you, you're dealing with Jonathan Bogarde, and I am not a man to let a little detail like being in prison stop me from going about my business. So, you do what you're proposing, and I will make sure that your wives, children, parents and grandparents, if they're still alive, end up suffering for your mistake in ways you couldn't possibly imagine. Now, I'll assume you don't want those terrible things to happen to your nearest and dearest, so that is why, my friend, we're at a stalemate. And just in case you think this is a bluff, let me assure you, Jonathan Bogarde does not lie when it comes to business.'

He stopped talking and let his visitors absorb the threat.

Wesley cleared his throat before speaking again. 'You know, I've never heard anyone talk about themselves in the third person like you just did. I mean, I've seen boxers doing it in interviews after a fight, but I didn't think real human beings actually spoke that way.'

Jimmy thought he saw a smirk pass across Mac's face for the briefest of moments.

It was a long time before Bogarde spoke again. 'Let me tell you something. I haven't been spoken to like that since 1989, and you want to know what happened to that idiot? I personally cut his tongue out whilst our friend here held him down. After we tortured him for three hours, I got my boys to cut his body into little pieces then shovel all the bits into a suitcase and throw it off Brighton Pier. They never did find him, did they, Neil?'

'No, Jon,' Mac said as he stared at Wesley. 'They didn't.'

'It's a pity he didn't have your diary,' Jimmy said, ''cos if he did, he could have made copies of it. Then, if anything did happen to him, those copies would have automatically been sent to the police. If he'd had that sort of insurance, I think he would have been just fine, don't you, Wes?'

'I do,' Wesley said, 'if he'd had that insurance, I think that, despite all the threats, he would have been pretty much untouchable. If you get what I'm saying.'

Bogarde made the grunting noise in his throat again. 'What exactly do you morons want from me?'

Wesley and Jimmy looked to each other before Wesley spoke. 'We want you to give a million pounds a year for the rest of your life to Sussex Fire and Rescue Service on the proviso that they use it to keep East Brighton fire station open. As it's now your local station, they shouldn't find your request too strange, and knowing what a persuasive man you can be, I'm sure you won't have any problem convincing them.'

Bogarde laughed, a long, pronounced chuckle that came from deep within the icy crevasse where his heart should have been.

After a few seconds, he turned to Mac, still laughing. 'Seriously, can you believe this?

Mac shook his head. 'No, boss, I can't. They're pretty fucking unbelievable.'

Bogarde turned his attention back to the firefighters. 'All the things that you could have asked of me, and this is what you decide to risk your lives for; a selfless act. You're even crazier than I thought.'

'We tried doing greedy,' Jimmy said, 'and it didn't work out too well.'

'Besides,' Wes said, 'it's not completely altruistic. You keep the station open, and we keep our jobs.'

Bogarde smiled at him. 'If you'd played this situation a bit smarter, you'd never have to work again.' He leaned back in his chair and took stock of the offer. 'Jonathan Bogarde, philanthropist. I never thought I'd hear those words together in my lifetime, but you know something, I kind of like the sound of it.'

'So, is it a deal, then?' Jimmy asked.

Bogarde shrugged. 'I'm not sure yet. Let me ask you something first.'

'Go for it.'

'What makes you do what you do?'

'What's that?'

'Let me rephrase the question. Why do you feel the need to help other people? To put their lives before your own. Personally, I think it's one of three things. One: you're religious men who think your good deeds are going to get you into heaven. Two: you're doing it because it makes you feel good, like real life superheroes, or three – and this is the one I think is more likely: it's because you think it's the right thing to do. Tell me, am I getting close?'

When neither of his guests answered, he carried on. 'That's what I thought, and that's what intrigues me about people like you. You live by this myth that governs everything you do in your lives. Let me tell you something, gentlemen; there is no right and wrong, there just *is*. You're like those people who waste their time trying to save the pandas. What they don't realise is those animals they're trying to protect will die off no matter what they do, it's inevitable. Ninety-nine percent of things that have ever walked this planet are

extinct. One day, we will be too. You may think that history will judge me for what I've done, but it won't, not in the long term anyway. Our time on the shitty little planet is finite, and by that I don't mean you and I. I'm speaking about the entire human race. One day soon, we'll all be gone, snuffed out, just like that, and nothing that any of us does right now will mean a single thing in the very near future. None of it matters, so stop hiding behind these rules and morals you've bound yourselves to, and do what needs doing. The day you realise that is the day you'll be truly free.'

Wesley looked surprised at the revelation. 'I never knew there was a philosophy to being such an evil bastard. I just thought it came natural to you.'

Bogarde laughed. 'That's the point; it *is* natural. The way I live is exactly how nature intended. Darwin would have been in complete agreement with me. It's your way of life that's at odds with the natural order of things. I'm just letting millions of years of evolution guide me. It's survival of the fittest, and no man is fitter than me.'

'Have we got a deal or not?' Jimmy asked, doing his best to look bored.

Bogarde thought about it before answering. 'Meet me tomorrow night. Bring the book, and you'll get your money.'

'Two things,' Wesley said. 'First, we're keeping the book. That's our insurance.'

'Not going to happen,' Bogarde cut in. 'You can keep as many copies as you like. They'll be just as good evidence as the real thing should you ever decide to take them to the police, but like I said, the book is of great sentimental value to me. You give it back, or it's no deal. Now, what was the other thing?'

'We can't meet tomorrow; we're working nights.'

Bogarde smiled. 'Understood. Meet me here on Thursday night, eight pm.'

'Tell you what,' Jimmy said. 'Why don't we meet at your new gaff? Dylan would love to see what it looks like on the inside.'

'Fine,' Bogarde said. 'But this time, I *do* expect you all to be there.'

Chapter 40

Wes

'Daddy!'

Olivia and Emily almost bowled Wesley over as they charged into him. He wasn't sure if it was the joy of seeing him or the break in routine his visit heralded, that excited them most.

'Why are you here today?' Olivia, the elder girl asked after kissing his chin. 'We're supposed to be in school.'

Wesley pinched at the girl's nose. 'You want to go to school, do you?' Come on, then. I'll drive you both there now.'

'No, Daddy,' the girls screamed as they hugged him.

'Where are you taking us?' Emily asked.

'Anywhere you like, darling. Now, get in the car, please. I need a quick word with Mummy before we go.'

The girls did as they were told and disappeared into the back of the vehicle. Wesley turned his attention to Nina, who had stood quietly back, saying nothing.

'Thanks for this,' he said. 'I know I've asked a lot, but you don't know what it means to me to see them.'

He wasn't supposed to be seeing the girls until the weekend, but the meeting at Bogarde's had unnerved him, and that was the polite version of events. In actual fact, it had frightened the living fuck out of him. Even though he had somehow managed to keep it together, he didn't think he had ever been as scared as he was with that evil old man staring him down. The real reason he wanted to see the girls was because, quite honestly, he wasn't sure if, come the weekend, he would still be alive.

The friendly smile on Nina's face had taken him back. He wasn't expecting her to agree to the visit, especially as it involved

pulling the girls out of school. The last time he had changed his visiting plans at short notice, there had been riots.

'Has something happened at work?' Nina said, her voice laced with understanding.

'Something like that. Sometimes, it takes something bad to happen to make us realise what's important to us.'

Nina laughed. 'Tell me about it.'

'I'll have them back by six and don't worry. I won't go filling them up with sweets and chocolate.'

'If you want,' Nina said, 'you can stay for tea. The girls would like that.'

'I'm sure they would. I can't imagine Gregg being too pleased about it though.'

Nina looked to the floor, 'Gregg's left me; he's gone back to Paula.'

She waited for Wesley to answer, but when nothing came back, she spoke again. 'Go on, say it. You knew it wouldn't last.'

Wesley shook his head. 'I'm sorry to hear that.'

'Are you?' she said. 'Sorry that he's not living here anymore?'

'No, but I'm sorry if you've been hurt again.'

'Don't be, he was an arsehole anyway. I realise now that I never really wanted Gregg. He was just a way of dealing with my loneliness.'

'I'm sure Paula will be glad to hear that.'

Nina reached out and grabbed Wesley's hand. 'It's you I want. Come home, Wes.'

When she touched him, it felt like he'd received an electric shock. He looked down at their embraced hands, then gently retracted his own.

'What?' Nina said. 'I thought you wanted this.'

'I did. I do, I think… I don't know what I want, if I'm honest.'

'Come home,' she repeated. 'The girls would love it. I would love it. We miss you.'

Whether he was aware of it or not, Wesley took a step backward. 'I miss you guys too. I'm just not sure I'm ready for it yet. This is all a bit much to take in right now.'

The smile on Nina's face fell away and was replaced with the accusing stare he had grown accustomed too over the past few months.

'Sorry, Wes, maybe I didn't make myself clear. If you want to keep seeing the girls, you'll come home now.'

'If you want me home, issuing threats is a funny way of going about it.'

'I'm serious. Do what I say and move back in, or you can treat today as a goodbye visit. It'll be the last time you see the girls for a long time.'

Wesley laughed. 'Tell you what. Let's speak about this again when you're in a less psychotic mood.'

'Don't laugh it off, Wes. I'm not messing around here. Come back or all you'll be seeing of those girls is the pictures I send you on Instagram.'

'Fine,' Wesley said, 'you do it. You stop me seeing the girls, and let's see how well you cope without me paying for this place. Perhaps your old boss will give you your job back, although I'm pretty sure you'll need a substantive pay rise to cover the mortgage and all the bills.'

Nina reacted like he'd just punched her in the face. 'You can't do that! I'll get the CSA on you.'

Wesley shrugged. 'Big deal. Like you said before, it'll take months, if not years, for them to stick their oar in. By then, the bank will have seized the house off you.'

Nina swallowed hard before speaking. 'And you'd do that, would you? Watch your little girls get brought up in some stinking council flat just to prove your point.'

'Those girls have had everything they could ever need and a bit more on top. They don't realise how lucky they are. I think a bit of adversity in their lives would do them the world of good; give them a better appreciation of the simple things. And besides, most of the council flats I see when I'm in work aren't that bad. Nothing that a lick of paint wouldn't solve. I'll even come round and do it for you, just to show there's no hard feelings.'

Nina opened her mouth to form words, but nothing came out.

'I don't blame you for leaving me,' Wesley said. 'I don't pretend that I was the best husband, and I am sorry for that. But one thing I am is a good father. Don't try and turn me into a bad one by denying me my kids. Maybe one day, I will come home. Maybe we will get back together, but it's got to be right for both of us, not just you. Let's take these things slowly and see what happens.'

He looked at his watch. 'We better be going, or it'll be too late to get in anywhere.'

He smiled at his wife. 'I'll have them back by tea-time, scout's promise.'

Still silent, Nina watched as Wesley joined his daughters in the car.

Chapter 41

Confessions

'What do you mean she's not coming?' Jimmy said.

Bodhi shrugged apologetically. 'She's not coming, Jim. That's it.'

'We've already pushed him far enough. If we want this deal to work, then she needs to be there.'

'She won't be,' Bodhi said. 'So just drop it.'

Jimmy gave Bodhi a look. 'And Jo's all right with this, is she? Playing the damsel in distress, I mean. Doesn't sound like her to me.'

'For once, we didn't even have to argue about it. She feels the same way too.'

'Fuck me, I've heard it all now.'

It was an hour into their second nightshift. The evening before, Jimmy and Wesley had laid out their meeting with Bogarde to the rest of the Watch over a cup of tea. They'd spelt it out in no uncertain terms that Bogarde wanted the whole of Red Watch there, and everyone had not only agreed, but said it was the fairest thing if they all accepted a share of the risk. This was why Jimmy was so shocked when Bodhi had pulled him aside and presented this new development.

'I understand where you're coming from,' Jimmy said. 'I know you've not been together long, and right now, you must be about as loved up as it's possible for two people to be. She's your woman, and you want to protect her, I get that, mate, I do. But let's just do this one last thing together, and then, it will be over for good.'

Bodhi smiled at his friend. 'I hear what you're saying, Jim, and I know it pisses you off, but she's not going, end of story.'

Jimmy went to speak, then stopped and sighed. 'You want to know something? Ever since that hoax call at my house when I thought something had happened to Jen and the kids, things have been good at home, and when I say good, I mean really fucking good. When you think you've lost the people you love, then find out you haven't, it changes you. Makes you realise how much you take for granted. I love my kids more than anything, and even though me and Jen spend half our time arguing, there's no woman in the world I'd rather be with. But despite that, I'm going to go to that prick's house tomorrow and put an end to this shit once and for all. It's got to be done, and we all need to be there.'

'She's pregnant, Jim.'

'Fffuck,' Jimmy said, the shock almost preventing him from overcoming the first syllable. 'Now I really have heard it all.'

'How do you think *I'm* feeling?'

Jimmy clapped his hands together. 'You're right, she ain't coming. Bollocks to that shit. Fuck Bogarde. He'll have to do without her, and you for that matter.'

'Don't be silly, Jim. I'll be there.'

Jimmy shook his head. 'No, you won't. You need to be home with her, just in case anything does go wrong. That baby's going to need the both of you.'

'What about your kids, or Wesley's or Lenny's little girl? Don't they need their parents too?'

'Yeah, and they will have them, 'cos nothing's going to happen. But Jo's going to need you more than anything in the next few months, even though she'd never admit it.' Jimmy put his hand on Bodhi's shoulder. 'Let us deal with this, you've got bigger problems coming your way.'

The door of the locker room burst open and Jo walked in.

'What the fuck are you two arseholes talking about?' she shouted, then looked to Bodhi. 'You better not have said anything.'

'Congratulations,' Jimmy said.

Jo rolled her eyes. 'For fuck's sake, Bodhi, we talked about this.'

Jimmy walked up to her, kissed her and gave her a bear hug, hunching his shoulders forward so he wouldn't crush the bump that wasn't even there yet. The hug that Bodhi received was far less gentle.

'Congratulations, the pair of you. You'll make great parents.'

'No, we won't,' Jo said. 'We'll be fuck-ups, just like the rest of you.'

'In that case,' Jimmy said, 'welcome to the club.'

Chapter 42

Reconciliation

Dylan went to open the car door then retracted his arm as if the handle was electrified. 'I can't do it.'

Lenny shook his head in disgust. 'Seriously, you need to stop being such a pussy. Man the fuck up and deal with this shit.'

They were double-parked outside Felicity's office building, and had been for the last twenty minutes; a situation that was testing what little patience Lenny had to its very limits. When he was tired, he became even more irritable than usual. They had spent the previous night at a ten-pump fire in Newhaven. The science block of the comprehensive school had been set alight at two o'clock in the morning, and their appliance had been there almost from the start until they were relieved by a retained pump at seven.

That was only three hours before Lenny had found himself acting as Dylan's chauffeur and moral back up, and he wasn't happy. He should have been tucked up in bed.

People often asked firefighters what was the biggest fire they had been to, associating biggest with best. Most of those firefighters would be quick to respond that more often than not, the bigger fires quickly turned out to be a massive ball-ache. Yeah, they looked pretty spectacular at first when the flames were thirty feet high, but the truth was, big fires attracted lots of fire engines, and worse, even more officers. Usually firefighting, when a blaze was that big and developed, was limited to keeping surrounding buildings safe. In other words, damage limitation. This was known as being in defensive mode, and that had been the case with the school.

The crew had spent most of the early morning directing a jet at any flames that licked up through the burnt-out roof, stopping

the heat travelling to the art wing. When the fire had finally died down and crews had been able to get in there and put it out, another two hours had been spent turning over and dampening down. The crews that replaced them would be continuing with the job for the rest of the morning.

No, most firefighters would tell you the best jobs were the ones they could get stuck into and put out before management had even turned up. A good bedroom fire, where the crews had to work like lunatics for twenty minutes and kept contained to the room of origin, was often far more satisfying than the bigger jobs that made the headlines.

'I can't, Len. What if she says no? It would ruin me.'

'I'll fuckin' ruin you if you don't get the fuck out of my car. How do you think you're going to face that bastard tonight if you can't even confront your own woman?'

'That's different.'

'Too fucking right it's different. If this goes tits up, at worst you'll get a slap around the face. If it goes wrong tonight, we could end up under the pier wearing concrete boots.'

'Thanks, Len, that makes me feel so much better.'

Lenny looked out of the car window to the street outside. 'You going to do it, then? If not, we're gonna do one, there's a parking Nazi coming.'

Dylan took a deep breath and nodded at his driver. 'I'm going. Wish me luck.'

'Good man. I'll stay here, just in case I need to move.'

'Really?' Dylan said. 'I was hoping you'd come up and serenade her for me. Where's that poem you wrote?'

'Shut up, knobhead,' Lenny laughed. 'Go and get your missus back.'

As he walked down the corridor, Dylan noticed a few sideways glances and whispered conversations from Felicity's workmates. Most of them had been at Nick's house on the night they broke up and clearly hadn't forgotten it. As he approached her office, he

could feel his heart rate increasing. Despite what Lenny had said, he was far more worried about this meeting than the one that would follow in a few hours' time.

When he was ten yards from her door, Nick came out of the room with a broad smile on his face. When he saw Dylan, he went white, and the smile fell away.

'Hi, Nick,' Dylan said, preventing the man from completing a 180 degree turn. 'Is Flic in?'

Nick tried to smile, but it came out as grimace, like he was swallowing razor blades, 'Nice to see you, Dylan.'

'And you, Nick, as always.'

'You know, I'm glad you're here. I wanted to tell you how sorry I am for what happened before, and I just wanted to let you know nothing like that will ever happen again.'

Dylan smiled. 'Thanks for that. Now run along and give us ten minutes alone. I need to speak to my fiancée.'

When he knocked on the door, Felicity's head was hidden from view behind her computer monitor.

'What now?' she said. Even though he couldn't see her face, Dylan was certain she was smiling. 'Haven't you got work to do?'

'Sorry to disappoint you,' he said. 'It's just me.'

When she leant out from behind the screen, the smile had already gone. 'Dylan, what are you doing here?'

He responded by walking closer to her desk. 'I need to speak to you. We can't go on like this.'

'No, you're right. You should come and get the rest of your stuff. I think it's best that you leave the flat for good.'

Dylan felt like he had been punched in the stomach. 'It's Nick, isn't it. Are you seeing him?'

'No, Dylan, I most definitely am not seeing Nick. He's my colleague and we have fun at work. That's it, end of story.'

'Then why do I have to move out? I love you.'

'Do you, though? How can you love someone you've got no respect for; whose job undermines the values you hold so dear?'

Dylan let out a nervous laugh. 'Don't be silly, I love you, and that's all that matters. Even if you were a serial killer, I would still love you.'

'Oh, right, so now, you're comparing me to a serial killer. I thought you were trying to put things right.'

Dylan held his hands up in surrender. 'I'm sorry, that's not what I meant. What I was trying to say is, I love you, no matter what. 'I know you're a good person, and I know that you love your job and you're in it for all the right reasons, even if some other people aren't.'

The look on Felicity's face stopped him. 'Sorry. But I mean it. I love you, Flic. I love you more than anything, and I would do or say anything to keep you with me. You're the best thing that ever happened to me, and I know I don't deserve you, but I want you in my life until the day I die. I want to have children with you, and I want us to get old together, and we can share a room in the care home when the kids don't want to look after us anymore.'

'I thought you weren't planning on living past forty-five?'

Dylan shrugged. 'You know me, I talk a lot of shit. Take me back, Flic, please.'

'I don't know… I do love you, but I don't want to spend the rest of my life feeling guilty for doing my job, which, like you said, I do love and I am proud of. I can't have you making me feel like I'm committing a human rights violation every time I leave for work in the morning.'

Dylan reached out and took both her hands in his. He was pleasantly surprised when she didn't pull away.

'I swear, I will never ever make you feel guilty again. You're one of the most honest people I've ever met, and if I could be half of the person you are, I'd be a very happy man.'

Felicity didn't answer. Instead, she stared at the hands that were still holding hers. After diverting her gaze to his face, she stood up and wrapped her arms so tight around his neck, he thought he was going to choke.

'I love you, Dylan,' she said, 'even if you are a fucking idiot.'

Chapter 43
Confrontation

'Forget about it,' Bogarde said, looking like he meant it.

When they'd arrived at his house, minus Jo and Bodhi, the crew had been expecting the worst. Bogarde, however, was taking the news in his stride.

'As long as you've got my little book,' he said, 'I'm willing to overlook your friends' absence. I can't blame you for your tactics. I imagine the two of them are sitting at home right now, making sure that copy you made is nice and safe.'

'There's more than one copy,' Wesley said, 'and we've got them squirrelled away in lots of different places.'

'So, don't even think about fucking us over,' Lenny added.

Bogarde laughed. 'We're friends now, gentlemen. There'll be no more animosity between us.'

Outside, the wind and rain lashed against the windows. An hour before they had arrived, it had been a pleasant, sunny day, but as their meeting loomed, the wind had suddenly whipped up, and the heavens opened. It was as if nature itself knew about the upcoming encounter with Bogarde and had decided to provide some mood lighting.

The house was as gaudy on the inside as the exterior suggested. It looked like Bogarde had made it as nouveau riche as possible just to wind up his neighbours. Elaborate murals decorated the wall, and tiled Roman mosaics ran the length of the hallway. The marble floors and internal columns complimented the theme, if compliment could ever be the right word. The room Mac had led them to was lined with walnut bookshelves full of burgundy and green leather-bound books that you would normally see in a reference library.

Dylan nodded at the books on display. He'd been squinting at them for the past few minutes, unsuccessfully trying to make out some of the titles.

'You read those,' he said, 'or are they just for show?'

Bogarde glanced over his shoulder, then back to his guests. They were seated on the opposite side of a ridiculously large table that would take weeks to circumnavigate. 'Some,' Bogarde answered, 'although I've never found them to be as useful as some people would lead us to believe.'

'You don't go for the old "knowledge is power" adage, then?'

'It's not, that's why.' He held his scrawny hand up and clenched his fist. '*This* is power. Doing to others what they lack the will to do to you first. That's what creates real, meaningful power. Now tell me, have you got it? And please don't say "got what?"'

'We've got it,' Jimmy said. 'You knocked that contract up yet?'

Bogarde smiled. 'It's done, not that it counts for much from a legal point of view. It's my word that matters, and I don't say something if I don't mean it. Give me the book back, and I'll make sure your fire station stays open as long as I'm still drawing breath.'

Jimmy looked at his friends, who responded by each offering him a nod. He dug his hand into the rucksack that sat between his legs and pulled out the book. The sight of it brought instant relief to Bogarde's face.

'I've got to hand it to you, gentlemen, you have been formidable opponents, haven't they, Neil?'

'They've been cunts,' Mac answered.

Bogarde smiled. 'He means that as a compliment.'

He nodded at Mac, who walked around the table, taking the book out of Jimmy's hand.

'And there we have it,' Bogarde said, 'our business is complete. You made the right call, gentlemen.'

When he looked back to Mac and his book, he was almost salivating. Rather than return to Bogarde's side, his man had stayed in situ, patting the book against his open hand. 'You know

you lot have proved yourself to be a stupid bunch of pricks over the last few months. Brave, too, I'll give you that, but stupid, mainly. But what you've done shows just what a bunch of dumb-fucks you really are. With this book, you had the chance to take down one of the most powerful men you're ever likely to meet. If you idiots had played it right, you could have had him on his knees by now.'

Bogarde's nose wrinkled as he listened. 'Bring that book back over here, will you. There's a good man.'

Mac ignored him. 'Do you have any idea how much he's worth? And what do you ask for? Small change to keep that piss-pot fire station of yours up and running.' He held the book aloft for them to inspect. 'You don't deserve it.'

Bogarde's voice deepened. 'Bring the book to me, Neil. Now!'

'Tell you what I'll do,' Mac said, focusing only on the firefighters. 'I'll show you fellas how to bleed someone dry properly. I'll let you take notes, just in case you ever get in a similar situation again.'

He turned his attention to his former employer and gave him the widest of smiles.

Bogarde's face went grey as he realised what was taking place. 'You son of a bitch,' he whispered. 'I'll kill you for this.'

Mac smiled. 'No, you won't. You won't do a goddamn thing. Now, shut the fuck up while I decide just how badly I'm going to screw you over.'

Bogarde sat back in his chair like he'd just been shot. 'I thought we were friends.'

Mac laughed from deep within his belly. 'Friends? I've been busting heads for you for over twenty years, and what have you given me in return? Twenty percent of a business that I created, that I took all the risk for. I've killed more people for you than I can remember, and you haven't even got the decency to give me a decent slice of the pie. That's not what friends do for each other.'

Bogarde held his palms aloft. 'We can sort that out. You'll get a better deal from now on, trust me.'

'Trust you?' He pointed at the guests. 'I'd trust this lot more than I'd trust you. See, it's not just the business, John. It's about respect, and you've got none for me.'

Bogarde shook his head. 'How can you say that? You're like part of my family.'

'Am I? When was the last time you invited me and Jane over for a social event, then? Do you even know my girls' names?'

'Neil,' Bogarde said, 'what are you talking about? I can still remember the look on your face when Faye and Rachel were born. How can you say these things to me?'

Mac brushed off his words with a shake of his head. 'I'm just a skivvy to you, always have been, always will. The only time you need me is when you've got shit that needs clearing up. That finishes here, this book changes everything.'

'I'll give you half of the coke business. You deserve it after everything you've done.'

Mac slammed his hand on the desk. 'I deserve all of it, and that's what I'm taking. You've made enough out of that little side-line for my liking.'

'Fine,' Bogarde said, 'it's yours. Consider it my retirement gift. We'll part company on good terms. You keep the business and I get the book. Deal?'

Mac laughed. 'What sort of cunt do you take me for? Don't you think after all this time I've learnt how your brain works, you nasty old bastard? I give you the book now and I'll be dead by the end of the night. It stays with me and I get all the profits from the coke from now on.'

Bogarde pretended to think about it for a few moments. 'Got no choice, have I? It's a deal. Real shame it had to come to this though.'

'Plus,' Mac said, 'I want ten million pounds in cash by the end of the week. Call it compensation for all the bullshit I've had to put up with over the years.'

Bogarde's face had turned from grey to crimson; his anger overcoming the threat. He pushed out his chair and stood up. 'Now, you listen to me, you horrible little prick, I've put up with

enough of this shit. Give me that book back right now, or I'll feed you to the fucking dogs.'

Mac smiled. 'Ah, there he is. Nice to see the real you back again.' He took his gun out of his belt and aimed it at Bogarde's chest. 'Now sit down, old man, and shut your mouth for once.'

'I'll kill you myself,' Bogarde snarled at him. 'I promise you now. You're a dead man, Neil. A fucking dead man.'

Mac put his finger to his lips. 'Hush, you're starting to annoy me.'

'I'm starting to annoy you? Why you little–'

Mac lowered the gun and shot Bogarde in the gut. The noise almost made the firefighters fall out of their seats.

'You can keep the ten million,' Mac said. 'Just shut your stinking mouth.'

Two of Bogarde's heavies ran into the room, seemingly unsurprised by what had taken place. Mac nodded at them, and in an instant, they had disappeared again. As Bogarde collapsed to the floor, Mac turned the pistol onto the guests.

'Thing is, fellas, no one would have believed he was willing to give you all that money out of the goodness of his heart. The son-of-a-bitch ain't got one. If you want your pay off, you'll have to earn it the hard way.'

As he spoke, the smell of petrol struck everyone's noses.

'And if you do get him out,' Mac said, 'don't forget to remind him that I've got the book, and I'm in charge now.'

He turned and headed for the door.

'Good luck,' he said without turning back. 'You're going to need it.'

After he'd left the room, the firefighters looked at each other in disbelief, not quite sure if what they'd just witnessed had really taken place. A groan from Bogarde kicked them back into life. Even though it was unnecessary, Lenny lifted up his nose and sniffed the air.

'They're torching the fucking place.'

Jimmy leapt from his chair and onto the floor, where he put his head close to the victim's. 'Are your wife and kid here?'

'Upstairs,' Bogarde said, with spit dribbling down his chin. 'Please, get them out.'

'Where are they, do you know?'

Bogarde tried to lift his head. 'My son's room. Top of the stairs, last room on the left.'

'I'll do it,' Dylan said, springing to his feet.

Wesley followed him up. 'I'm coming with you.'

Dylan looked at his boss like their roles were suddenly reversed. 'You sure you're up for it?'

Wesley nodded. 'I can do it.'

'Go,' Jimmy said as he inspected the casualty's injuries, 'and be careful.'

Bogarde's groans of pain cut him off.

'Keep your hands pressed to your stomach,' Jimmy said, as the pair ran out of the room. 'It'll slow down the bleeding.'

He stood up and looked at Lenny. 'If we want this finished, we've got to stop Mac.'

'Fuck Mac,' Lenny said, then looked down at Bogarde. 'We've still got our copies of the book. If he doesn't die now, then he ain't going to fuck with us again.'

'If Mac's got the book, it don't matter. He's going to be the one calling all the shots, and when he realises Uncle Jashari's not really related to the dead Albanians, how long do you think it's going to take him to come back for us?'

'He's not going to give a fuck about us anymore; he's just taken over Bogarde's empire.'

'We broke into his house,' Jimmy said. 'We blackmailed him, threatened his family. You choked him out, for Christ's sake. He'll want to settle the score sooner or later. The only way to stop that happening is to keep Bogarde alive and give him the book back. We do that and Mac will have to move to the other side of the world if he wants to keep breathing.'

Lenny shrugged. 'Then, let's find the prick before he gets away.'

'I'll get him. You get Bogarde outside and call an ambulance. If he dies, we're all fucked.'

'Be careful,' Lenny said. 'He's got a gun.'

Jimmy tried to smile. 'I know.'

He left the room and ran into the central hallway as the smoke alarms bellowed out their warning. A place this fancy should really have a built-in sprinkler system, Jimmy thought, but that was Bogarde for you, always trying to save a coin. He went past the stairway that Wesley and Dylan would have gone up and headed in the direction the thick black smoke was emanating from. In a normal fire, the conditions would have taken far longer to develop, but they'd clearly gone to town with the petrol; one of the best accelerants you could find when you really wanted to get things going. In minutes, the whole place would be alight.

Jimmy had to pull up sharply when he spotted the two heavies leaving the front door. Both men were carrying a can of petrol in their hands and were coughing heavily. Due to the amount of smoke, they were oblivious to his presence, and as the smoke layer continued to lower, he had to crouch to be able to breathe properly. Seconds after they left the house, Mac emerged from a separate room and followed their path to the door. He still had the book in one hand and the pistol in the other.

When he was about to reach the fresh air, Jimmy charged at him, rugby tackling him from behind. As they hit the deck, the book left Mac's hand and slid five feet across the floor. Jimmy crawled up his back, letting off a couple of kidney punches on his journey towards Bogarde's prized possession. Stretching out, he almost had it in his hand when Mac managed to roll over beneath him. Remembering the pistol, Jimmy gave up on the book and lunged with both hands at Mac's wrist.

As they struggled, two rounds went off, almost deafening Jimmy. One of the bullets had been so close to his face, he had felt the pressure of it passing his cheek. Mac's grip was solid. No matter how hard he tried, Jimmy couldn't get the pistol away from him. Instead, he changed tactic and butted the older man in the nose. As Mac's head went back and crashed against the tiled floor, Jimmy yanked at the pistol with both hands, yelling

as he exerted every fibre in his body. Mac finally released the gun, causing Jimmy to fall back onto his arse as the resistance to his efforts disappeared. He quickly stumbled to his feet, turning the pistol around so the muzzle was now pointing at Mac.

'You haven't got the bollocks,' he said, wiping away the blood that was running down his face.

Before he could answer, one of the heavies stuck his head back around the front door, craning his neck to find his boss through the smoke. Jimmy shot a hole in the timber, inches from his head.

'Get him out of here,' Jimmy said, nodding to Mac, 'before I blow both your fucking heads off.'

As the heavy gingerly crept forward and assisted his boss to his feet, Mac continued to smile at Jimmy.

'You should have killed me,' he said. 'You boys are too soft.'

'Yeah, well, that's our problem. We're all heart.'

'It'll cost you,' Mac said as he and the other man backed towards the door. 'Believe me.'

As he got to the door, he glanced at the book. It was less than three feet from his left leg.

'Go on, try it,' Jimmy said. 'Then you'll see how soft I am. Now, jog on, before I show you how big my bollocks really are.'

Mac smiled before stepping out of the house. When they had gone and the smoke layer had dropped another foot, Jimmy picked up the book before running to the bottom of the stairs. It was impossible to see anything up there, the smoke had done what it was meant to do and risen to the highest part of the building. If his friends were going to get that kid out safely, they would have to be quick.

'Wesley! Dylan!' he yelled up. 'You okay up there?'

He wanted to wait for an answer, but when the smoke forced him down to his knees, he had to turn and crawl towards the front door, hoping Mac's boys weren't waiting there to put a bullet between his eyes.

Chapter 44

Building Well Alight

By the time they'd got to the top of the stairs, Dylan and Wesley were already coughing heavily. The smoke was black and acrid, and they could taste the petrol contained in it. After taking ten steps down the corridor that seemed to go on forever, they were forced to their hands and knees. A dozen steps more, and with at least another dozen left until they reached their destination, they were on their bellies, army crawling as they sought out the breathable air.

'You okay, Wes?' Dylan shouted behind him as they progressed towards the child's room.

'I'm fine!' Wes yelled back. 'Just keep moving.'

Except he wasn't fine. In fact, he was about as far from fine as it was possible to get. All he could think about, as they made their way down the corridor, was the last time he had been in a similar situation to this; when he'd abandoned his partner and fled the building. What struck him, as the smoke filled his lungs, was that the feeling of panic he was experiencing was exactly the same as it had been all those years before. He desperately wanted to do the same thing as he had done on that occasion; turn and leave the building as quickly as he possibly could.

Except this time, he didn't. Instead, he did the thing that countless other firefighters had done before him. He took that fear, panic and self-doubt that was rising up his throat, swallowed it down and got on with the job in hand. He pushed his nose closer to the floor to avoid the smoke and did his best to keep up with his partner.

'I've found it,' Dylan said finally. 'I've got the door.'

He turned and grabbed his boss, directing him towards the area in question. It wasn't uncommon for BA partners to manhandle each other in such circumstances; it was quicker and easy than explaining to them when visibility was this poor.

'We need to get in and get the door shut behind us as quick as possible,' Dylan said. 'We don't want them breathing in this shit.'

'Fine,' Wes coughed. 'Let's just do it.'

The door was only open for a matter of seconds, but in that time, they managed to fill the child's room with smoke. Dylan moved quickly to the French doors that led to a small Juliet balcony and opened it up, allowing in the roaring wind.

Within seconds, it had diluted the smoke and taken it back outside to an area of lower pressure. At the same time, Wesley took a blanket off the child's cot and laid it across the bottom of the door to prevent any further ingress of smoke.

When the visibility and conditions had improved, Wesley cast an eye around the room. 'They're not here,' he said, peering under the bed.

Before Dylan could answer, they heard a child's cry coming from behind the closed door of the en-suite bathroom. He tried the handle, but it was locked.

'Mrs Bogarde,' he said as gently as he could, 'we really need to get you out of here. We don't want to hurt you, we're not the bad guys, but your house is on fire, and you and your baby's lives are in danger.'

When no answer came, Dylan looked to Wesley then gave the door three gentle raps with his knuckle. 'Mrs Bogarde, we really need to go.'

'How do I know you're not going to hurt us?' a female voice asked after a pause. English was definitely not the owner's first language. Dylan looked at Wesley who shrugged back at him.

'We just want to help you,' Dylan said. 'We're firefighters.'

A few seconds later, the door opened. Dylan put on his friendliest smile for her, but when she saw him she screamed and slammed the door in his face.

'Fucking liar!' she yelled. 'You say you were fucking fireman.'

'We are!' Dylan shouted back through the door.

'Then why no uniform? Lying fuck.'

Wesley approached the door. 'He's not lying. We are firefighters. We came here tonight to speak to your husband. He's been shot but not by us. Our friends are downstairs trying to save his life. If you and your baby don't come with us now, then you may not make it out at all. You need to choose quickly because it's not safe for us to be here much longer.'

Except that wasn't necessarily true. When firefighters carried out their Home Safety Visits to the public, they would tell them that if, for any reason, they couldn't get out of their property should it be on fire, then the safest thing was to stay put rather than attempt a potentially dangerous escape. You were more likely to get injured scaling down sheets or jumping out of windows onto mattresses. The solid oak wooden doors *should* provide them with at least half an hour's fire protection, and the fire service *should* be there within minutes. But staying put wasn't an option for Wes and Dylan, and there was no way they were leaving the mother and child in the building whilst they escaped. They were firefighters. Their job was to protect people, not abandon them. They couldn't rely on *should*.

After a pause, the door opened again. The woman looked scared and not sure if she should believe them. In her hands, she cradled her baby who, despite his quiet cry, seemed oblivious to the danger around him.

'You promise you're not going to hurt us?' the woman asked.

Despite the fear in her face, she was beautiful in a glamour model way. She wasn't his type, but Dylan could see what had attracted Bogarde to his much younger wife.

'We just want to get you and your baby outside safely,' Wesley said. 'I promise.'

The woman looked down at the child in her arms and sobbed. 'Please, don't let my baby die.'

Dylan placed his hand on her shoulder. 'We're going to get you both out of here, I swear, but you need to trust us.'

'What's your name?' Wesley asked her gently.

'Katya,' the woman said. 'But most people call me Kat.'

'Can I?'

'Yes.'

'Good stuff. Now, we just need to think of a way to get out,' Wesley said, to himself more than anyone else. 'There's no way we can take you through that smoke.'

When they stepped onto the balcony, the wind almost knocked them off their feet. Within seconds, all of them, including the child, who now screamed like his life depended on it, were soaked through. Dylan peered over the edge, it was at least a twenty-foot drop to the lawns below. Do-able for an adult, if you landed right, but not a fall you'd want to put a baby through. He considered lowering himself down and getting Wes to drop the child to him, but remembering what a useless goalkeeper he was, and doubting Wesley's skills were any better, he quickly dismissed the idea.

'When we came in,' Wesley said, as if picking up on Dylan's thoughts, 'we drove past a garage that had a load of scaffolding and other builder's gear stored against it. I think I may have seen a ladder there.'

Dylan was already over the balcony railings and in the process of lowering himself down when he spoke again. 'I can't see any other options.'

He landed with a thump, turning his ankle awkwardly. If it had been concrete he had landed on, he probably would have broken a bone. Before leaving, he looked through the window of the room directly below the one he had just leapt from. It was engulfed in flame from floor to ceiling. The quantity of accelerants used by the arsonists meant that it must have flashed over in minutes. The rooms either side of it had also followed a similar pattern. As he tried his best to sprint towards the garages, he thought that it didn't matter what the bedroom doors were made of and how much fire protection they offered. Those people needed to get out of that building and fast.

The relief he felt when he found the double extension ladder was immense. It took a couple of minutes to get it from the garage back to the balcony, and every time he stumbled or the ladder bumped into something, he cursed his clumsiness. He'd always hated ladder drills in training school, but Dylan had never done a better pitch than he did that evening when he positioned the head of the ladder three rounds above the top of the railing, in text-book fashion.

When he got to the top, he was met by Kat, who Wesley had shepherded to the railings.

'Go on,' he said gently. 'Give him the baby. I swear he'll be fine.'

Dylan held out his hands and did his best to smile at her.

'Please, look after my boy.'

'I will,' he said, scooping the child into his arms.

When he was at the bottom of the ladder, Wesley helped the woman over the railings, watching as she slowly made her way down in the pouring rain. He waited until she was reunited with her baby before he climbed down himself. Just as he got to the bottom, the window in the room below gave out, allowing the thick black smoke to escape. If they had still been on the balcony when it had happened, the four of them would have been engulfed.

Less than a minute later, they made it to the front of the house to see Lenny and Jimmy kneeling down next to Bogarde's prone form. Jimmy was using his jacket to try and stem the blood escaping from the bullet wound. Seeing her husband, Kat let out a scream before quickly composing herself. It was then that they finally heard the distant sound of sirens.

Jimmy looked to the rest of the team. 'We need to get the fuck out of here.'

'Thank you,' Kat said, then wrapped her free arm around Dylan and pulled him closer. 'You saved my baby,' she said after kissing her rescuer on the cheek. 'I'll never forget that.'

Dylan inspected the soaking wet, screaming child and smiled.

Bogarde attempted to sit up, his shirt was drenched with rain and blood but somehow, Jimmy had succeeded in slowing down the flow of red. 'Neither will I. Don't worry about this mess. I'll make sure you stay out of it.'

Jimmy threw the book on the floor next to him. 'Let's hope so.'

No one else said anything. Instead, they turned and ran towards Jimmy's car.

They were only just out of the gates and onto the main road when the fire appliance flew past them as it raced towards the ten-million-pound bonfire.

'Fuck,' Jimmy said when they'd made it a safe distance from the scene. Up until that point, they'd sat in silence. No one had known what to say.

'Fuck,' he repeated. 'If Mac's wants to get out of this in one piece, he's going to need the book.'

'Tough shit,' Lenny laughed. 'Bogarde's got it.'

'I know,' Jimmy said. 'So, now, he's going to go after the next best thing.'

He slammed on the breaks and turned the car around, driving west as fast as he could.

Chapter 45

All Aboard

Jo clung to the arm of the sofa as the boat lurched up and forward for the umpteenth time.

'If I'd known it was going to be like this,' she said, looking a little green around the gills, 'I would have stayed at home. Where the fuck did this shitty weather come from?'

Bodhi laughed and gripped her hand. 'What? You're Wonder Woman. I didn't think anything bothered you.'

'It doesn't bother me, I'm just saying.'

'Yeah, I can see that. Anyway, you're a triathlete. You're meant to like water?'

'I like being in it,' she said, pointing at the sanded boards below her feet, 'not on top.'

As the boat moved again, she returned the grip on Bodhi's hand with interest. 'How often does it get like this?'

Bodhi gave her his usual carefree smile. 'Not that often, but the tides in, so we're going to have to sit it out for a few hours 'til the water drops.'

'I'm going to take a piss,' she said, 'then I'm going home. The roller coaster ride is doing nothing for this baby.'

If anyone else had heard her, they would have thought she was lying. She was nearly three months and was showing hardly any sign of a bump.

'Then I'll come with you,' Bodhi said as she clambered to her feet.

Jo gave him an I-don't-think-so look. 'Really? I thought you knew me better than that by now.'

'I'm serious,' Bodhi said. 'You know what the others are doing. Until it's over and Bogarde's got his book back, I don't want to let you out of my sight.'

Jo studied her boyfriend before breaking into a smile. ‘Oh, Mr Bodhi, I like it when you’re forceful. Keep that up and you could be in for a treat when we get back to mine. Now, hold that thought. I’m bursting.’

As she disappeared down the galley, Bodhi sat back and took a slug from his beer bottle, thinking about how crazy it was. A few days earlier, the most important thing to him was how big the waves were or what the wind speed was and the direction it was blowing from. Now, though, he was getting ready to be a father. To paraphrase Lenny; shit just got real. Bodhi and Jo had created another life, a life that was growing and developing inside her right at that second. Soon, that child would be born, and it was to the two of them it would look to for its moral guideline. It was them the child would ask why the sky was blue and why it was important that we share with our friends and eat our vegetables. The responsibility was immense, and it excited and scared the shit out of him in equal measures.

He was so busy thinking about these life-changing issues, that it wasn’t until he was almost at the bottom of the steps that he noticed bruiser number one; the big one they called Frank, who he had knocked out cold a few weeks previously.

‘I got to say…’ He was soaked through, the leather jacket he was wearing had provided little resistance to the almost horizontal rain outside. ‘You’ve done a good job of getting this place straightened out after our last visit. Very cosy, indeed.’

Bodhi sat up in his seat, trying to show his usual calm and not the panic that was racing through his body. He had to summon all his energy not to turn and look to the bathroom door. ‘What do you want?’

‘I think you already know that,’ the man said. As he came off the final step, he ruffled his hand through his cropped hair like a dog shaking water from its fur. ‘Where’s the book?’

Bodhi caught his breath and tried to slow his heart rate. ‘You’re brave coming here on your own, after what I did to you and your friends last time.’

Frank shrugged. 'Wasn't planned. Just got a call from the boss. I don't know what this is all about, but he wants that book pretty bad.'

'And you reckon you can take it?'

The man buried his hand into his coat pockets and brought out a small but deadly looking pistol. 'I reckon so. I came prepared this time.'

Bodhi gave the weapon an impressed nod. 'Yeah, looks like you did, bud.'

'So, like I say, where's the book?'

'Where are my friends? What's happened to them?'

Frank raised the gun's muzzle. 'I'm the one who asks the questions. Don't make me ask again.'

What the fuck to do. Bodhi wanted the guy out of his home as quickly as possible before he realised Jo was there. But something had obviously gone wrong at Bogarde's house. By giving him the book, he could be putting their lives in danger. *What the fuck to do.*

'It's not here,' he said. 'The book's gone. If we go now, I'll take you to it.'

It *was* there. They had made two copies. One was sitting under the sink in the kitchen cupboard, and the other was hidden in the spare locker at the fire station. Bodhi had no intention of taking him there; he just wanted to get him off the boat and buy some time while he figured out what the hell he was going to do.

The big lump took in Bodhi's words. 'Really, are you sure about that?'

'It's not here, it's at my girlfriend's place. I'll take you there.'

Shit. He hadn't meant to say that. He didn't know what he was thinking. He just wanted him out, and fast.

'No need.' Frank smiled. 'I already know where she lives. Bet she'll be glad to see me again.'

'She won't let you in,' Bodhi said, thinking fast. 'She doesn't let anyone in at night after what you and friends did to her. She's had an intercom installed, and the only way she opens that door is if she hears my voice.'

Frank thought about it some more then nodded to the stairs. 'C'mon, let's go.'

As Bodhi walked past him, the man grabbed his arm. 'I'd put a coat on, if I were you. It's pissing down.'

Bodhi took his hoodie from the edge of the sofa and went up the steps, two at a time.

When they were on deck, he had to turn his head to escape the slashing rain. As the boat rocked forward, both men almost fell over and had to put out their arms to steady himself. Bodhi grabbed the rail and quickly found his feet, but the goon fumbled forward with both arms outstretched like a blind man searching for his cane. Bodhi hadn't intended to play the hero, he really hadn't. All that had been on his mind was to get the trespasser off the boat and away from his lover and unborn child, but when he saw the look of helplessness on the face of the man he had once bested, the opportunity was too good to ignore.

Bodhi lunged at the pistol and was about to twist and rip it away when his opponent's clumsiness worked in his own favour. As they struggled, his legs slipped from underneath him and went straight up in the air. At the same time, his body crashed down onto the deck with such a violent motion that Bodhi was unable to maintain his grip on the pistol. Frank laid on his back with both hands on the gun pointing straight up at Bodhi's head.

'Stand back,' he said, his arms shaking, 'or I'll blow a fucking hole in you.'

Bodhi held up his arms and took a large step backwards as the man slowly and carefully rose to his feet.

'You know what I'm going to do to that girlfriend of yours after I get the book?' he said, smiling.

Bodhi stayed silent as the rain soaked him to the bone.

'Let me tell you anyway,' Frank said, when Bodhi didn't answer. 'I'm going to take you with me to her place and you're gonna watch me fuck her senseless before I kill her… or maybe I'll kill her first and then fuck her, I haven't worked it out yet… Decisions, decisions.'

'You're not fucking anyone, you fat piece of shit,' a voice behind him said.

When the man turned to see who was talking, he was met with a fire extinguisher smashing into his face at speed. He staggered backwards with blood pouring from his nose, but miraculously, considering how hard Jo had hit him, he had managed to keep hold of the gun. Through watering eyes, he aimed it at her head.

'Fuck you, bitch,' he said. 'I'll fucking kill you both.'

Before he could shoot, Bodhi charged into him taking both of them over the side into the water below. When they came back to the surface, the man gasped and lunged at Bodhi. They had fallen into the relatively calm water between his and Vera's boats. As he thrashed around, it was clear the bruiser was far from comfortable in the water, but Bodhi knew that in this confined space, the man had his best chance of beating him. Before he could compose himself, Bodhi grabbed the collar of Frank's jacket and dragged him into the rougher waters. The tide had changed and was now sucking them back towards the sea at a rapid speed. Within seconds of getting into the channel, they were already fifty feet from the safety of the boat.

Frank managed to twist around as he was being towed, and in his panic, grabbed at the front of Bodhi's hoodie. Bodhi was unsure if he was trying to drown him or cling to him for safety, but either way, the bigger man's efforts were forcing him under the water. Bodhi didn't panic; he knew that was pointless. Instead, he did a trick some of his old lifeguard buddies in Cornwall had taught him. Rather than resist, he grabbed hold of the man's wrists and pushed himself under the water, expelling all the air in his lungs and taking his opponent down with him. They'd only gone under a few feet when Frank let go and desperately swam back to the surface for a gulp of fresh air.

When he surfaced, Bodhi saw the man's arms waving in the air, grabbing at nothing as he floated off towards the sea. He thought about swimming out to rescue him; he knew he was a strong enough swimmer to get him back to the shore. He was

also aware of his responsibilities as a firefighter; it was in his DNA to try and help people, but then, he remembered what Frank was about to do to the woman he loved and his unborn child. He gave the drowning man another look, watching his arms flail as his head disappeared under the water, then Bodhi turned and swam to the bank.

When he got back to the boat, they were all there waiting for him; Jimmy, Lenny, Dylan, Wesley and, of course, Jo. He was soaking wet, freezing cold and covered in mud, but when they saw him, none of them thought twice about squeezing the life out of their friend. Except for Jo, that is. She slapped him across the face first, cursed him for being a stupid twat for doing what he'd done, then gave him the biggest kiss on the lips she could manage.

'What happened?' Bodhi asked. 'Did it go bad?'

'It did,' Jimmy said, 'then it didn't. I'm guessing you took care of that guy?'

Bodhi gave them a shamed nod. He wasn't proud of what he had done, even if it was necessary.

'Then, that's it. I think we're off the hook.'

Jo put her arms around him and squeezed Bodhi tightly; she already knew how guilty he was feeling.

'Don't feel bad,' she said. 'You saved my life and our baby's too. That's all that matters.'

Bodhi placed his hand on her miniscule bump and gave her a tired smile. 'Yeah, you're right,' he said. 'It is.'

When he came out of the bedroom, freshly showered with a new hoodie on that looked just like the one he'd been wearing earlier, Bodhi was met by the sight of his friends huddled around the television staring at the news. The female reporter, wrapped in a yellow mac to protect her from the driving rain, was standing in front of what had once been Jonathan Bogarde's house. The shell of it was still standing, but it was clear that everything on the inside had been destroyed.

'In what was believed to be a dispute over money,' the reporter said, raising her voice to be heard over the wind, 'an employee of Mr Bogarde's broke in to the property, shot the owner, then set fire to the house which he had only recently moved into following nearly five years of construction. Despite his injuries and with the building ablaze, Mr Bogarde was able to rescue his wife and young son from an upstairs bedroom and lead them to safety. However, it was the firefighters who arrived to put out the fire that Mr Bogarde said were the real heroes, and has pledged to help them save their fire station from closure in any way he can.'

Lenny threw a cushion at the TV, cutting off the reporter. 'Fuck this guy. I can't believe he's managed to come out of this smelling of roses.'

Jimmy shrugged. 'Who cares, it's over. Mac's gone, the station stays open and we're out of the shit.'

Dylan didn't look convinced. 'So, what's the moral of the story here? The way to fund a public service is by getting some ruthless businessman to bail us out? I know it's good the station is going to be saved an' all, but it just doesn't sit right.'

Lenny threw a second cushion and struck Dylan in the side of the face. 'How about you shut the fuck up and enjoy the moment, for once.'

He looked across to Bodhi. 'You got any more beer in that fridge of yours?'

Bodhi nodded. 'Course, what do you think I am?'

'Then, what are we waiting for? I think we need a toast.'

'I'll get them,' Dylan said.

As he went to get up, Lenny put his arm on his shoulder, pushing him back onto the sofa. 'I'll get them, you're not the new boy anymore.'

Lenny went to the fridge and filled his hands with beer bottles. After handing them out, the others stood around not knowing quite what to do.

Wesley elbowed Jimmy in the arm. 'Come on, Jim. I reckon you should say something.'

'You say something,' Jimmy said back. 'You're the governor.'

'Yeah come on, Wes,' Lenny said. 'You're one of us now, you massive bell end.'

Wesley laughed. 'Thanks, Len.'

He took a second to clear his throat. 'To be honest, I don't really know what to say. A lot has happened over the last few months, much of it due to my inability to take charge and stop us from losing our heads like we did. But it happened. We made our mistake, and hopefully, now, we've managed to rectify the situation. I've learnt a lot about you guys lately, and if it means anything, I just want to say how proud of you all I am. But I've also learnt something about myself. I know you guys didn't think much of me when I started on the Watch, and I don't blame you either. Hopefully, your opinion has changed now, because I know I have. Whether it's for the better or not, I'm not too sure.'

He paused whilst the others laughed.

'With any luck, Harrison will get off with this charge they've put against him, and very soon, we can get back to business as usual.'

He held his beer bottle up in the air. 'Cheers… you bunch of cunts.'

The others cheered at his profanity, held up their bottles and threw the contents down their throats.

'I was thinking,' Bodhi said to Jo who had substituted her beer for an orange juice. He had lowered his voice for her alone to hear. 'Maybe I should sell the boat and move into your place. I want our kid to have a normal life living with both his parents.'

'I've got a better idea,' Jo said. 'How about I rent the flat out and come and live here with you.'

'Really?'

'This boat is part of you. It's part of what makes me love you, even if you and it drive me crazy sometimes. I don't want you to change, and if you can get some of your ways to rub off on our little one, then all the better. Perhaps, then, they won't end up like their neurotic, competitive mum.'

'Don't talk bollocks,' Bodhi said. 'I love that you're determined and driven and don't take shit off anyone. I want our kid to be like that too.'

Lenny groaned. 'Jesus, are you two going to start wanking each other off or what'

Jo shot him a look, then returned her attention to Bodhi. 'So, you up for it, then? Could your precious boat handle family life?'

'Are you sure *you* can? You didn't look too hot earlier when it got rough.'

Jo laughed. 'I'm Wonder Woman, I can handle anything.'

'Except Bodhi's penis,' Lenny said.

Jo clenched her fist and directed at him. 'One more word, dickhead, and you'll be getting this.'

'Seriously, though,' Lenny said, smiling, 'isn't anyone else thinking that maybe Mac had a point? Don't you think we should have squeezed a few quid for ourselves out of Bogarde? Nothing silly, just twenty or thirty grand each to compensate us for our troubles.'

Jimmy nodded to Jo who responded by punching Lenny straight in the stomach. As he doubled over and gasped for air, the others held their bottles up and sank the rest of their beers.

Chapter 46

Scores to Settle

Three Months Later

'Seriously,' Dylan said, shaking his head, 'that's so gay.'

'How can it be gay, knobhead?' Lenny said. 'If it was a bloke sticking his finger up my arsehole, that would be gay. But it wasn't. It was a twenty-eight-year-old lap-dancer.'

Jimmy picked his cup of tea off the canteen table and blew at the contents. 'I thought you said you were staying away from dancers after last time.'

'I was,' Lenny said, 'but you should see this one.'

He held both hands a foot away from his chest and looked down at the imaginary cleavage.

'You're right,' Jo said.

She was now working light duties, and despite her bump having grown considerably, she was still in the gym every day, putting in times on the running machine that no one else could touch.

'It's not gay, it's fucking repulsive. How can you make the poor girl go near that hairy A-hole of yours?'

Lenny smiled. 'That's just it, she wanted to do it. It's *her* thing. And just so you know, my arse ain't so hairy anymore. She made me get a back, sack and crack wax.'

Jo made a gagging face. 'I didn't think it was possible to make this story any worse, but well done, Len, you've just managed it.'

'Don't try and bring me down with your negative bullshit,' Lenny said, but in a cheerful manner. 'I got a woman who likes to do stuff to the holiest of holes, and my brother and me are talking to each other for the first time in far too fucking long. Life is good right now.'

Since the fire at Bogarde's house, life had improved for everyone on the watch. Dylan had moved back in with Felicity, and the wedding plans were back on. His rescue of Kat and her baby had also removed his desire to transfer to Central, and he had withdrawn his application. He was more than happy working at East with his Red Watch comrades.

Jimmy had cut back on his work with Bob and was seeing far more of Jen and the kids. Despite spending most of his time moaning about being skint since this new arrangement, he was far happier with his work-life balance, and so were the rest of his family. Something else that had cheered him up was that he had recently gone back to the training centre to retake his BA refresher. His pride had been seriously dented by his previous failure, but free of external worries, he had gone up there and passed it with ease. He could now call himself a firefighter again without the nagging doubt that had been lurking at the back of his mind. The nightmares hadn't gone away, but since Mac's disappearance, their frequency had dwindled, and he was seeing less of the dead men's faces when he closed his eyes at night.

Jo had kept to her word and put the flat up for rent. She'd moved onto the boat a month prior and was trying to adapt to its limited space before the baby came. Bodhi had been working hard converting the spare room from a kite storage area and workshop into a nursery. The colours were being kept neutral to cover all eventualities.

Jo pursed her lips and blew out, rubbing her bump as she did so.

'You okay?' Bodhi said. 'Baby giving you a good kicking?'

Jo shook her head. 'I'm starving. My breakfast didn't stay down again.'

She leaned back in her chair and looked to the canteen. 'Harrison, how long are those sandwiches going to be, mate? My stomach thinks my throat's been cut.'

Harrison poked his head out the door and gave her a smile. 'Not long now, but like they say, you can't rush perfection.'

'He better not watch me eat it, then,' she said under her breath as he disappeared into the kitchen. 'I'll fucking demolish it in seconds.'

Harrison's disciplinary investigation had already gone down in station folklore. When Dylan turned up to the meeting with his arms full of A4 binders, Phil Collins and the Brigade's human resources manager had looked at each other, as if not knowing quite what to expect. Over the next two hours, their concern would prove to be well founded. The meeting had been Dylan's finest hour. He went at them from the off, referring them to the Bill of Rights, the Magna Carta and the Declaration of Rights; some of the most important acts in history that protected a person's freedom of speech. He talked of the struggles of the suffragettes and the Tolpuddle Martyrs, quoting text at them from Nelson Mandela, Gandhi and Martin Luther King.

Yes, he said, Harrison had said a word that they could possibly construe as offensive, but *their* actions he argued, were far more offensive to Harrison and his colleagues. At one point, he launched into a theoretical discussion, about the English language itself, and if Harrison had used any other word than "scab," would it still be considered offensive. He dropped Shakespeare in at this point, referencing Juliet's "a rose by any other name" speech. Dylan, the arch-atheist, had even quoted the bible at them. 'Whatever one sows,' he had said, 'that he will also reap,' before launching into a final tirade at the officers that had undermined the union that had served them extremely well, and were refusing to take responsibility for their actions. Phil and the other guy eventually dismissed the charges against Harrison rather than hear any more of Dylan's lecturing.

By the end of the day, everyone who worked at the station had heard about what he had done and were ready to accept Dylan as their new union rep with open arms. Harrison, who had enjoyed the time off and the chance to rekindle his relationship with Janet, was nonetheless happy to get back to work and get some decent meals back into the Watch. He had spent over an hour of his first day on duty getting the canteen cupboards back to a way he found acceptable. It was criminal, he had complained,

that people were stacking the tinned tomatoes amongst the baked beans, and the herb and spice rack was a total mess. When he looked inside the fridge and saw the state of the vegetable tray, he almost fainted. *Welcome back, Harrison.*

Five minutes later, he returned to the room, handing Jo her sandwich.

'The rest of you miserable bastards,' he told them, 'can get your own.'

'Ketchup?' Jo asked.

Harrison tutted. 'I'm hurt that you even had to ask.'

Jo winked at him and patted his bum as he walked past.

After pulling up his seat at the table, Harrison turned his attention to Jimmy. 'Now that the station is staying, do you think you can order us some more knives for the kitchen? I might as well have been using the side of my hand to cut that onion.'

'I'll ask Wesley when he gets back,' Jimmy said. 'I'm sure Phil Collins won't mind helping out his favourite Watch.'

Bogarde's offer to bankroll the station had been reluctantly accepted by the fire authority in an emergency meeting held earlier in the month. Some of the councillors on the panel were happy to endorse his offer, whilst others felt it reflected badly on them, with a U-turn suggesting they had made a mistake in the first place. Eventually, the yeses and their belief that it was the people of Brighton that were the priority won the day by the slimmest of margins. The station would stay open as long as Bogarde was happy to finance it.

'How do you think Wes' little family holiday is going?' Lenny said. 'You reckon they're sharing the same bed yet?'

'If a week in Butlin's doesn't bring them together,' Dylan answered, 'I can't imagine what else could.'

Wesley had been spending much more time with the girls, and as a consequence, his wife too. They hadn't got back together, but their relationship was healthier than at any time since they'd separated, and there had even been tentative conversations about him moving back in again. The holiday was their first step in an attempt at reconciliation. Another development for Wesley was

that he had decided to stay put as an operational firefighter and forego his job in fire safety. He had already proved to the crew that he was up to the task but on the night at Bogarde's house, his own actions had convinced him that he was capable of the challenge.

'Don't be a snob, you knob,' Lenny said. 'When you've got little ones, you'll think Butlin's is the best thing since sliced bread. Especially when you can pack them off to kids club so you and the missus can get jiggy.'

The bells went down, interrupting their conversation.

'What we got, Jim?' Dylan said from the back of the lorry as he did up his fire tunic.

Jimmy stared at the computer screen in front of him. 'Fire in the open, Bevendean Woods.'

'Little bastards,' Lenny said from the driver's seat. 'They've only been on holiday for a couple of days. Usually takes a week or two before they get bored and start burning stuff.'

Pulling out of the bays, he cursed every child under sixteen that lived in the vicinity of the woods and continued to do so until they arrived at the incident a few minutes later.

Lenny parked up at the bottom of a track that led into the offending area. It wasn't that large a space, but the track was far too narrow for an appliance to get down. The only way the crew could get to the fire was on foot.

At the pump bay, Lenny filled up two buckets and, with a smile on his face, handed one each to Bodhi and Harrison.

'You sure you're going to be all right with this?' Lenny asked the senior member of the crew. 'A man of your age shouldn't be doing this sort of work. Let laughing boy do the heavy lifting.'

He nodded at Dylan who was wearing the flex-pack; a back-pack full of water that made him look like he'd gone to a fancy-dress party as one of the Ghostbusters. The flex-pack was the least effective piece of equipment on the fire engine, if not the planet. The nozzle required a vigorous pump-action in order for water to be ejected out

of it, so much so, that after getting a few litres of wet stuff on the fire, the mug doing the job would be well and truly knackered. If he was on duty, Dylan always got dumped with the flex pack.

'Take care in there,' Lenny said as the crew traipsed off into the trees. 'If you get scared, give me a call, and I'll come and hold your hands.'

After walking for less than a hundred yards, Jimmy stopped and sniffed the air. He turned to his left and looked to the tops of the trees. Grey wisps of smoke could be made out rising above them and drifting north. He turned and pointed in the direction of the fire.

'This way, troops.'

In the clearing, a small bonfire was burning at a lazy pace. All that was left of the mattress that laid on top was the springs. When the call came, it was probably chucking out heaps of black smoke, looking far worthier of a visit by the brigade.

Jimmy turned to Dylan. 'Hopefully, the buckets will do it, and you won't have to waste your time with that thing.'

'I knew it,' Dylan said. 'I told Lenny not to fill it up so much. My spine feels like it's about to snap.'

As Bodhi and Harrison made their way to the fire, a familiar figure stepped out from behind a tree and smiled at them. He had a pistol in his hand, and it was pointing in their direction.

'Gents,' Mac said, 'I've been waiting for you.'

The firefighters stopped dead, not knowing what to say or do.

Mac nodded at the fire. 'Go on then, put it out. We wouldn't want it causing a mischief.'

Bodhi and Harrison looked at each other then walked forward and poured the buckets over the fire. The steam produced made Mac take a half-step backwards.

'What do you want?' Jimmy asked the intruder.

'What do you think I want? You and your team of do-gooders have ruined my life. I want revenge, Jim. I want retribution. I want you fuckers to pay for what you've done.'

'Take it easy,' Harrison said, 'and think about what you're doing for a minute.'

'You should have stayed retired, pal,' Mac answered without bothering to look at him.

Dylan put out his hands and stepped forward. 'Despite what you think, we're not your enemy. We were just trying to stay out of trouble, that's all.'

Mac laughed. 'You *were* out of trouble, you streak of piss. I was through with you, I told you that. Why the fuck did you have to stick your noses in where they weren't wanted? Because of you, I had to leave my family and run off to Spain. They don't even know if I'm still alive. Do you know what that feels like? Abandoning the people you love, knowing there was fuck all I could do to protect them from that bastard. Why the fuck didn't you just let it go?'

'Because we didn't believe you, that's why,' Jimmy said, 'How long would it have been before you came back and wanted more from us? We did what we had to do to protect *our* families.'

'You had it coming to you after what you put us through,' Bodhi said, 'or have you forgotten what your goons did?'

Mac shook his head. 'That's nothing compared to what they're gonna do. After I've killed you lot, I'm going to wait for that dumb-fuck driver to come and look for you, then I'm going to kill him too. After that I'm going to go to each and every one of your homes and kill your families, and that includes that pregnant bitch you've shacked up with. I'm going to make sure she suffers worst of all. It's you who's got it coming, son, and believe me when I say it ain't going to be pretty.'

Bodhi dropped his bucket and stepped forward. 'You touch her, and I'll fucking kill you.'

'Go on, Blondie,' Mac said, pointing the gun at Bodhi's face. 'Just fucking try it!'

Jimmy's radio crackled into life with the gruff tones of Lenny's voice. 'Everything okay, Jim? You boys need anything?'

Before Mac could protest, Jimmy lifted the radio and spoke into it. 'All good, Len. We've got a number of potential Code Ones down here. Hopefully we'll have it sorted soon.'

'You, what? Yeah okay, got it,' the voice came back.

When he lowered the radio, Mac looked ready to use the pistol on him. 'What did you say that for, and what the fuck is a Code One?'

'A Code One is a suspicious fire, and the reason I said it was because if I *didn't* answer, he would have come down here looking for us. If you're gonna do us in, I'd rather you didn't kill him too.'

Mac shrugged. 'No big deal. I'll get him later. Just after I've gutted your wife and made your kids watch.'

Jimmy snorted. 'You're full of shit. You're not going to kill my family, or anyone else's for that matter. You may be a cunt, but you're not that much of a cunt.'

Mac walked up to him and hit him on the side of the head with the butt of his pistol. Jimmy dropped to his knees before quickly stumbling back to his feet. He didn't want to give Mac the satisfaction of seeing him stay down.

'I owed you that. But, yeah, you're right, I'm not going to kill them, but I am going to kill you. Then, when I'm finished, I'm going to go to Bogarde's office and kill him. After that, if I'm still in one piece, I'm going to get my family out of this shitty country and back to the sunshine. That's the advantage of being a smuggler; passports are not essential to international travel.'

Mac stopped talking and studied the faces of the men in front of him. 'So, come on, let's get on with it… Who wants it first?'

The crew stared at each other, sharing a look that spoke of fear and desperation, but there was also something in it that said that none of them were going to give up their friends.

Mac studied the pistol's muzzle. 'Come on, boys. I haven't got all day.'

'Me,' Jimmy said as he put his hand to his head to stem the flow of blood. 'Do me.'

'You'd better put me down first,' Bodhi said. 'Otherwise, I'm coming for you.'

Harrison looked at his friends and shrugged. 'Fuck it, it might as well be me.'

Like a schoolboy requesting the attention of his teacher, Dylan put his hand up in the air. 'I'll go first.'

Mac laughed. 'Isn't that just the sweetest thing. I'm Spartacus. No, I'm Spartacus. You boys crack me up.'

Jimmy stepped forward and walked to within three feet of Mac. He lifted his head in the air like he was waiting to receive a punch in the face. 'Come on, you wanker. Just get on with it.'

Mac raised the pistol, bringing it to within inches of Jimmy's skull. 'Good choice,' he said. 'I'm glad it's you.'

He was about to pull the trigger when he heard the sound of cracking twigs behind him. Mac turned just in time to see something rushing towards his face. The impact lifted him off his feet and back to the floor with a thump. He was unconscious before his head hit the ground.

Lenny smiled and kissed the head of the shovel he was brandishing. 'Gotcha, motherfucker!'

He looked around at the others. 'So, is everyone all right or what?'

Jimmy placed his hands on the bigger man's shoulder. 'We are, now that you're here.'

Lenny checked that Mac was definitely sleeping, then put the shovel down. 'Was he really going to do you?'

'I reckon so. It's a good thing you caught on.'

Lenny gave him a look. 'You said a number of potential fatalities. I may not be the brightest spark, but you don't have to be Stephen fucking Hawking to know that something wasn't right.'

'Good job,' Harrison said. 'Usually, I don't condone violence, but in this case, I'm willing to make an exception.'

'Me too,' Dylan chipped in.

'I've always found violence to be a pretty effective means to an end,' a voice said.

The small, wiry man they all recognised stepped out of the forest. It was Al, the assassin they had escorted to the Albanian's house to carry out his work.

Bodhi peered into the woods in the direction the man had just come from. 'Anyone else hiding out there, bud?'

Al smiled. 'Nope, just me.'

A light bulb went off in Lenny's head, and he pointed his finger at the new guy. 'You're the prick who stabbed me.'

Before he could go for the shovel again, Al nodded at the gun in his belt. 'I wouldn't go down that road, if I were you. I'm not here for you boys. It's our mutual friend I'm interested in.'

'Mac?' Dylan said unnecessarily.

'Clever boy. I've been keeping an eye on him for the past couple of days.'

'You've done what?' Jimmy said.

The man stepped into the clearing and inspected Mac's prone form before nodding his approval. 'I've been following your man since he got back in the country. As I'm sure you can imagine, Mr Bogarde is rather keen to see him again.'

'You mean, you've been standing there the whole time?' Jimmy said. 'Were you going to let him shoot us?'

Al shrugged. 'I just wanted to see how things panned out. You fellas have been pretty resourceful lately, and so you've proved again. If you ever fancy a change of vocation, you should consider a life of crime… Now, do yourselves a favour and get back to your fire engine. I'll deal with things here.'

Bodhi nodded at Mac. 'What are you going to do with him?'

Al followed Bodhi's gaze. 'Does it matter?'

'Not really.'

'Then, fuck off. You boys are done here.'

Without saying another word, the five men turned and headed back down the track. Dylan attempted to look and see what fate would befall Mac, but Bodhi grabbed his arm and pushed him forward.

When they were back on the appliance, Jimmy turned and inspected his crew. 'Is everyone okay?'

'Yeah, Jim,' Harrison said. 'We're all good.'

The End

Acknowledgements

The first people I have to thank when it comes to the writing of this book are all the firefighters I have worked with over the past seventeen years. I love my job and the people I work with. People often take the piss out of us for playing pool and drinking tea, but my colleagues are some of the most professional and caring people you could wish to find. I have worked on some great watches with some genuinely great people, many of whom could tell a great story about their experiences in the job.

I felt like I had a wealth of tales to draw from when I started writing the book, and although the main theme is purely fictional (I swear I, nor anyone I have ever worked with, have stolen anything at an incident), many of those stories have been reworked to fit into my tale. There were also many true stories I have also left out, for fear that you would never believe them! Many of the characters in the book are based on a mixture of the very interesting people I have worked with, and I'm sure if they read it, they will recognise parts of themselves. Other people like Dave 'Trigger' Sommer, and Leanne Emery Garner (by far the nicer of the firefighting Garners), I have pretty much cut and pasted into the novel.

So thank you Red Watch, High Wycombe, my first watch where I learnt so much. Keith Carmichael, I remembered one of your jokes and worked it into the plot. Thank you Green Watch, Hove for welcoming me to East Sussex. Mark Moss I hope you don't mind me stealing your unique style of texting. Thank you, Blue Watch, Preston Circus for turning me into the belligerent prick that I am today and ruining my chances of future promotion (I mean that in a good way), Dean Clark, I'm sure you'll recognise

some of your old tricks. Finally, thanks to Green Watch, Preston Circus, for somehow managing to put up with my shit for the last ten years. You are *literally* awesome. I also want to praise the work of the FBU, who despite brutal government cuts to fire services nationwide, have continued to watch our backs and fight the good fight.

Thanks to David Gaylor for reading the book and offering me some incredibly helpful feedback. Thanks to Mark Taylor, for helping with things from the point of view of the police, and explaining how I could smuggle drugs more efficiently. Dave Statham, my gaffer, cheers for your advice on managing operational incidents. Morgen Bailey, thank you for editing the book and teaching me a great deal about the English language. Sorry for not removing all the rude words, but firefighters swear a lot!

Thank you so much to Betsy and Fred at Bloodhound Books for taking a chance on me and publishing the novel. After dozens of rejections from agents and publishers, I was ready to give up on the book, but then I was contacted by Betsy. That was definitely the best moment of my writing career to date. Thanks also to the rest of the team at Bloodhound; Sarah Hardy, Sumaira Wilson, Alexina Golding and anyone else who was involved in getting the book out into the world. Thank you all, Bloodhound rock!

Buddy and Sylvie, thanks for being you, and Ange, thanks for everything x

Printed in Great Britain
by Amazon